Nursing Homes and Public Policy

Drift and Decision in New York State

Nursing Homes and Public Policy

Drift and Decision in New York State

by William C. Thomas, Jr.

CORNELL UNIVERSITY PRESS

ITHACA AND LONDON

Library of Congress Catalog Card Number: 69-18217

PRINTED IN THE UNITED STATES OF AMERICA
BY VAIL-BALLOU PRESS, INC.

To my wife, Jean, and
my daughters, Meg and Julia

Foreword

by Martin Cherkasky, M.D.

The brilliant successes of medical science in the last fifty years have resulted in substantial control of the acute illnesses that have affected our population. The life expectancy for the average American has increased roughly thirty years since the turn of the century. Because of this increase we have an aging population, and as a result the crucial medical care problem of our time is chronic illness.

The usual course of chronic illness is long, measured in months and years. Almost inevitably the illness is accompanied by disability and handicap along with emotional and social aberrations and economic difficulties. The result is a wide variety of needs for medical, nursing, and rehabilitative services. This is the silhouette of chronic diseases.

While hospital care is usually necessary for diagnosis and treatment of the acute stage of heart disease, cancer, stroke, diabetes—all chronic diseases—frequently patients then require a variety of services at home and in institutions other than the hospital. These institutions, generally under the name "nursing homes," have developed in response to the most serious needs of patients, families, and physicians. While in large cities hospitals have in some way been responsive to the needs of patients and community, the same cannot be said for nursing homes. All too often they have been a disgrace to our society. The oldest, most pitiable, most helpless persons have been left to linger without hope in these institutions; medical care and services have been poor; rehabilitative therapy has been nonexistent; and the physical surroundings and ambiance have been unappetizing and deadening. This is because nursing home care for the most part has been outside the mainstream of modern medicine.

As a physician-administrator I am impressed by the story that Professor Thomas tells in this thoughtful study of public policy and nursing homes in New York State. It is clear from the sweep of the author's story that the problem of adequate care for the long-term patient crept much too slowly into the field of consciousness of legislators and administrators. Despite significant progress, nursing home care remains a major problem requiring resolution. The modern hospital has the excitement, the drama, the science, the equipment, the personnel. By the very nature of the patients it must deal with, the nursing home in a sense has none of these—and yet the need is great.

One is impressed by how far we have come since even the early 1930's. The whole controversy, described in detail by Professor Thomas, of "indoor" versus "outdoor" relief and the unwillingness of legislators to reimburse local governments for long-term patients in public and voluntary nursing homes is testimony to how difficult progress has been.

Today we accept as social and public policy the fact that medical care is a right for all people and not a privilege for some. It is my conviction that the acceptance of this idea by contemporary politicians has resulted in state legislation, including the Folsom Law, and in nursing home codes for New York State and New York City that at last approach the standards we have a right to expect. Further, reimbursements to long-term care institutions throughout the state now approximate cost, so that the indigent or medically indigent patient can be protected by his government.

Unfortunately, public policy in the 1930's and 1940's in this state, as shown by Professor Thomas, led to a mushrooming of proprietary nursing homes. It is questionable whether such a crucial service should be substantially in the hands of entrepreneurs who frequently make large sums of money from the operation of these institutions. It is interesting to note that new laws and codes, and new public policy on financing for long-term care, may lead to an increase in the proportion of facilities under the auspices of nonprofit organizations.

While it is clear that important progress has been made in improving the quality of care in nursing homes of the state, the ultimate solution to the chronic illness problem must lie in a reorganization of the medical care delivery system. The care and treatment of the long-term patient must be part of a broad continuum of service—preventive, diagnostic, treatment, rehabilitative, ambulatory, and institutional. This is what we mean by comprehensive, continuous, well-integrated patient care services. The nursing home must be part of a medical care system—it cannot be isolated or outside that system.

It is my view that fundamental to the restructuring of health services must be a new understanding of the crucial and central role that the hospital must play. The hospital of the future must be a social instrument that will serve as the core facility in the vast spectrum of health services. Quite clearly, every practicing physician must have ready access to the hospital's resources if he is to provide the best medical care. The ambulatory services of the hospital must be prepared to treat all patients, not only the indigent or medically indigent, and the model for such treatment must be a group practice unit based at or related to the hospital to provide total care to all patients in its geographic area.

Implicit in the new definition of the hospital is its direct responsibility for the care of the long-term patient. Constructive planning for medical care services implies that all chronic care or nursing home facilities should be physically or functionally related to the core institution—the general hospital. The real disaster in nursing home care has been its isolation from the hospital. Today community leaders, medical care experts, and the federal and state governments through recent legislation have all recognized that good-quality chronic care must be delivered as part of a system related to the general hospital. This does not suggest, however, that the long-term patient must be kept in the general hospital. On the contrary, the hospital is just the place where he should not be, both from the point of view of the patient's progress after the acute stage of illness has passed and in terms of the costs to the community. But around the core of the hospital there must be a series of related facilities and programs designed to treat the patient according to his needs at varying stages of his illness, with continuity of care through the coordinated efforts of the hospital's staff and program. This not only relates to institutional facilities such as nursing homes but also means organized home care services, visiting nursing services, and a variety of rehabilitative services —all integrated by the hospital to assure that they are rendered in a continuous and coordinated fashion and are of high quality.

It is only through the creation of an organized system of health care services that the community can be assured that its nursing homes will provide patients with the best that medical science has to offer. There is no question that we are moving in this direction. The Governor's Committee on Hospital Costs, which stimulated the enactment of the Folsom Law, understood and accepted this concept. The New York State and New York City Health Departments and the various regional and hospital health councils are committed, at least in theory, to these principles. The recent comprehensive health planning legislation and the Regional Medical Programs, both federally supported, are essentially based on the concept of the integration of health services. The question then becomes when and how will it be done.

I have every reason to believe that this excellent study will help in the movement toward this goal.

The Bronx, New York
October 1968

Preface

This study undertakes to illuminate the processes by which public policy grows and is shaped. It attempts to seek out and describe the ways in which people determine what they want from their community and how they go about influencing their social institutions to produce the desired effects. To a great extent, however, it illustrates that public policy on a given matter does not always develop in an orderly, step-by-step procedure. It describes how policy may emerge as a relatively clear statement of what is desired or thought needed in a particular area, but then may lose form and content and meander in aimless confusion. That this occurs in modern society is known in a general way. Nonetheless, it is often bewildering when it does occur. Understanding of why it has occurred, in any given situation, can be gained only through a detailed examination of the various factors that have influenced the evolution of the policy.

This is a case study and hence does not employ a general approach to the understanding of all policy development, but rather explores a substantial body of historical, factual detail in one area. The case studied is not a particular decision or event, but the whole historical development of public policy influencing the growth and elaboration of a new kind of social contrivance, the nursing home, in New York State.

The "publicness" of public policy has to do with its adoption, or potential for adoption, as government policy. The concept is concerned not only with formal manifestations of government intent such as laws, rules, and regulations. It con-

siders as well government administration on the firing line
—where actual government action, whether or not guided by
articulated policy or vigorous leadership, has its impact upon
individual citizens. It sees policy as often shaped through usage.
It is concerned with the absence, as well as the presence, of
policy and also with the presence of streams of opinion in the
community whose holders are striving for their adoption as
government policy. It recognizes that public policy is a
process, a matter of dynamic relationships between people, and
that its being either "public" or "policy" is only a matter of
degree. The pages that follow are intended to demonstrate the
validity of this concept of public policy.

About Nursing Homes

The nursing home is to be distinguished from homes or
other institutions providing only custodial, or domiciliary, care
in that its services include not only board, lodging, and help
with the daily personal chores necessary for comfortable living,
but also continuous skilled nursing care. It is also to be distinguished from hospitals—if they are performing their proper
function—in that it does not offer intensive physician care and
its patients typically stay much longer than those in hospitals.

The arrival of the nursing home on the health care scene
is essentially a consequence of three developments, each relatively recent from a historical point of view. First, the improvement of the hospital as a curative, remedial facility called for
a division of labor separating the historical sheltering function that hospitals performed in the past from acute care. Second, with the increasing urbanization of society there occurred
a change in the character of domestic social structure, the con-
jugal family assuming a much greater importance than the
extended family. Old people, especially if they are sick, are not
accommodated as conveniently within the family as they once
were. Third, there has been an increase in life span and, as a
result, in the proportion of aged persons in the population.

The number of persons sixty-five years of age or over in New York State grew from 784,845 in the mid-1930's to 1,876,616 in 1964. This constituted an expansion from 6.10 to 10.71 per cent of the state's population. These factors, combined with the fact that old age is frequently accompanied with debilities requiring long-term nursing care, created a new need.

WILLIAM C. THOMAS, JR.

Glen Rock, New Jersey
September 1968

Acknowledgments

Let me first thank Aldred E. Duncker, whose hard-digging research efforts and tireless analyses enabled me to outline the main historical developments of the story told in this book. Credit should go as well to I. Jay Brightman, Assistant Commissioner of the New York State Department of Health, who originated the idea that tax and administrative structures had been sufficiently important in the development of facilities for the care of the aged to justify special investigation. Dr. Brightman approached the Columbia University School of Public Health and Administrative Medicine (CUSPHAM), where I am a faculty member, with a proposal for this research. The State Health Department financed the work, in part. Ray E. Trussell, Associate Dean at Columbia and Director of CUSPHAM, carefully read an earlier version and the near final version of the manuscript. Beatrice Mintz not only made many helpful suggestions after a searching examination of the original version of the manuscript, she also patiently attended my many needs that could be met by the Archives of CUSPHAM, of which she is the Director. Herman E. Hilleboe, currently of the faculty of CUSPHAM, was New York State's Commissioner of Health for sixteen of the years during which important developments in health planning were occurring. His readings of this work provided a reassuring test of my judgment. His generous and warm encouragement is also gratefully and affectionately acknowledged. Virginia Brown has kindly and consistently helped me over a number of years to learn about the work of health facilities.

I am also indebted to David Schneider and Gertrude Binder. As Administrator of the Office of Medical Economics of the State Department of Welfare, Dr. Schneider—and his Senior Research Analyst, Miss Kathryn Miller—provided much of the data on beds and institutions that make up the quantitative base of this study, and in Chapter 2 I have drawn upon Dr. Schneider's exemplary studies of the history of public welfare in New York State. Miss Binder, Chief of the Bureau of Adult Institutions of the Department of Social Welfare (now the Department of Social Services), was extremely helpful in my efforts to understand enforcement problems in nursing home regulation. I am obliged to many others of the Department of Social Welfare. Ray Gramm I shall never forget. Byron Hipple, Deputy Commissioner for many years, called my attention to the important phenomenon, specialization of institutions. There are still others.

To Cyrille Gell for help in preparing the manuscript, and to Anna Luchessi, Shirley Karlin, Ruth Warren, and Ada Weingarten for secretarial assistance, go my thanks.

Some two hundred public officials and other persons who have been involved in one or another phase of the development of nursing homes and health facility planning have talked to me or Al Duncker, corresponded with us, or opened their files to us. Differences of opinion were encountered, but obstructions other than those posed by the inherent difficulty of the research problem were truly minimal. Research is especially rewarding under these conditions.

The encouragement, instruction, and aid I received I gladly acknowledge; yet I alone accept responsibility for all errors of judgment and fact—and also for some of what is useful—to be found in the pages that follow.

                                                                W. T.

Contents

Tables

Figures

Nursing Homes and Public Policy

Drift and Decision in New York State

CHAPTER 1

Introduction

A Study of Change

Traditionally, where health care has been provided through institutions, the organizations involved have been predominantly nonprofit. Hospitals are the most obvious example. However, in the provision of nursing home care, which has grown to become a major consideration in the field of health services since the 1930's, institutions operating on the principle that income should render a profit above costs have come clearly to outstrip nonprofit facilities—those operated by government and voluntary agencies. This change has had profound consequences for the rendering of care. The purpose of this study is to explain in some measure the reasons for it and for other important modifications in the health care field, demonstrating that they have been intimately related to public policy.

Modern health care institutions evolved from medieval precursors that were fundamentally ecclesiastical in character. Public hospitals and dispensaries emerged as urban populations developed. In time, secular voluntary organizations appeared alongside these and the church-promoted hospitals. These different kinds of facilities had a common quality: all were organized around the primary purpose of rendering a service. To this end, the organizational model they adopted was not designed to produce material gain for those sponsoring the institution, or for any others, save perhaps the patients. Such institutions are to be distinguished from business concerns, which are designed for the gain of their promoters.

Consonant with the tradition of institutional care being administered by nonprofits agencies is an unmistakable predominance of opinion among leaders in the public health and welfare fields that profit is not an appropriate motive for ministering to the needs of nursing home patients, who are as a whole unusually dependent because they are aged, chronically ill, and are often confused or emotionally disturbed. The development of this belief is not recent.

Probably underlying this professional opinion are inarticulate premises regarding motivational principles in organizations that have been spelled out somewhat by organizational theorists. For example, Peter M. Blau and W. Richard Scott, in their book *Formal Organizations*, distinguish between "business concerns" (profit-making), "service organizations," and governmental agencies. In business organizations, they state, the prime beneficiaries are expected to be the owners. In service organizations the basic function is to serve clients. Government agencies are expected to serve the public at large.[1] The clear implication is that organizations based on the principles of business concerns are inappropriate for the provision of service to sick people.

With the advent of the nursing home, proprietary homes—businesses operated for profit—grew from virtual nonexistence to dominate the whole field of long-term health care in the face of the hundreds of years of health facility tradition and despite the predominance of critical judgment of professionals and leaders. And they continue to grow today. Nationally, beds in proprietary homes outnumber those in voluntary and government nursing homes combined by a ratio of about 70 per cent to 30 per cent.[2] In New York State, historically the heart of the philanthropic movement of the country and the seat of much

[1] *Formal Organizations: A Comparative Approach* (San Francisco: Chandler, 1962), pp. 45–57.

[2] Calculated from E. Earl Bryant and Carl A. Taube, *Utilization of Institutions for the Aged and Chronically Ill*, United States Public Health Service Publication No. 1000, Series 12, no. 4 (Washington: Government Printing Office, 1966), Table 1, p. 14.

liberal political philosophy, proprietary institutions do not dominate so strongly. But they do dominate, representing some 73 per cent of the institutions and 57 per cent of the beds.

Considering the circumstances, the abrupt and marked departure from established organizational forms is remarkable. But the development of proprietary institutions is only part of the story. The nursing home, as a facility providing a novel and specialized kind of service whether under proprietary, voluntary, or governmental auspices, is a relative newcomer to the spectrum of institutions that provide health care for people. The emergence of need, the recognition of the need and the evolution of a new concept are also important threads of the historical fabric. Still other threads are processes of change that have occurred within each of the three types. As the reader will see, proprietary homes have undergone considerable metamorphosis from their primitive origins. Changes in voluntary institutions are of possibly equal significance. Public homes, the precursors of all nursing homes, would hardly be recognized today by one accustomed to their predecessors of fifty years ago.

Still another theme of importance to the matters under consideration here is the relationship of nursing homes and of other kinds of institutions, particularly hospitals, to each other. Historically one of the major problems concerning health care facilities generally and long-term care facilities, of which nursing homes are one kind, in particular, has been the absence of any ordering principles or instrumentality fashioning the association of institutions with each other so that each might handle patients most appropriately. There was and is, in other words, an absence of coordination. The point was graphically made by Dr. Ernst Boas' foreword to a study by Mary Jarrett in the early 1930's:

Thus we find a very confused picture—patients at home who should be in hospitals, patients in hospitals who should be in less complex institutions, patients in homes for the aged that are not prepared to minister to their needs, patients in convalescent homes occupying beds needed for another purpose. A mad confusion of patients and institutions. . . . It is really a scene of the greatest disorder that presents itself as the report unfolds the many types of agency that contribute to the care of the chronic sick: public and private hospitals, homes for the aged, convalescent homes, nursing and visiting doctor services, after-care agencies for sheltered work, medical social service departments, and family service agencies.[3]

The reader may note with interest that in 1933 the "nursing home" was not part of the scene. Its later appearance, however, only aggravated the conditions described by Dr. Boas. This was particularly so because, with rare exceptions, proprietary nursing homes were administratively and financially unassociated with any other medical care facility. Two major efforts to improve order have been the moves to have nursing homes associated with general hospitals and to establish a system of organizing health care institutions on a community-wide basis, assuring the provision of proper numbers of the proper kinds of beds in the proper places, and staffed by the proper kinds of personnel to meet the discernible needs of the community.

Closely related to this matter, and even an integral part of it, is a deeper and more general theme to be found in the historical development to be spelled out here. It is the halting, sometimes ebbing, progression to broader and broader areas, both geographically and in subject matter administered, for the basis of public administration and finance. At the beginning of the story, in the post-Revolutionary War period, public administration is characterized by a strident localism. From that point on there occur many moves, some successful, to include more under single administrative umbrellas. At one time the effort would be to broaden the tax base by moving it from the town to the county, at another to have a more comprehensive code for the regulation of nursing homes, and at a third to have uniform state reimbursement to local governments for all kinds, rather than only some, of the care they provided at public expense. A list of almost infinite length could be

[3] Mary C. Jarrett, *Chronic Illness in New York City*, Vol. 1: *The Problems of Chronic Illness* (New York: Columbia University Press, 1933), p. xiii.

made of such examples. It would be a mistake to see this phenomenon as growing centralization. In some instances it did involve greater centralization; in some it did not. What it did attempt consistently was the casting of wider and wider organizational boundaries to encompass more people, needs, and resources within one integrating network.

It is the thesis of this study that public policy has been important in determining what was to be done about new kinds of health service needs. There has been an interplay of policy with other factors, of course, such as traditions of private charity, traditional organization of private charitable institutions, and economic considerations, that have not always been direct consequences of governmental action. And, the influence of public policy has often not been direct and simple—often it has been oblique and always it has been complex. Because the story about to be told is an intricate and involved one, the reader may find a preliminary exposition of its main contours helpful in understanding it.

Synopsis

BACKGROUND

Public policy affecting the poor, sick, and aged from the post-Revolutionary War period through the nineteenth century tended to follow, rather uncertainly, the philosophy of indoor relief—persons could not get help except in almshouses. Financing was on the basis of small, local jurisdictions. The development of specialized institutions, such as those for children and the insane, left a residual population in almshouses comprised of aged, sick persons. New York State legislation of 1929 and 1930 embraced the philosophy of outdoor relief, emphasizing care given outside of institutions, preferably in one's own home.

Despite recognition of a growing need for systematic provision of institutional care for long-term illness, the state passed, in 1930, the Old Age Security Act providing state aided pensions to aged persons not in institutions. The federal Social

Security Act of 1935 resembled New York's law in that Old-Age Assistance and Aid to the Blind brought federal financial support, but not to those in public institutions. In implementing the federal law, New York left to local governments the sole financial responsibility for any welfare recipients in "a public or private institution of a custodial, correctional or curative character."

EARLY DEVELOPMENT OF PROPRIETARY NURSING HOMES
IN UPSTATE NEW YORK

In upstate New York social welfare investigators faced the imperative of finding places to care for increasing numbers of sick, homeless, aged people. Private family homes seemed the only answer that would allow the local governments to draw the substantial state and federal aid available. But the homes lost their family character as the numbers of their clients increased and became proprietary nursing homes. An explosive growth in their number occurred. Yet they were not part of any health care system and were virtually unregulated.

Concern grew about the legality of the use of these homes for public charge patients and about the quality of services they were rendering. The State Board of Social Welfare and its agent, the Department of Social Welfare, which supervised institutional care in the state, conducted studies of them. They concluded that proprietary homes were inappropriate facilities for sick people, but in the face of need, sought and obtained state legislation legalizing partial reimbursement, with state and federal money, of the amounts spent by local governments for the care of public charge patients in such homes and in other private, but not governmental, institutions. The new law, passed in 1944, made reimbursement for care of persons in proprietary homes contingent upon such facilities being inspected by the local government concerned. (Inspection of nonprofit facilities had long been a responsibility of the Social Welfare Administration.) The following year the State Health Preparedness Commission called for state regulation of proprietary homes. In 1951 legislation providing for the registration and inspection of these institutions was passed and a mild code of regulations promulgated.

VOLUNTARY AND PUBLIC HOMES UPSTATE

Meanwhile, voluntary facilities offering nursing home care had not grown appreciably. The legislative strictures on "custodial" and "curative" care in institutions had been important—there was no question about voluntary homes being institutions as there had been about the proprietary homes. A second important limiting factor was the traditional image of these places as philanthropic institutions, supported by and serving the members of, specific religious, fraternal and other nongovernmental organizations. Close ties of the homes to their parent bodies—and to the hospitals operating under their auspices—generally assured considerate, responsible care of patients. On the other hand, such ties gave rise to reluctance for voluntaries to become involved in the care of public charges. Probably even more important, in the minds of the members of the voluntary organizations and those of government officials, the philanthropic image dictated that a significant portion of the cost of giving the care should be borne by the organization —which in time created a financial crisis for voluntary health care institutions.

Public nursing home institutions, ineligible to receive any but local government money for care given, languished in neglect. Amendments to the Social Security Act in 1950 finally provided that federal money could flow on to public facilities, but New York State was caught in a stalemate of upstate-downstate politics and was unable to contrive a similar modification of policy in regard to state money. A 1946 change in the formula of state aid to local governments for welfare purposes had, as a matter of fact, aggravated the disadvantage under which the public facilities were working.

THE 1950'S AND ATTEMPTS AT REDRESS

During the 1950's there were further modest efforts to redress the imbalance between proprietary and nonprofit nursing homes. State reimbursements became available to public homes in 1954. In the same year the Hill-Burton law was amended to provide federal funds to aid in the construction of public and voluntary nursing homes. Proprietary homes, operating largely through the American Nursing Home Association, failed in attempts to share Hill-Burton benefits, but succeeded in 1959 in securing from Congress loan guarantees administered by the Federal Housing Administration.

The FHA program stimulated the growth of institutions unrelated to any systematic network of community health facilities. The Hill-Burton Program, designed to develop such a network, ultimately proved more worth while, at least so far as nursing homes are concerned, more because of its design than because of the funds it provided. Voluntary and public homes were stimulated slightly during the 1950's, but the proprietaries continued to race far ahead of them in number in upstate New York.

In this race, the proprietary homes encountered reverses at the end of the decade. The typical proprietary home had been small, somewhat amateurishly operated—although it had had a nursing orientation—and not well financed. Supply began to overtake demand and government-imposed standards raised costs. The confluence of these factors resulted in a reduction in the number of proprietary beds from 1958 through 1962. A trend for financially strong, management-oriented persons to be attracted to the field and to build large homes intensified. The character of the proprietary nursing home was changing significantly. The character of the trade organization, the New York State Nursing Home Association, showed signs of reflecting that change.

NEW YORK CITY VARIATIONS

Until 1952, New York City had followed a policy, quite different from that of upstate New York, of regulating proprietary nursing homes and of eschewing their use for public welfare recipients. Proprietary growth had been minimal in the city even though the city's hospitals had become crowded with aged, long-term patients. Realizing that the use of proprietary homes was reimbursable, and capitulating at last to the pressure of bed shortages, the city shifted its policy and began to transfer patients from city hospitals to these homes. The owners and administrators were counseled to undertake self-regulation.

An immediate and continuing expansion of proprietary facilities followed. Then, in 1958, scandal broke. Homeowners were charged with defrauding the city of huge sums of money and were required to pay it back—at a discount. Strong reform measures were instituted. Licenses of numerous homes were revoked. Homes were closed. A new code was formulated—the most demanding in the country. A new organization, the Metropolitan Nursing Home Association, took shape under these pressures.

Voluntary institutions in the city showed much less reluctance than their upstate counterparts to assume the responsibilities of caring for public charges. Yet, partly because the government paid them less than cost for such work, they did not expand their nursing home services significantly. The city public nursing home facilities emerged from the nineteenth-century almshouse stage only in the 1950's. The development was unique in that nursing home units were developed in close relation to hospitals rather than to residential quarters. The city encountered substantial resistance from state authority in breaking this tradition. There was also resistance on the part of teaching hospitals in the municipal hospital complex—doctors feared that little could be learned from tending to the aged. Nevertheless, the concept became well established, although public home infirmary care—as it is called—did not grow to any imposing dimension.

THE PRESENT: PUBLIC POLICY CONSOLIDATED

The 1960's brought a consolidation of policy related to nursing homes in New York State. Under the pressure of rising hospital costs, the utility of the nursing home as an efficient alternative to the acute-care hospital was broadly recognized. Under the same impetus, state authority was instituted to determine that unneeded new health care facilities, including hospitals and nursing homes, would not be constructed. In 1965 legislation provided that all facilities caring for public charges should be paid at cost, transferred the responsibilities of regulating all health care institutions from the Board and Department of Social Welfare to the more qualified Department of Health, and strengthened the regulating powers considerably. In 1966 statutes provided long-term, low interest loans for the construction of voluntary nursing homes and grants similarly supporting public institutions of this type. A strong state-wide code was promulgated soon thereafter. Thus governmental structure to assure a properly deployed set of facilities to provide nursing home and other institutional health care on a planned, community-wide basis was established.

There were other developments in the 1960's. Many of the old proprietary institutions, weak from a financial and managerial standpoint, had ceased existence, and the industry plunged ahead with renewed growth. Proprietary homes were becoming big business. Nationally, proprietary nursing home people moved to strengthen their organization. The federal legislature produced the 1965 amendments to the Social Security Act—providing Medicare and Medicaid—which promised unprecedented financial support for nursing home care. Elsewhere on the national scene, a nongovernmental program of nursing home accreditation to be administered by the Joint Commission on Hospital Accreditation under the auspices of the American Medical Association, the American Hospital Association, the American Association of Nursing Homes (proprietary) and the American Association of Homes for the Aged (voluntary) was established in 1966, after a protracted imbroglio.

Public policy related to nursing homes apparently was becoming directed in a comprehensive, meaningful, and deliberate fashion in the mid-1960's. Many of the policy options had already been eroded away by history. But this is probably inevitable in the development of all concerted community action.

Definitions

Up to this point I have casually referred to proprietary, public, and voluntary "nursing homes." To continue this usage would obscure some important differences between these different kinds of institutions. From now on, therefore, it is necessary to use the clumsy generic rubric "nursing-home-type facilities" and, by and large, public and most voluntary facilities will not be referred to as nursing homes.

The most complete data available on the numbers of facilities and beds in the state are those collected over the years by the Department of Social Welfare. The classifications followed by the Department to distinguish between kinds of facilities are not ideal for present purposes in every respect but they are useful and, since the needed data are cast in these terms, are used here. The classifications are four in number: Infirmaries of private homes for the aged, incorporated nursing and convalescent homes, public infirmaries, and proprietary nursing homes. Data on the numbers of these various kinds of institutions at different times from the mid-1930's down through 1964 are presented in the six master tables of Appendix I of this study, from which most of the tables and figures in the text are drawn.

"Private homes for the aged"—the descriptive language is in statutory form—are voluntary, nonprofit organizations established under the membership corporations law of the state. They are tax-exempt and solicitation for philanthropic contributions for their support is permitted. Historically, private homes for the aged were institutions offering domiciliary and personal care services almost exclusively. Now many have infirmary sections where skilled nursing care is given. Such sections are generally regarded as nursing home-type facilities and are so regarded for the purposes of this study. They may provide charitable care, may charge private patients, or may accept patients supported at public expense.

"Incorporated nursing homes" and "incorporated convalescent homes"—again the specific words have a statutory base—similarly are tax-exempt, nonprofit voluntary institutions, with charters of incorporation and privileges of philanthropic solicitation. They may accept the same classes of patients as private homes for the aged. Incorporated nursing homes are to be distinguished from private homes for the aged in that they have no domiciliary sections but are devoted fully to the rendering of care with skilled nursing. Incorporated convalescent homes, under definition by a rule of the State Board of Social Welfare, have not given nursing care.[4] Historically, however, this has not always been the conception of a convalescent home; in 1945 some appear to have been giving such care, at least in New York City.[5] Moreover, the state Hill-Burton agency, the Division of Hospital Review and Planning of the State Health Department, regards incorporated convalescent homes as the equivalents of incorporated nursing homes. Finally, the table kept by the Department of Social Welfare in which data on incorporated nursing homes are available lumps these latter with the convalescent institutions. Figures for the two kinds of

[4] See *Charter for the Aging: New York State Conference Convened by Governor Averell Harriman at the State Capitol in Albany, 1955*, pp. 202–203, for some of the distinctions between these various classes of facilities.

[5] New York State Health Preparedness Commission, *Planning for the Care of the Chronically Ill in New York State—Some Medical-Social and Institutional Aspects*, Leg. Doc. No. 66A (Albany, 1946), pp. 22–23. A 1959 study of nonprofit convalescent homes serving New York City reported that "they are not nursing-convalescent homes as the term is applied to the proprietary nursing home or the chronic care facility." It found them largely oriented to short-term care and varying extensively in the kinds and levels of care they offered. Magda Gislaine Pendall, *Convalescence and Institutional Convalescent Care*, Columbia University School of Public Health and Administrative Medicine (New York, 1959), pp. 1–3.

facilities are combined in this study. Incorporated convalescent homes have decreased in importance over the years. The relevant 1964 directory listed only four in upstate New York and one in New York City.[6]

Public home infirmaries are institutions owned and operated by local governments, almost exclusively for the care of public charges. They make up parts, or in some instances the whole, of county and city homes, and, as with infirmaries of private homes for the aged, are to be distinguished from the domiciliary sections of the homes in that they add skilled nursing care to the other services given. Not all public homes have infirmaries.

Proprietary nursing homes are privately owned and may not be incorporated. They provide food, lodging, personal and skilled nursing care, for compensation and profit, to both private patients and those maintained at public expense.

About This Study

The research techniques employed for this report have been, for the most part, those traditionally used in historical studies. There has been a considerable reliance upon the files of various governmental and private agencies. Some of the most troublesome research problems encountered have been those associated with establishing a set of satisfactory statistics indicating the growth of different classes of nursing-home-type institutions. The primary resources have been the files of the State Health Department, the New York City Department of Hospitals, and, as noted, the State Department of Social Welfare. The statistical problems are discussed in the note preceding the master tables, of Appendix I, and in the footnotes to those tables.

The presentation of the material in the following pages is in essentially chronological order, the major exception being that public policy in New York City after 1930, and the impact

---

[6] New York State Department of Social Welfare, "Incorporated Non-Profit Nursing Homes, Convalescent Homes and Homes for Adults in New York City and in Upstate New York," March 1, 1964.

of that policy upon nursing home development in the city, are described separately in Chapter 6, after state policy and its influence upstate have been examined. We begin this chronological treatment in Chapter 2 by turning to New York State in the post-Revolutionary War period. For public attitudes and opinions of public leaders, reverberating out of the clashes of the industrial revolution, were to remain as impressions important to the development of nursing-home-type institutions until the middle of the twentieth century.

CHAPTER 2

Early Background
in Welfare Policy

Local Responsibility, Outdoor and Indoor Relief

As the State of New York emerged from the Revolutionary War period, it began developing what was probably its harshest and most stringent set of measures for the provision of public welfare. The central concern was the fixing of financial responsibility for relief, and the aim was to limit such responsibility within narrow and specific confines. After going so far as to break the parishes down into districts (parishes were divisions of towns) as the basis for support of the poor in 1784, the legislature, in a 1788 law entitled An Act for the Better Settlement and Relief of the Poor, determined that every city and town should maintain its own poor. "The new act dealt more with the problems of settlement and removal than with those of relief," according to David Schneider.[1] Settlement—that is, entitlement to relief from a given jurisdiction and involving residence—was hedged about with thorny qualifications to make it difficult to get. Paying rent or taxes or serving as a bound apprentice for two years, or as a public official for one, were qualifications for acquiring settlement. Being born in a community was not enough; children born out of wedlock were considered as settled in the same places as their mothers. A good many of the legal provisions described procedures for

---

[1] David M. Schneider, *The History of Public Welfare in New York State, 1609–1866* (Chicago: University of Chicago Press, 1938), p. 112.

"removing" a needy person from town if he had no settlement there. Upon a finding that a newcomer was likely to become a public charge, he was to be passed from constable to constable through jurisdictions until he reached his place of legal settlement. Those so audacious as to return after having been removed could be whipped.[2]

Welfare administration as well as financial responsibility was tied to a low organizational level. The Poor Law of 1788 was the first general authorization for almshouses, or poorhouses. It provided that any town or city might establish such an institution.[3] A second law of the same year required that all counties be divided into towns and that two overseers of the poor, who would run the almshouses, be elected in each town and city.[4] Two selected overseers for each ward had already been prescribed for New York City,[5] but responsibility for management of the almshouse was centralized into the hands of the Mayor and Aldermen and delegated in 1788 to thirteen Commissioners of the Almshouse and Bridewell (jail).[6]

Assessments and Proposals

Although there were differences between the American and English poor laws, the former were largely an inheritance of the latter and the phases that each went through were remarkably similar. And, although America lagged behind the mother country, at times New York, if not the United States as a whole, was somewhat ahead.

About the turn of the century there developed in both countries a flurry of investigations into poor laws and their administration. Major redirections of policy grew to fruition in 1824 here and a decade later in England. The immediate

---

   [2] *Ibid.,* pp. 112–114.   [3] *Ibid.,* p. 118.   [4] *Ibid.,* p. 119.
   [5] Paul E. Malone, *The Fiscal Aspects of State and Local Relationships in New York,* New York State Tax Commission Special Report No. 13 (Albany, 1937), p. 325.
   [6] Schneider, pp. 117–118.

stimulus for the New York change was a study of poor relief, the most comprehensive to its time, made by the Secretary of State, John W. N. Yates.[7] The actual purpose of the study and the report that followed was that of a trial balloon, to test responses to the idea that a system of almshouses should be established throughout the State and that relief should be granted only to those in residence in such institutions. At this time, only about thirty of the towns and cities had taken the option allowed under the law of 1788, or had acted under laws specifically empowering them to set up poorhouses. Of a total of some 22,111 public relief recipients in the State, Yates estimated that less than a tenth were maintained in almshouses. The remainder were generally given relief in their homes, contracted out for care to those who would keep them for a set fee, or to those who offered the lowest bids for their care. Such contractors had the privilege of putting their charges to work.[8]

We may summarize the liabilities of the contemporary poor relief laws and administration as reported by Secretary Yates by dividing them into three general areas: first, the operations were expensive; second, there was inadequate education or supervision given to relief recipients; third—and after this mention we shall go no further into the matter—"idiots and lunatics do not receive sufficient care and attention in towns, where no suitable asylums for their reception are established."[9]

Chief among Yates's criticisms of the existing poor law system was its expense. He reported that poor relief expenditures had risen from $245,000 in 1815 to $470,582 in 1822.[10] The uneconomic nature of the operations showed up in high costs of administration—in the state as a whole, almost one-ninth of the costs were going to pay overseers, lawyers, constables, and justices; and in Orange County more tax money actually went to overhead than to direct care of the poor.[11] The disadvantages of having recipients dispersed in towns, and such a large proportion dispersed outside of institutions, also made costs run

---

[7] *Ibid.*, p. 218.   [8] *Ibid.*, p. 221.   [9] *Ibid.*, pp. 226–227.
[10] *Ibid.*, p. 119.   [11] *Ibid.*, p. 224.

higher, it was argued. Especially was this presumed to be so with the sick, whose medical care accounted for a substantial share of the expenditures.[12]

The second fault was thought to be the lack of supervision over recipients. This was considered important because opinion gathered from all over the state by Yates for his study, and reflected in his own report, was that most dependency arose out of individual dependents' faults and weaknesses. The observation of a Poughkeepsie Overseer of the Poor, for example, was that "a great portion of the paupers are voluntary, in consequence of drunkenness, idleness and vice of all kinds."[13] Secretary Yates himself confused symptoms and cause; he believed that most dependency was attributable to intemperance.[14] Specific aspects of this lack of guidance were spelled out. Children grew up in ignorance, it was noted, or were schooled only in the ways of undesirables. The poor as a whole learned no habits of industry. Indeed, it was argued that the prevailing system encouraged beggary, reliance on public relief, and crime.

As Secretary Yates was criticizing the poor law system in New York, similar moves were being made in England that were to produce similar results, though for somewhat dissimilar reasons. After the establishment of a workhouse system in 1722, England had encountered great problems in caring for the able-bodied, the aged, the sick, and children all within the confines of single institutions, even though it found this principle an economic one. Outdoor relief for the able-bodied poor became mandatory with the passage of the Gilbert Act in 1782. The outdoor relief policy was pressed even further by the Speenhamland system of 1795, which gave public grants to all whose income fell below a certain level. The arrangement proved a boon to employers, who cut wages with the assurance that government would provide for employees, and a near disaster to government, which soon was subsidizing employers' payrolls heavily.[15]

[12] *Ibid.,* p. 229.   [13] *Ibid.,* p. 220.   [14] *Ibid.,* p. 219.
[15] Charles W. Pipkin, "Poor Laws," *Encyclopedia of the Social Sciences,* ed. Edwin R. A. Seligman, XII (1934), 331.

These troubles in England, and the growing relief expenditures in New York, gave rise to increasing doubts about the wisdom of outdoor relief, and even to questions about the justification of any public relief whatsoever. In England this movement culminated in the milestone poor law amendment of 1834, which adopted the policy of exclusive indoor relief, the principle of "less eligibility," and a measure of centralization in the administration of relief measures.[16] The seat of the rationale that underlay the English change was philosophic radicalism and its purpose there was largely to rationalize labor —that is, to make labor mobile and readily available for employment in industry by relaxing settlement laws and making relief decidedly less appealing than employment.[17] New Yorkers were swayed by English arguments that the existing relief system was bad even though the industrial revolution had not progressed nearly so far here as there.[18]

Despite the difference in English and American conditions, the influence of English thinking was strong enough that the New York reform proved to be remarkably similar to that eventuating in England even though it came ten years earlier. Secretary Yates had gathered communications from poor law authorities throughout the state, and from other states and countries, and the weight of opinion reflected therein favored a thoroughgoing shift to relief given only in institutions. He recommended the establishment of a state-wide system of county almshouses, each having a farm, where indigents could be maintained and would labor according to their abilities.[19] There was no question but what one intention of the proposal was to discourage persons from seeking public aid. This was

[16] Ibid. See also George Rosen, A History of Public Health (New York: MD Publications, 1958), p. 200.

[17] Pipkin, Encyclopedia of Social Sciences, XII, 231; Rosen, pp. 195–196.

[18] "There developed a tendency to apply English observations to the American scene, where conditions were not at all analogous to the situation in the mother country except for some surface similarities." Schneider, p. 216.

[19] Schneider, p. 227–228.

the principle of "less eligibility": "Those able to labor would prefer to work themselves outside than to work for others within the institutions," and "only those in most desperate need would accept the restrictions and humiliation entailed in such institutionalization." Yates reasoned not only that fewer would accept public relief, but also that indoor, or institutional, relief would not exceed $35 in annual per capita cost, where outdoor relief was averaging about $65. Also in consideration of effecting economy, but for the sake of ameliorating harshness as well, he recommended a relaxation of the settlement laws and the abolition of removal orders.[20]

Indoor Relief Attempted

In 1824 the State Legislature accepted the principles of Secretary Yates's report but failed to apply it consistently throughout the state. State leadership was not so strong as to prescribe modes of relief for all local government; or perhaps local government was too strong for such state leadership. The statute required County Boards of Supervisors to build almshouses, the construction and subsequent operation expenses to be maintained by county taxes—but excepted thirty-eight of the fifty-four counties. Supervisors were required to appoint superintendents of the poor houses, who in turn were to employ keepers of the institutions. Keepers were empowered to require inmates to work and were given sanctions of imposing solitary confinement and bread and water diets upon those who refused to obey orders. Finally, the law forbade the removal of persons across county lines.[21] Considerable relaxation of the settlement laws came later, in 1827.[22]

Even with this partial adoption of the proposed reforms, the lawmakers departed substantially from established policy. In a large sense, they accepted indoor relief and "less eligibility" as desirable over outdoor relief. They took steps toward centralizing relief administration—relief was to be handled through

[20] *Ibid.*, p. 229.   [21] *Ibid.*, pp. 235–236.   [22] *Ibid.*, p. 239.

the almshouse, and the almshouse was a county, not a town or city, institution; they moved upward one level of government in regard to fiscal responsibility—the town and the city were no longer solely responsible for their own poor in those places where the new plan applied, but shared that responsibility with other towns and cities in the county.[23] Moreover, the impact of the legislation was not all immediate. A measure was included to permit any of the thirty-eight excepted counties to adopt the new system; in a short time a number had done so.

The county poorhouse system proved, as had been predicted, to be impressively economical. Centralization and the principle of "less eligibility" were evidently effective factors. This, apparently, accounts primarily for its widened adoption. By 1832 forty-eight counties had almshouses and the principle of county financial responsibility—which had been made optional also—was being applied in thirty-five counties. By 1835 the comparable figures were fifty-one and forty counties.[24] Widespread sentiment in favor of the system developed. Governor Enos T. Throop declared in 1832 that the county poorhouse system

has had the effect of providing more effectually and comfortably for the needy, and of repressing idleness; and when in complete operation, it will save to the people of the State, in poor rates alone, an amount equal to one-half, and probably much more, of the ordinary expenses of administering the government.

By 1840 the proportions of county to town paupers had been widened—there were 52,764 of the former, but only 3,797 of the latter.[25]

In 1840, however, in Schneider's words, "the pendulum started to swing back toward town responsibility." Some of the forces generating such a swing had actually begun in 1826, when Schenectady County had secured special permission from

---

[23] But annual almshouse deficits were prorated for payment among the more local units at the end of each year according to the number of inmates in the almhouse each unit had.

[24] Schneider, p. 242.   [25] Ibid., pp. 242–243.

the legislature to grant outdoor relief. Justices of the peace in the county were empowered to conduct the investigations involved and grant temporary relief. Evidently it seemed necessary to give some applicants aid in their homes instead of sending them to the poorhouse. It is of importance that the justices were not county, but town and city officials. In 1827 such temporary—outdoor—relief was extended to certain applicants in all counties, conditional upon the approval of justices of the peace.[26] This proved to be a crack in the indoor relief system. Soon there was an increase in outdoor relief and a return to the principle of each town and city being responsible for their own poor. The ratio of town paupers to county paupers increased. By the time of the passage of the Public Welfare Act, in 1929, only two counties were not using towns as a basis for fixing financial responsibility.[27]

In 1840 charges mounted that the justices of the peace were being far too generous in allowing outdoor relief. The objections were not so much to outdoor relief, per se, as to officials representing only part of the county granting relief without the stigma of the poorhouse to persons from their own small part of the county, while the expenses would be borne by the county as a whole. This condition, it was argued, resulted in too much leniency.[28] The exercise of the taxing power at one level of government and of spending powers at a different level often raises problems of delineating and effectuating responsibilities of smaller units of government within larger units. Here is a theme woven throughout the whole of public policy regarding nursing homes.

The distribution of costs was not the only factor promoting outdoor relief. In 1838 a committee of the State Assembly investigated conditions in almshouses and found them unbelievably shocking in Genesee County. "Indiscriminate hearding" (sick and well, normal and insane, married and single, children and adults not separated even as to rooms); overcrowding in

---

[26] *Ibid.*, p. 239.   [27] Malone, p. 343.   [28] Schneider, p. 243.

unrepaired buildings; and uncared-for illnesses were the three most prominent characteristics of the institution reported. The pleas of the County Superintendent of the Poor for repair and enlargement of the institution had been ignored by the County Supervisors.[29]

In 1839 the legislature permitted Genesee County to grant outdoor relief—to give people support in their own homes—through town officials as an alternative to using the poorhouse, and to use the town as the base for financial responsibility. By 1843 five counties had been allowed to restore the town as the base, and before 1849 permission had been granted to eighteen others. In that latter year a general statute was passed granting any county the power to return to the town base,[30] which signaled the collapse of the principle of spreading financial responsibility for poor relief over the whole county.

It also signified a lessening, in a measure, of the commitment to indoor relief, although most county almshouses were still in operation and outdoor relief was still to be given only in exceptional cases. It is significant that in the conflict between the values of county financing and outdoor relief for exceptional cases, county financing yielded. Outdoor relief did, of course, have a powerful ally in the unwholesome conditions in almshouses, to which welfare leaders and the public became more and more sensitive.

In 1856 a committee of the State Senate undertook a comprehensive survey of poor law operations. The conditions they discovered in some of the fifty-seven almshouses then operating were the most deplorable reported in the history of the state. The recommendations ensuing were remarkably progressive for their time. After a finding that there were worthy people in poorhouses, pauperized through no fault of their own, the committee proposed that such persons be provided with the absolute necessities of life in their own homes, without the degradation of almshouse living. It also recommended that

29 *Ibid.*, p. 244.   30 *Ibid.*, pp. 245–246.

children and the insane be removed from almshouses to specialized institutions and that an organ of government be established at the state level to supervise almshouses and other
institutional operations.[31] Many years were yet to pass, and
other studies were to be made, before these reforms would be
instituted. But in 1867 a Board of State Commissioners of
Public Charities was created. Children were excluded from
almshouses in 1875, the mentally ill in 1890.

Nowhere, throughout the period being discussed, had opposition to outdoor relief been greater than in New York City.
And, paradoxically, nowhere had the reliance upon outdoor
relief been greater. The impact of depressions on the com-
mercial-industrial community, the influx of immigrants of low
economic status and the problems of large-scale administration
had frequently made resort to noninstitutional alms necessary
to cope with obvious destitution. Legislators, recognizing these
circumstances, had excepted the city from the poorhouse act of
1824.[32]

There was turmoil in the city. As the expenditures for outdoor relief mounted during the 1840's, the thirteen Commissioners of the Almshouse and Bridewell were replaced by one
official, a Commissioner of the Almshouse, in 1845. When this
official estimated, in 1848, that one-ninth of the population was
on public outdoor relief, and one-quarter on either public or
private outdoor relief, his office was replaced with a ten-man
Board of Governors. The Board was in turn supplanted by the
Department of Public Charities and Correction, headed by
four Commissioners, in 1860.[33]

Involvement in the scandals centering on Boss Tweed and
the demands of the depression of 1873–1878 gave the Department considerable trouble in regard to outdoor relief.[34] Political abuses in the distribution of aid were obvious and in the

---

[31] *Ibid.,* pp. 250–251.   [32] *Ibid.,* p. 246.   [33] *Ibid.,* pp. 247–248.
[34] David M. Schneider and Albert Deutsch, *The History of Public Welfare in New York State, 1867–1940* (Chicago: University of Chicago Press,
1941), pp. 35–36.

course of the investigation that resulted, the commissioners found it advisable to stop public outdoor relief entirely for some months during 1874–1875, which worked great hardship upon the thousands of employed. Mass meetings and militant demonstrations were common.

Throughout these times opposition to the use of outdoor relief remained strong and aggressive, both in New York City and in upstate urban areas as well. Private welfare leaders objected to soup lines as encouraging pauperism. The major trend, supported most strongly by the unemployed themselves, was toward the development of public works projects; but this trend became considerably more significant during the depression of 1893–1895. There was a marked recrudescence of the philosophy of the English poor law amendment of 1834—all relief should be given in institutions and the principle of less eligibility should apply.

Private charitable agencies, which, incidentally, were increasing in number during these times, were receiving large grants of public money from New York City for distribution as outdoor relief among the poor.[35] And a number of these organizations, joined by members of the State Board of Charities, engaged in a campaign against public outdoor relief in the downstate area.

In 1876 the City Board of Estimate and Apportionment sharply reduced the amount allocated to outdoor relief, and channeled what it did allocate toward private agencies. In succeeding years there was further limitation, cash grants to the blind and coal for others being all the noninstitutional help given by the city. In Brooklyn, after three Commissioners of Charities had been convicted of malfeasance in office and Seth Low, a leading reformer of the time, had excoriated outdoor relief as a "sore on the body politic" under which "the underlings connected with the distribution" reaped most of the benefits, this mode of aid was abolished. When the charter of

35 *Ibid.*, p. 47.

1898 combined the five boroughs into greater New York, it prohibited outdoor relief.[36] With a few specific exceptions, institutional care remained the only kind of aid that could be given by the city until the barrier was specifically removed by the State Old Age Security Act of 1930.[37]

Specialization in Institutional Care

Over the next three decades there was significant evolution in the almshouse and the outdoor-indoor relief policy. It was in a large measure attributable to changing attitudes of leadership bodies actively concerned with public relief, which came to see the almshouse as inappropriate for certain classes of persons. One factor that facilitated and reflected such change was the establishment of the State Charities Aid Association in 1872. This organization, though an interest group specializing in social welfare and public health, ranged broadly through the whole of those fields and established visiting committees in virtually every county in the State.[38] Louisa Lee Schuyler, granddaughter of Alexander Hamilton, developed the idea for the association after visits to the Westchester County poorhouse, and the avowed purpose at the time it was organized was the amelioration of conditions in almshouses.[39] The Board of State Commissioners of Public Charities welcomed the activities of the SCAA; with its support, the association was granted, by the laws of 1881, the privilege of receiving from State Supreme Court Justices the right to inspect any almshouse in the state, a power already residing with the Board. There was hardly a step in almshouse development between this time, through the passage of the Public Welfare Act of 1929 and the

[36] *Ibid.,* pp. 47–48.

[37] New York State Commission on Old Age Security, *Old Age Security, Report,* Leg. Doc. 67 (Albany, 1930), p. 21.

[38] Belle Zeller, *Pressure Politics in New York: A Study of Group Representation before the Legislature* (New York: Prentice-Hall, 1937), p. 134.

[39] *Ibid.,* p. 133.

Old Age Security Act of 1930, in which the SCAA did not play a significant, if not major, role.

The chief modification of policy affecting almshouses from the time of their official endorsement by public policy in 1824 through today—today they are no longer called almshouses but public homes—has been the emergence of other, specialized, charitable institutions that have drawn off various segments of the heterogeneous populations that once inhabited them. Indeed, the process of specialization had begun long before. An infirmary was set off in the New York City Almshouse in 1735; it became Bellevue, a hospital primarily for the poor, in 1825.[40] New York Hospital began receiving mentally ill patients in 1792, acquired state aid beginning in 1806, and could contract with overseers of the poor to care for mentally deranged persons who otherwise would be kept in almshouses beginning in 1809.[41] Later, other specialized agencies appeared. A school for the blind had its beginning by taking children from the New York City Almshouse in 1831. Public financial support for it started in 1833.[42] A state school for the feeble-minded began in Albany in 1851;[43] legislation provided for a House of Refuge for "vagrant and degraded" women to open at Hudson in 1884;[44] Craig Colony, in Livingston County, for epileptics was similarly established in 1894.[45]

Profound changes in the character of the almshouse were wrought through the exclusion from it of children. After the Senate committee of 1856 recommended that children be cared for elsewhere, a number of counties began placing minors in orphanages or with families; by 1874 half of the counties had discharged all children from their poorhouses.[46] Meanwhile, the State Board of Charities[47] and the State Charities Aid Association had allied themselves in a campaign to forbid the

---

[40] Schneider, p. 194.   [41] *Ibid.*, pp. 197–199.   [42] *Ibid.*, p. 372.
[43] *Ibid.*, p. 367.   [44] Schneider and Deutsch, pp. 103–104.
[45] *Ibid.*, p. 101.   [46] *Ibid.*, p. 61.
[47] The name had been changed from Board of Commissioners of Public Charities to State Board of Charities in 1873. *Ibid.*, p. 22.

use of almshouses for child care. Supported by the press and the County Superintendents of the Poor, they succeeded in bringing about the passage in 1875 of legislation forbidding the commitment of any child over three years of age to an almshouse.[48] There ensued considerable growth in private establishments for the care of children. Of undoubted significance for this development was the fact that, although a few counties set about creating public homes for children, state policy in general discouraged this practice.

The exclusion of the mentally ill from county institutions was probably as significant as the exclusion of children and was far more difficult to bring about. An act of 1865 required the transfer of all insane persons in poorhouses to state hospitals. Because of inadequate space in state institutions, however, fourteen counties were soon exempted from the law, and in 1881 thirty-eight nonexempted counties were still keeping the insane in their almshouses.[49] Repeated investigations revealed that at the county level these people were the subjects of brutality and inadequate medical care. The County Superintendents of the Poor bitterly opposed the move for state care, even though at a special conference in 1855 they had favored that plan. The reason for the change in their position evidently lay in a provision of the 1865 law levying a charge back to the county of settlement for each state patient.[50] The State charges were $2.00 per week or more per patient, while in many county institutions the weekly cost per inmate was less than $1.00. The State Charities Aid Association adopted a resolution favoring state care in 1886. Enlisting the support of medical associations, and in league with the State Commissioner in Lunacy, it secured the passage of a measure in 1890 that provided for care in state hospitals of all insane persons, wholly at state cost.[51] With this law, the State Care Act, effective provision was made to move another class of persons out of almshouses.

Although the process did not work with clocklike precision,

---

[48] *Ibid.*, p. 63.   [49] *Ibid.*, pp. 91–92.   [50] *Ibid.*, p. 93.
[51] *Ibid.*, pp. 96–97.

and although growth of specialized facilities to receive different classes of almshouse inhabitants was often far behind the numbers of persons waiting in almshouses to occupy them, in the long run there was an unmistakable change in almshouse population. Schneider and Deutsch have reported that, because of the rise of specialized institutions and changing public opinion toward dependency generally, "by the end of the [First] World War [the almshouse] was looked upon as an institution mainly for the care of the aged and infirm."[52] The *Hearings* and the *Report* of the New York State Commission on Old Age Security of 1929–1930 give no reason to question that conclusion.

The Shift to Outdoor Relief

A major development that chronologically preceded the emergence of the old age security issue was the renovation of the poor law as a whole—the passage of the Public Welfare Act of 1929. Once again it was the State Charities Aid Association, the private interest group, that was the driving force behind the reform. The State Board of Charities and elements of the legislature had made moves as early as 1924 and 1925 to have the law overhauled,[53] which undoubtedly helped create a climate favorable to change. The Association created a Committee on the Revision of the Poor Law in 1925, and adopted an ambitious plan for modernization.[54] In 1926, the Association of County Superintendents of the Poor got its own bill for codifying the law—which Charities Aid thought inadequate—introduced into the legislature. SCAA then hurriedly introduced a bill that would have made the county the welfare base and the county relief officer appointed rather than elected, which was distinctly unpalatable to the county officers. The result was stalement—neither bill was passed—which was tantamount to victory for the SCAA for the time being.[55]

The private organization then set about with painstaking

[52] *Ibid.,* p. 278.   [53] *Ibid.,* pp. 284–285.   [54] Zeller, pp. 144–146.
[55] *Ibid.,* p. 147.

care to develop grass roots support for the measure they were drawing up. Their representatives in various counties thoughout the state consulted with local politicians and other community leaders. Religious bodies were consulted and in some instances their suggestions were incorporated in the proposed legislation; a great number of civic and other community groups were brought into the movement. The opinions of various state departments were sought.[56] Pamphlets and speaking tours were used. However, although a genuine attempt was made to generate broad public support, the Association used the "utmost care" in soliciting the support of key persons in each county.[57] And after defeat of its proposals a second time, in 1927, by the Association of County Superintendents of the Poor, the SCAA brought this key body into the fold, setting up a Joint Committee comprised of County Superintendents, Charities Aid people, and representatives of the State Board of Charities.[58] The compromise that this committee produced—making the adoption of the county as the welfare financial base and the appointment or election of county welfare officers discretionary[59]— finally made possible the renovation of the poor law, the passage of the Public Welfare Law of 1929.[60]

The most significant feature of the welfare act, by far, was the degree to which it reversed public policy on the outdoor-indoor relief issue. Since the County Poorhouse Act of 1824, the law had definitely sponsored indoor relief—public aid was to be given only to those in institutions—although there had been exceptions to the principle arising out of inadequacies of institutional facilities and financial squabbles. The new law adopted an opposite principle: "Whenever practicable, relief shall be given to a poor person in his own home." The new provisions sought to prevent dependency and restore self-sufficiency through the giving of relief, rather than by withholding it or deterring its acceptance.[61] However—and this is

---

[56] *Ibid.,* pp. 149–150.   [57] *Ibid.,* p. 151.   [58] *Ibid.,* p. 148.
[59] *Laws of New York, 1929,* chap. 565, secs. 4, 25.
[60] Zeller, p. 148.
[61] *Laws of New York, 1929,* chap. 565, sec. 77.

of major importance for the purposes of this study—relief and care could also be provided "in a boarding home, the home of a relative, a public or private home or institution, or in a hospital."

In passing, we may note that there was no such clear change in the administrative machinery for handling public welfare as there was in policy statements. With the exception of five cities, counties were constituted public welfare districts, the principal administrative division.[62] The election or appointment of a new officer, a Public Welfare Commissioner, in each district was prescribed. The tug of parochialism was still extremely strong, however. The administration of home (outdoor) relief was left at the town level, to be carried out by appointed welfare officers.[63] County Boards of Supervisors were to decide if towns were to be financially responsible for maintaining town poor or whether the county would serve as the financial base for all welfare.[64] In 1937 six counties had chosen to operate under the county unit plan.[65] And a critic, writing in that year, declared that local fiscal responsibility "has been one of the most positive deterrents to developing welfare activities commensurate with the requirements of the new social and economic order."[66]

[62] *Ibid.*, sec. 17.   [63] *Ibid.*, sec. 24.   [64] *Ibid.*, sec. 25.
[65] Malone, p. 343.   [66] *Ibid.*, p. 340.

CHAPTER 3

Grants-in-Aid for Noninstitutional Relief

The New York State Old Age Security Act

It is with the passage of the New York State Old Age Security Act of 1930 that the background material discussed in the previous pages joins clearly into the stream of development of nursing-home-type facilities. That legislation, which for the first time provided substantial and permanent state grants-in-aid for a public relief program, prohibited the granting of the state-aided relief, old-age pensions, to any person living in an institution:

> Old age relief is to be given to any person who is not at the time an inmate of any public or private home for the aged, or any public home, or any public or private institution of a custodial, correctional or curative character, except in the case of temporary medical or surgical care in a hospital . . . and . . . is not because of his physical or mental condition in need of continued institutional care.[1]

This limitation, there can be no question, constituted a serious restriction upon the development of the public home (the Welfare Act of 1929 had altered the nomenclature from almshouse to county, city, or town home) and of other institutions that might have cared for the aged.

---

[1] *Laws of New York, 1930*, chap. 387, sec. 123.

The reasons for the restriction, it would seem, have been popularly misunderstood. In the light of the historical development of institutional care for the indigent, as it has been sketched out in previous pages, it appears reasonable to deduce that the limitation grew out of the general rejection of any indoor relief whatsoever as an inadequate, inefficient, and parsimonious approach to welfare tasks. Certainly there were pendulum swings of policy from the English workhouse system of 1722 to the Speenhamland system of 1795, and then, in New York, back to the poorhouse system that dominated most of the nineteenth century. It seems natural to expect that a new swing of the pendulum, this time supported by complicated developments in the socioeconomic system, brought back public rejection of the negative welfare philosophy, indoor relief. This is undoubtedly partly the case, but by itself it is an inadequate explanation for what happened. It leaves out of account the trend toward the development of specialized institutions that had built up during the nineteenth century. And it ignores the fact that while new ways of life were creating large groups of needy for whom pensions, annuities, and unemployment insurance were far more reasonable than public home care, they were simultaneously casting up greater numbers of people for whom institutional care was the only answer.

Nor are the reasons why the Old Age Security Act of 1930 barred institutional doors to its beneficiaries to be found exclusively in the broad evolutionary stream of concepts and attitudes concerning welfare. They are related, also, to the political situation in the state out of which the law developed. It is quite clear that there was no comprehensive, systematic body of ideas to which the principals involved in shaping the policy subscribed. Although there was a general desire to expand public home care and improve its level, a number of groups were promoting different causes and the various participants exhausted their ability to act in concert in reaching agreement on other issues that had a higher priority.

The Move for Old Age Pensions

During the second and third decades of the twentieth century there arose an awareness that there were increasing proportions of aged persons in the population and that increasing proportions of these aged were not economically self-sufficient. Paul H. Douglas, in his book *Social Security in the United States*, ascribes some of this increasing dependency to the "decrease in the proportion of persons who were self-employed as agriculture, the handicrafts and small trade gave way to large-scale industrialism and [to] the increasing speed of industry which made it more difficult for old people to be reemployed once they had lost their jobs."[2] "The phenomenal progress of medical science and its contributions to public health"[3] in lengthening life was also a contributing factor. Private interest groups—fraternal organizations, led by the Order of Eagles, The American Association for Labor Legislation, and the American Association for Old Age Security—began to press in various states for special relief for the needy aged. Even before 1929, when the depression began, eight states had inaugurated systems by which their counties might distribute old age pensions. There occurred contemporarily a number of investigations of almshouses, which did much to further discredit this traditional facility and to underscore the extent to which it had become an institution for the aged and infirm.

Estelle M. Stewart worked with the U.S. Bureau of Labor Statistics to produce one study,[4] and with the Women's Department of the National Civic Federation to turn out another.[5]

[2] Paul H. Douglas, *Social Security in the United States*, (New York: Whittlesey House, 1936), pp. 5–6.

[3] David M. Schneider and Albert Deutsch, *The History of Public Welfare in New York State, 1867–1940* (Chicago: University of Chicago Press, 1941), p. 344.

[4] *The Cost of American Almshouses*, U.S. Bureau of Labor Statistics Bulletin No. 386, 1926.

[5] *Study of a Group of Almshouses in Connecticut, New Jersey, New York, and Pennsylvania* (New York: National Civic Federation, 1927).

A book by Harry C. Evans, *The American Poorfarm and its Inmates*, was somewhat in the muckraking tradition.[6] Its genesis lay in addresses to national congresses of fraternal organizations by the United States Secretary of Labor, James J. Davis, during the early twenties;[7] no less than sixteen fraternal or auxiliary organizations took up Secretary Davis' proposals to sponsor an almshouse study, a fact that undoubtedly added to the impact that the book had upon its appearance.

While there was increasing desire to better the welfare of the aged as the 1920's drew to a close, there was a definite split in New York as to the means by which the vaguely agreed upon goal should be achieved. The report of a State Joint Legislative Committee recommended in 1929 that there be an "unbiased" investigation of retirement and pension plans.[8] Meanwhile, Franklin D. Roosevelt, campaigning for the governorship in 1928, had called for old-age pensions. However, Roosevelt strongly favored a contributory, or insurance, program wherein workers would themselves accept part of the responsibility for providing for their declining years.[9] Upon becoming Governor, he sought the creation of a nine-member commission—seven of the members to be appointed by himself—to undertake study of the matter and to make recommendations. The Republican-controlled legislature, however, passed a measure providing for the appointment of three Commissioners by the Senate Leader, three by the Assembly Speaker, and three by the Governor. Roosevelt reluctantly approved the move, fearing that the Commission's recommendations would not incorporate social insurance provisions and threatening to veto the resulting legislation if they did not.[10] The Governor's fears were well grounded. The weight of political influence fell against social

---

[6] Harry C. Evans, *The American Poorfarm and its Inmates*, (Des Moines: Royal Order of the Moose, 1926).

[7] *Ibid.*, p. 1.   [8] Schneider and Deutsch, p. 283.

[9] Bernard Bellush, *Franklin D. Roosevelt as Governor of New York* (New York: Columbia University Press, 1955), p. 175.

[10] Bellush, p. 177.

insurance. In fact, it later became clear that the battle had been lost with the establishment of the legislature-dominated Commission.[11]

Institutional Care in a Political Crossfire

The fact that the central political issue in the New York State government was whether or not there would be contributory social insurance for old age was of great importance to the evolution of institutional care. While much of the contemporary opinion on the old age issue concerned the public home and its proposed conversion to a modern institution—and the Commission on Old Age Security considered this matter extensively —the central issue so overshadowed other considerations that no concrete recommendations for legislation were offered by the Commission for the modernizing of institutional care. A desire to make the specific legislative recommendations for pensions above suspicion, in the highly charged political atmosphere, was at least partly responsible for the exclusion from private institutions of all beneficiaries of the pension law.[12] Inmates of public and private institutions were excluded as beneficiaries in an attempt to detach pensions from the stigma of traditional indoor relief and also to avoid the mechanical problem of having two relief systems operate on single individuals. These provisions were of particular importance because, as the system

[11] The Commission operated for several months without a director of research because the factions within it were unable to agree upon any candidate. Dr. Luther Gulick was eventually appointed because, although he had a good reputation as a research director, he had done no work in the field of social welfare and was considered neutral in his opinions. The conservative membership was sufficiently strong that practically from the outset the real question, within the Commission, became whether there would be a pension system at all rather than whether a social insurance system would be adopted. Interview with Luther Gulick, June 4, 1963.

[12] There was concern that there would be accusations that religious charitable institutions—the faiths were duly represented on the Commission—would benefit if they were allowed to care for pension recipients. This is the recollection of Luther Gulick. Interview, June 4, 1963.

was adopted, the pension costs were shared equally by the state and the public welfare districts. Outdoor relief was therefore less expensive to the local governments, the primary administrators of the law, than institutional care, a condition that created artificial pressures for "noninstitutional" care.

The net consequences of the Commission's activities and recommendations did not advance, and in fact probably retarded, the development of institutional care. Its influence, moreover, had effect not only at the state but at the national level. New York's system served as something of a model for the national social security legislation.[13] In a few years the impediments growing out of these developments to the advancement of public homes contributed to a sudden growth in the new commercial institution, the proprietary nursing home. The *Hearings* held by the Commission and its *Report* to the legislature make it abundantly clear, however, that these developments were not at all in accord with the Commission's intent, or with the intent of any opinion held by persons who appeared as witnesses before the Commission.

The Concern for Institutional Care

Although the Commission, in its report, took a strong stand for outdoor relief, it also made a vigorous declaration in favor of moving the public institution system abreast of the need, which it found considerable. On the opening page of its recommendations to the legislature, and as part of its first recommendation, it stated that "some counties in this state have constructed modern, well-equipped, sanitary county institutions providing nursing, medical, and hospital care," but that much more progress in this direction was needed. It asked that "the recommendations regarding the improvement in our almshouses or county homes, . . . the building of modern and up-to-date institutions more in the nature of hospitals or in-

13 See below, p. 51, n. 69.

firmaries rather than almshouses, should be given further and careful consideration by your Honorable Body."[14]

Perhaps the most eloquent statement on the public institutions was made (as a witness before the hearings of the Commission) by Dr. Abraham Epstein, Director of the American Association for Old Age Security and to whom, along with Senator Robert Wagner and Dr. I. M. Rubinow, Paul H. Douglas later dedicated his book on social security: "Everyone knows that today the population of our almshouses is an entirely different one than the population of half a generation ago. There are very few shiftless and indolent people in almshouses today." After reporting that public home inmates of 1929 were older and sicker, from higher as well as lower socioeconomic status, and were people "whom fate has simply cast aside in their old age," Epstein went on to say: "There has been a complete change in the population of the almshouse . . . while the almshouse, in the majority of instances, is the same as it existed in the days of Queen Elizabeth." He then called for "well equipped medical institutions where [this new population] can be given proper medical and nursing care."[15]

There was a substantial predominance of opinion among the witnesses testifying before the Commission that only a small number of almshouse inmates would be able to live outside institutions even if provided with the economic wherewithal. Eight public home superintendents who dealt with the question quite uniformly believed that few could leave the institutions. Such proportions as "a half-dozen" of those in one large county home, 3 per cent, and less than 10 per cent, were the kind of estimates these officials made. A ninth spoke merely for better institutions for the better class people, without directly commenting upon the proportion who needed institutional care.[16] A representative of the National Civic Federation,

---

[14] New York State Commission on Old Age Security, *Old Age Security, Report*, Leg. Doc. No. 67 (Albany, 1930), p. 13.

[15] New York State Commission on Old Age Security, *Hearings*, State Legislative Library, Capitol, Albany (typescript), p. 173.

[16] See *ibid.*, pp. 354, 436, 682, 773, 881, 907, 1100, 1114, 1193.

an organization opposed to the granting of public pensions on the ground they would lead to social insurance,[17] reported on studies that showed that many noninstitutionalized aged in urban communities "need nursing and other institutional care, not now provided, and cannot be properly assisted by indiscriminate pensions."[18] A second spokesman for the same group stressed the need for infirmaries as part of the county homes.[19] Comment of the Commissioner of Public Welfare of Erie County was also addressed specifically to the matter of county infirmary care: "Most of the cases that we commit to the County Home today are infirm cases, cases that practically need hospital care and still they are chronic cases, and the hospitals will not take a chronic case, and it is necessary to commit them to the infirmary."[20] Similar findings were reported by the President of the Metropolitan Life Insurance Company, who cited a 1925 survey by the Massachusetts Commission on the Aged Population. Figures developed from that study, he said, indicated that only 31 per cent of those sixty-five years of age and over, and 25 per cent of those seventy and over, could leave Massachusetts almshouses. He also used supporting data gathered by the National Civic Federation and concluded that not lack of knowledge, but of support, was the primary problem of institutional care.[21]

It is significant, of course, that some who emphasized the infirmities of the dependent aged, and their consequent need for institutionalized care, were not among the most stalwart supporters of the proposed pension system which was an elaboration of outdoor relief. The positions of the conservative, business-backed National Civic Federation, the private insurance interests, and the county welfare officers ranged from open hostility to the pension proposals to lukewarm neutrality. Their testimony must be judged accordingly. The attitudes of the county officers are particularly interesting. Their general opinions that pensions would not improve things much were prob-

[17] *Ibid.*, pp. 1036–1037.   [18] *Ibid.*, p. 1041.   [19] *Ibid.*, p. 1057.
[20] *Ibid.*, p. 436.   [21] *Ibid.*, pp. 943, 957.

ably colored by tendencies to cling to the old poor-relief philosophy and desires to avoid state supervision.[22]

However, the belief that institutional care needed special attention was shared by many who can be considered far more objective in their judgment. Homer Folks, Secretary of the SCAA, who had led the battle to adopt outdoor relief as a public policy, was probably the most emphatic of all those testifying before the Commission on the matter:

A great deal is said about the pension as an alternative to the almshouse. . . . I think we must not be led astray too much by that. It is in a certain number of instances the real thing; a very small percentage of the people in the almshouses of the State could take care of themselves with a pension. I should say [sic] a recent inquiry we made in a number of counties, maybe 15 per cent, or something like that. The others are physically infirm and sick, and have various kinds of ailments and conditions that require personal attention of the kind that you could not get in an individual home, even in your own home . . . which require nursing or medical attention . . . in some sort of institution, and I hope that you feel yourselves charged with the duty of considering what kind of . . . and form of institutional provision for the aged who are sick, should be had, which is not had now.

Folks went on to note that "this is a very outstanding problem, particularly upstate."[23] The sentiments were echoed by Richard

---

[22] Homer Folks took the local officials severely to task for clinging to old traditional attitudes: "The almshouses are not what they ought to be and the public outdoor relief is worse yet, and all the neighbors know about it and people would rather die than came to get it." *Ibid.*, p. 276; see also p. 996. There was an abundance of collaborating testimony. The Commission *Report*, pp. 370–371, also found the administration of outdoor relief unreformed.

[23] New York Commission, *Hearings*, pp. 278–279. Contemporary expert opinion ran much in the same vein. Dr. Ernst P. Boas concluded, in the pioneering book *The Care of the Aged*, edited by Dr. I. M. Rubinows: "Almshouse statistics show that most of their inmates are sick; about 75 per cent of them are suffering from some chronic disease. Yet they receive almost no medical care." And, "An analysis of the customs and practices of the almshouses, their administrative methods, and housing

W. Wallace, Assistant Director of the State Department of Social Welfare.[24] The Commission showed its inclination to agree with these judgments in its analysis of questionnaires submitted by five almshouses. It confidently reported that 66 per cent of the inmates were sixty-five years of ago or over,[25] but it expressed substantial skepticism about figures indicating that only 12 per cent of the total needed nursing or infirmary care.[26] However, the Commission cautiously suggested that something just under half of all almshouse inhabitants could leave "if the proper investigation and social case work and financial help were available.[27] The Chairman of the Commission, Senator Seabury Mastick, opened the Buffalo hearings with the following statement:

I think to allay the apprehensions of the county poor-law officials, I might state that so far as I am aware, the Commission does not believe that any old age security system would do away with poor farms or poor houses or county hospitals, because there are places for all of that. The work that we are trying to do is something that is complementary to that instead of being an alternative.[28]

Assemblyman Francis X. Bernardt, a member of the Commission, a past State President of the Fraternal Order of the Eagles and sponsor of the Eagles' model pension law in the State legislature, argued that "there are 85 or 90 per cent that need institutional care instead of being in a poorhouse." Which, seemingly, was a call for a higher level of care.[29]

As the population of the almshouse had changed, and therefore the kind of care required for almshouse inmates, ideas about the relative costs of outdoor and indoor relief changed

---

facilities shows them to be antiquated survivals of medieval institutions." He then went on to call for improvements in the public institutions, "The Care of the Aged Sick," *The Care for the Aged*, ed. I. M. Rubinow (Chicago: University of Chicago Press, 1930), p. 45.

[24] New York Commission, *Hearings*, pp. 650, 666.
[25] New York Commission, *Report*, p. 409.   [26] *Ibid.*, p. 421.
[27] *Ibid.*, pp. 431–432.   [28] New York Commission *Hearings*, p. 347.
[29] *Ibid.*, p. 289.

too. One important argument advanced by those supporting specialized outdoor relief for the aged was that institutional care was wasteful unless needed. According to Dr. Epstein, "everybody knows that . . . it costs from two to three times as much to support a person in a well equipped institution, than it does to provide them with home attention or home relief."[30] The cost element was an important consideration in the shift from indoor to outdoor relief philosophy that was taking place. However, the matter was not as simple as it had been in the days of Secretary Yates, when a switch from one to the other was all that was involved. The Commission and others argued that economies could be effected by greater reliance upon outdoor relief,[31] but it was also clearly recognized that for those needing institutional care, the amounts being expended were, for the average case, grossly inadequate. The proposal was frequently ventured, during the hearings, that smaller counties should combine into groups and establish joint facilities where higher quality services would be rendered at manageable cost.[32]

Among the many others who thought that progress in institutional care was of great importance were Father Brennock, representing Catholic Charities, and Mr. Lawson Purdy of the Charity Organizations Society. Father Brennock hoped that the pension law would give Catholic organizations "a better leverage to change the character of our institutions for the care of the aged and sick."[33] Mr. Purdy reported that there was exclusion by private homes for the aged of all who were not well. He spoke of increasing age and concomitant illness among the members of a professional group that he served and the lack of facilities where these kinds of people might be cared for, the public almshouse being an unthinkable resource for them.[34] The Commission itself found private institutional care—which

[30] *Ibid.*, p. 175.

[31] *Ibid.*, p. 585; New York Commission, *Report*, p. 17. See also John H. Walker, "Labor's Point of View," *The Care of the Aged*, p. 25.

[32] New York Commission, *Hearings*, pp. 173, 645–646, 1061, 1090. Dr. Boas made the same recommendation in *The Care of the Aged*, p. 45.

[33] New York Commission, *Hearings*, p. 298.   [34] *Ibid.*, p. 310.

was virtually all charitable—of a much higher level than alms-house care, but inadequate in financial resources and facilities; long waiting lists were the rule.[35]

Although the predominant opinion expressed on the pension proposals showed a marked concern for the improvement of institutional facilities as well as for providing new kinds of outdoor relief to meet the problems of the new society that had evolved, a few interested parties weighted pensions heavily and de-emphasized institutional care. Mr. Almus Olver, of the Council of Social Agencies of Syracuse, favored the bill "chiefly because we feel that it sets up machinery by which large numbers of our own men and women who are today being forced into the almshouses of this State may be provided for properly and decently in their own homes."[36] Michael H. Sweeney, Grand Trustee of the Fraternal Order of Eagles, gave the following testimony: "Our organization believes that you will still have to continue with your county homes the same as you have in the past, but the people that are able to take care of themselves, and I believe there are many of those in the institutions today, as has been said, if they were given a pension of a dollar a day, they could be cared for among their friends."[37]

The Eagles had passed a resolution favoring old age pensions at a national convention in 1918 and had been openly and energetically campaigning for pensions among the states for years. The Eagles' proposals for legislation had been introduced into the state legislature four years before the Commission began its study.[38] It is quite possible that the order's massive membership—600,000 strong—gave its interest in pensions an unusual propagandizing character and made its perspectives somewhat less critically perceptive than those of such groups as the State Charities Aid Association. Professor Douglas saw the

[35] New York Commission, *Report*, p. 388.
[36] New York State Legislature, Assembly Committee on Ways and Means, Assembly Committee on Pensions, and Senate Committee on Pensions, *Hearings on the Bill for Old Age Security*, Albany, N.Y., March 11, 1930, p. 27.
[37] New York Commission, *Hearings*, p. 586.   [38] *Ibid.*, p. 584.

Eagles' work for old age security as propaganda,[39] and it seems reasonable to conclude that the leadership of large, popularly based organizations finds problems in being sensitive to nuances and in including subtle qualifications as it maps out its stand on policy.

Institutional Care as Public Responsibility

Associated with the prominent concern for institutional care was the expectation that such care should be provided, at least in a large measure, by government. The advice of the Commission to the legislature (see above, pp. 37-38) clearly assumed a public responsibility to care for indigent aged and chronically ill. That recommendation was quite consistent with the main trend of testimony from witnesses. Mr. Folks, the SCAA Secretary, expressed the hope that the Commission would be continued another year to deal specifically with "the institutional provision of the aged, the almshouse."[40] Also, in its annual report the Association noted that the Commission "proposed no legislation," expressed disappointment, and reiterated the hope that there would be further study of the matter.[41] A spokesman for the Charity Organization Society of Buffalo testified that the indigent sick aged "should be the burden of the public agency rather than the private, because . . . it is a case of chronic dependency that goes on from year to year, and private societies are not in as good a condition financially to take care of those cases."[42] Another witness said that the private institution he was associated with did not have a great many aged people who could not take care of themselves, because such cases were either cared for in their own homes or were sent to county homes.[43] Finally, it should be noted that there were no voices raised during the hearings to deny an essential public

[39] *Social Security in the United States*, p. 6.
[40] New York Commission, *Hearings*, p. 1005.
[41] *The Year in Review: Annual Report of the State Charities Aid Association for the Fiscal Ending Sept. 30, 1930*, p. 58.
[42] New York Commission, *Hearings*, p. 452.   [43] *Ibid.*, p. 490.

responsibility to care for indigent chronic cases in need of institutionalization. Even Harry C. Evans' book on the poor farm, which probably lashed out more strongly against almshouses than any other statement of the times, saw the responsibility involved as a public one and called for its fulfillment primarily by the institutionalization of the feeble-minded.[44]

Institutional Improvement Neglected

The greatest change in policy to grow out of the Commission's recommendations was the acceptance by the state of the responsibility for sharing in the financial support of, and its assumption of a major supervisory function in, the old age pension program. The state undertook half the costs and assigned the other half to the public welfare districts.[45] The districts were not allowed then to assess the towns for their respective costs.[46] The spelling out of rules for administration of the program was charged to the State Department of Social Welfare,[47] and appeals from the decisions of local public welfare officials could be heard by that Department, its decisions to supersede those made locally.[48] Thus, major breaks were made simultaneously with the principles of local responsibility and indoor relief, which the Welfare Act of 1929 had already substantially weakened. However, state supervision and financial aid were stimuli applied only to outdoor relief, despite the great concern shown by the Commission for institutional care during its investigations.

"We didn't know what was going to happen"[49] is probably the best explanation of why the new pension system excluded as its beneficiaries all persons who lived in institutions. The designers of the system had a number of considerations that were far more immediate and obvious, and therefore drew more of

---

[44] *The American Poorfarm*, pp. 93–100. Evans was of the opinion that 75 per cent of almshouse inmates were feebleminded.
[45] *Laws of New York, 1930*, chap. 387, sec. 124d.
[46] *Ibid.*, sec. 124b.   [47] *Ibid.*, sec. 124l.   [48] *Ibid.*, sec. 124h.
[49] Luther Gulick, interview, June 4, 1963.

their policy commitment than concern for the future development of institutional care for the sick and aged could draw.
Most important, Governor Roosevelt's veto threat was thought
to be very real; it motivated the designers to make the plan
as simple and invulnerable to political attack as possible. The
problem was to get any law for the aid of the aged passed, not
necessarily a broad one.[50]

Furthermore, there was a desire to make the pensions reflect
an entirely new welfare policy, to be completely untainted by
the old poor-relief philosophy that had used the institution as
its organizational focus—the pendulum swing was of some
significance. Homer Folks thought that the Public Welfare
Law of 1929 could have brought about the desired changes to
outdoor relief for the aged had its administration not been
left in the hands of the local welfare officials, whose traditional
perspectives had not changed.[51] The Commission itself noted
that two distinct types of old age assistance systems had developed among the American states. In one, there was "a
definite attempt to merge the improved methods of poor relief
with the special consideration of the aged needy and their
specific problems." In the other, a definite effort was made "to
distinguish between these two forms of relief."[52] The Commission acknowledged that when this separation went so far as
to disqualify residents of private institutions, it was "stringent."[53] But it then went on to note that "old age assistance
developed as a movement to remove certain classes from the
jurisdiction of the poor law," and it endorsed the discrimination between relief for aged and for others, thereby opening
the door for the disqualification for pension purposes of those
in not only public, but even private institutions.[54]

Making people in public homes ineligible to receive pen-

[50] According to Dr. Gulick's recollection, this was the most important
consideration.
[51] New York Commission, *Hearings*, p. 996.
[52] New York Commission, *Report*, p. 234.   [53] *Ibid.*, p. 226.
[54] *Ibid.*, p. 235. For further evidence of sentiment that old-age pensions
should be distinguished from ordinary public welfare, see New York
Commission, *Hearings*, pp. 503, 609; and New York State Legislature, As-

sions was seen as a much simpler matter. Of the ten state plans in operation in 1930 providing for pensions, nine permitted no pensions to go to persons in public institutions,[55] the purpose being to prevent any person from receiving double public relief. However, only one of those nine states provided any state subsidization of the pension plan; in eight of the nine cases the local government footed the whole bill whether they emphasized outdoor or indoor relief. This was not to be the case in New York. Until 1936, the state would pay half of the pension costs while the localities would have to pay for all of the costs of institutional care. In 1936 local welfare district responsibility for outdoor relief costs to the aged would move down to 25 per cent, and in 1946 to 20 per cent, while costs of care in public homes would be carried solely by the localities, and counties could continue to splinter their financial bases by allocating costs to towns. That such differentials would cramp the development of institutions was clearly not recognized by even those whose concern was unquestionably sincere. They saw the matter as one of simple bookkeeping. For example, Homer Folks, possibly the staunchest advocate of the improvement of institutional facilities, said: "We would think that people already in public or private institutions . . . should not while they are getting that aid also get the other aid."[56]

The consequences of the new legislation must have been a

---

sembly Committee on Ways and Means, Assembly Committee on Pensions, and Senate Committee on Pensions, *Hearings on the Bill for Old Age Security*, Albany, March 11, 1930, p. 60.

[55] New York Commission, *Report*, p. 226. The Miller-Love Bill, the measure backed by the American Association for Old Age Security in New York, did not prohibit any person in an institution from receiving a pension but prohibited anyone on a pension from receiving any other government relief. New York State Legislature Index, Jan. 7, 1930, Assembly Bill No. 12, sec. 187. Persons living in institutions could pay such institutions out of their pensions. Sec. 186.

The Fraternal Order of Eagles' Bill, introduced by Assemblyman Bernhardt, specifically disqualified persons in public but not in private institutions from receiving pensions. *New York State Legislative Index*, Jan. 17, 1930, Assembly Bill No. 264, sec. 397.

[56] New York Commission, *Hearings*, p. 1005.

disappointment to those who had foreseen any great exodus from the almshouses. Although undoubtedly the broad effect of the law was extremely wholesome, less than 25 per cent of the public home population was moved to new quarters.[57] Moreover, with the deepening of the depression, public home residents became more rather than less numerous. Their number, 10,974 in 1930, swelled to 14,117 in 1933. It was not until the World War II years that the figure once again dropped to its approximate 1930 size, where it leveled off.[58] Without question some of this growth was attributable to a lack of the "proper investigation and social case work and financial help" that the Commission had advised should be available.[59] However, Schneider and Deutsch observed in 1941 that "it is now generally recognized that, regardless of any liberalization of home care for the needy aged, there will necessarily remain some who require institutional care because of physical or mental infirmity or disability."[60] It had been the welfare system as a whole that needed to have the stigma removed, and not old age pensions alone.

Preoccupation with the Depression

The admonition to the legislature by the Commission to give further and careful consideration to the improvement of public homes and to "the building of modern and up-to-date institutions more in the nature of hospitals or infirmaries rather than almshouses" was swept aside by the rush of attention to large-scale outdoor relief efforts that came with the worsening depression. Governor Roosevelt studied unemployment and old age insurance for a good part of the next two years.[61] Senator Mastick, who had been Chairman of the Commission on Old

---

[57] U. S. Congress, Senate, Committee on Finance, *Hearings on S. 1130, Economic Security Act,* 74th Cong., 1st Sess., 1935, p. 189.

[58] Figures gathered from the *Annual Reports* of the New York State Department of Social Welfare, 1930–1957.

[59] See above, p. 00.

[60] *The History of Public Welfare in New York State, 1867–1940,* p. 348.

[61] Bellush, *Roosevelt as Governor of New York,* pp. 183–186.

Age Security, introduced unemployment insurance legislation in 1931 and 1932.[62] A special session of the legislature set up the Temporary Emergency Relief Administration in the late summer of 1931 and appropriated $20 million to help the unemployed.[63] The mounting numbers of unemployed and the waves of federal legislation to help them further overshadowed the issue of institutional care for the aged and chroncially ill.[64]

The Old Age Assistance Provisions of the Federal Social Security Act

It was with the federal government's moving into the field of aid to the aged, however, that public policy on the matter was not only raised to a higher level of social significance but was also crystallized into a pattern not completely hostile to all institutional care. The difficulties that voluntary hospitals were having, as charitable institutions in the mid-1930's, apparently prevented a thoroughly strict outdoor relief cast from being given to the new policy. The old-age assistance provisions of the federal Social Security Act of 1935 were initially framed to disallow aid to persons who were "inmates of public or other charitable institutions."[65] The alarm of voluntary hospital associations and the concern of a few others, expressed before House and Senate Committee hearings, seemingly persuaded the legislators that public aid for institutionalization under private auspices was justified. For, as the law was enacted, it prohibited benefits from going only to those who were inmates of public institutions.[66]

[62] *Ibid.*, pp. 186, 188.   [63] *Laws of New York, 1931*, chaps. 798, 799.
[64] Even though Mary C. Jarrett turned out, in 1933, an impressive study of chronic illness in New York City. *Chronic Illness in New York City*, Vol. I: *The Problems of Chronic Illness*; Vol. II: *The Care of the Chronic Sick by Different Types of Voluntary Agency* (New York: Columbia University Press, 1933).
[65] United States Congress, House of Representatives, Committee on Ways and Means, *Hearings on H.R. 4120, Economic Security Act*, 74th Cong., 1st Sess., 1935, p. 438.
[66] 49 *U.S. Statutes* 620, sec. 3.

Institutional Care Was Not a Major Issue

The background staff work and legislative considerations of the Social Security Act are striking, from the perspective of the present study, in the extent to which they did not consider the effects of public assistance upon institutional care. The reasons, of course, were not only that outdoor relief had gained public acceptance, but also, and more important, because the problems most urgent by far were matters of welfare and economic stability that involved multitudes of people for whom institutional care was obviously inappropriate.

The initial proposals for the law grew out of the work of the Committee on Economic Security, which President Roosevelt had appointed during the summer of 1934, and which was chaired by Secretary of Labor Frances Perkins, who had been his State Industrial Commissioner in New York. Staff reports to the Committee listed ten states among the twenty-eight that had passed old-age assistance laws as denying aid to go to any aged person in a "benevolent, charitable, or fraternal institution." Three others, New York among them, were shown as disqualifying persons in "need of institutional care." Six states were named as currently allowing old age assistance to go to "charitable or benevolent institutions if pensioner is an inmate." In the nine others, people in institutions could apparently receive pensions.[67]

No clear pattern of strict outdoor relief policy or flexible pensions-in-institutions emerges from these figures. In the absence of any substantial established drift one way or another, and apparently without really considering the matter of great importance, the Committee seems to have decided that New York's practice should set the tone for the nation. It recommended casually that "no federal aid is to be extended for aged

[67] Social Security Board, *Social Security in America: The Factual Background of the Social Security Act as Summarized from Staff Reports to the Committee on Economic Security*, Social Security Board Publication No. 20 (Washington: U.S. Government Printing Office, 1937), Table. 36.

persons cared for in institutions"[68] and then went on to offer the relevant sections of the New York law as a model for state legislation to enable states to participate in the proposed federal old-age assistance program.[69]

With the exception of the objections of a few witnesses to the strict outdoor relief policy proposed by the Committee on Economic Security, there is little or no evidence to indicate that thinking about institutional care had advanced beyond where it had been in New York in 1930. In fact, very little attention was paid to institutional care, compared to the New York examination of that problem in 1930.[70] Of course, the federal deliberations covered the issues of federal participation in welfare, of aid to dependent children, to the blind, public health measures, unemployment insurance and old-age annuities as well as public assistance to the aged; the focus was not sharply upon relief for the aged as had been the case in New York State.

To be sure, some of the same arguments about outdoor relief versus indoor relief that had been heard earlier in New York did reappear. A representative of The Fraternal Order of Eagles saw old-age assistance as intended "primarily to do away with the poorhouse."[71] He went on to say, however:

I do not believe that old-age pensions alone are going to solve the picture fully, because before you have done that . . . quasihospital institutions will have to be established where the old people who are mentally or physically afflicted and cannot live in their own environment can be sent and receive proper medical attention and nursing.[72]

Dr. Edwin E. Witte, Executive Director for the Committee on Economic Security, informed the Senate Finance Committee

[68] Senate Finance Committee, *Hearings*, p. 1333.

[69] *Ibid.*, pp. 634–635.

[70] A research staff report to the Committee on Economic Security noted specifically that there had been no almshouse survey for ten years. Social Security Board, *Social Security in America*, p. 154.

[71] House Ways and Means Committee, *Hearings*, p. 471. See also p. 476.

[72] *Ibid.*, p. 476.

that only a limited number of people could leave almshouses when given financial assistance.[73] He stressed that most people in public almshouses needed not only financial support but physical care as well. The relatively higher cost of institutional care over relief given to people living in their own homes was noted.[74] Abraham Epstein pleaded that federal efforts should promote, and not diminish, the distinction between old age assistance as honorable and deserved public aid, and old-fashioned poor relief.[75] Finally, there arose again the concern that persons getting aid in public institutions might get old-age assistance at the same time.[76]

Spokesmen for Charitable Institutions

The major new consideration on the issue of aid to aged in institutions was raised not by proponents of private or public homes but by representatives of voluntary hospitals. These people argued that government was not assuming enough of the financial responsibility for hospital charity work. Robert Jolly, of the American Hospital Association, told the House Ways and Means Committee that, in general, assistance was cut off when one became a patient:

Hospitals have had an increased burden of indigent sick without Government relief except in three or four States. Relief agencies have fed and clothed and housed indigent but the moment they need hospitalization the relief agencies have taken the attitude that the hospitals have always cared for the indigent so let them do so now, ignoring the fact that in addition to an increase in free patients the hospitals have had a falling off of earnings from pay patients and a falling off of donations from philanthropically-minded people to about 40 per cent of what were such donations in 1929. We had had no relief at all, the hospitals, except in three or four States where the local relief association does that.[77]

[73] Senate Finance Committee, *Hearings*, p. 189.   [74] *Ibid.*, p. 178.
[75] House Ways and Means Committee, *Hearings*, p. 556.
[76] *Ibid.*, p. 438.
[77] *Ibid.*, p. 433. Mr. Jolly repeated the same testimony before the Senate Finance Committee. See *Hearings*, pp. 457–458.

The hospital people were dismayed at the suggestion of the Committee on Economic Security that old-age assistance should not be available for institutional care. The Right Reverend Monsignor Maurice F. Griffin, Vice-President of the Catholic Hospital Association of the United States and Canada, testified:

We view with alarm such provisions as this, that make the beneficiaries of this act ineligible to receive its benefits just because they are inmates of public or charitable institutions. We all know that these people sixty-five years and over are going to be inmates of charitable institutions, and such we consider ourselves. We know that they are going to be in the hospitals in large number. We express great surprise that that provision was written in this act to make them ineligible.[78]

Monsignor Griffin went on to report, among other things, that approximately half of the 450,000 patients in vountary hospitals were cared for solely at hospital expense.[79] Mr. Jolly stated that nearly 400 nonprofit hospitals had ceased to operate since 1930 because the financial burden had become too heavy.[80] A statement submitted by the Joint Committee of the American Hospital Association, the Catholic Hospital Association of America, and the Protestant Hospital Association of America recommended the inclusion in the legislation of the following:

That no provision of this act be ever interpreted as prohibiting the use of funds made available under this act for disbursement to a public or private nonprofit charitable institution for any service rendered to any person who is a beneficiary of this act and that no person otherwise a beneficiary of this act be deprived, by reason of being an inmate of a charitable institution of benefits provided by this act.[81]

Twice again, in the Senate hearings, the proposed ineligibility for old-age assistance of persons in private institutions was questioned. Almost as an afterthought, and with the qualifica-

[78] House Ways and Means Committee, *Hearings*, p. 438.
[79] *Ibid.*, p. 443.   [80] *Ibid.*, p. 434.
[81] House Ways and Means Committee, *Hearings*, p. 438.

tion that it was not a very important point, Abraham Epstein commented that

the present bill would eliminate the possibility of giving attention to a man or woman who prefers to reside in the institutions in a private home for the aged. It does not affect many people, but it seems to me that socially it is advisable to permit a person's freedom if he so desires, to reside in an institution.[82]

Also, the Administrative Committee of the National Catholic Welfare Conference saw fit to send a short letter to Senator Pat Harrison, chairman of the committee holding the hearings. The letter called attention to the importance of private charitable organizations and then requested that the private institutions

be not further burdened because of any unfavorable interpretations of any of the provisions of the proposed Economic Security Act, but that such legislation make it explicit that no State is prohibited, through the acceptance of Federal funds, from using as agencies of relief and prevention the private institution, hospital, or home.[83]

Doors to Private Institutions Opened

The proposals of Mr. Epstein, those of the hospital representatives, and those of the Catholic Welfare Conference elicited no argument and little discussion during the Senate and House Committee hearings. The qualification or disqualification of aged in private institutions for assistance was regarded as a marginal issue relevant in only a limited number of cases, as Epstein had suggested, or to short-term hospital care.

At any rate, both the House and Senate Committees reported out bills that disqualified only persons in public institutions[84]

---

[82] Senate Finance Committee, *Hearings*, p. 511.   [83] *Ibid.*, p. 370.

[84] U.S. House of Representatives, 74th Cong., 1st Sess., 1935, Report No. 615, to accompany H.R. 7260, p. 18; Senate Report No. 661, to accompany H.R. 7260, p. 30.

and the relevant sentence in the Act, as signed by the President, did the same. Thus, there became available federal aid to any state, amounting to half of what the state spent giving assistance to persons sixty-five years of age or over (with a maximum federal aid of fifteen dollars per recipient), and such aid was available whether the recipient lived in his own home or in a private institution but was not available if he was "an inmate of a public institution."[85] Aid in the same amount was also made available for assistance to the blind.[86] The same sections also extended federal aid for the administrative costs of both the old-age assistance and the blind programs.

The Problem for the Future

Soon afterward, in telling the story of the passage and the purposes of the Social Security Act, Paul H. Douglas wrote that "pensions should not be denied to those in private institutions for the aged or in public nursing homes or infirmaries." He then went on to argue that although there had been political abuse in the management of poor farms, the opposition to institutional care had been carried too far. He noted, as many had before him, that there were large numbers of aged who like the congregate life of an institution or who could be cared for better in an infirmary or home than in their own private dwelling.[87] His subsequent comments are so germane to our concern that they deserve extensive quotation:

There is also no sufficient reason as a State develops competent nursing homes, infirmaries, hospitals, etc., why persons needing treatment there should not receive a pension while residents of them. Before the days of federal action, this could have been opposed on the ground that it was unnecessary since the State would be paying for them anyway as patients and to furnish pensions would merely mean taking money out of one pocket and putting it into another. The same objection no longer holds with the coming

---

[85] 49 *U.S. Statutes* 620, sec. 3(a).   [86] *Ibid.*, sec. 1003(a).
[87] *Social Security in the United States*, p. 244.

of federal aid for old age pensions. The cost of maintaining the State or county institutions is borne by these governments and they are not federally aided. *Aged persons in need of institutional treatment who are sent to such places will, when they are taken off the pension rolls, increase the expenditures of the State and decrease the aid given by the federal government. It is certainly unfair to penalize a State for thus giving superior treatment to its aged.* But under no conditions should the old and discredited poorhouse system be brought back under another name. . . .

It will of course need skillful administration to prevent the old abuses from coming back and to lead to such an integration of institutional and home care for the aged as will best serve the purpose. As the administration improves it will, therefore, be well to remove the present absolute prohibition upon federal aid being given for pensions to those in public institutions and to qualify this in such a fashion as will permit institutional care to be utilized for the ill and infirm as needed.[88]

[88] *Ibid.*, pp. 246–247. Italics added.

CHAPTER 4

Government Policy, Institutional Response, and Upstate Development, 1936-1952

The Over-all Growth Picture

The provisions of the Social Security Act of 1935 made it possible for federal money to come to the aid of local government revenues in the support of persons living in private institutions. New York State quickly took advantage of this opportunity and contributed to such support itself in the process. Over the next two and half decades the relatively new commercial establishments, proprietary nursing homes, flourished under this arrangement. Public home infirmaries, laboring under the decided disadvantage of being dependent upon local government for virtually all support, improved and increased their capacities modestly. Meanwhile nonprofit nursing homes and homes for the aged, having had their basic precepts, orientations, and legal standings established during an earlier era, found it difficult to make the adaptations necessary to grow commensurately with the increasing need for institutional services.

The general growth pattern is outlined in Table 1. Of particular interest is the growth in proprietary facilities in upstate New York from the mid-1930's to the early 1950's. The number of proprietary beds zoomed from an insignificant 325 in 1935 to over 11,000 in 1952, which represents the most remarkable change to be found in the table. Over the same period neither public nor voluntary facilities so much as doubled upstate, and although both were far more important than the proprietaries in the mid-1930's, by the early 1950's their combined bed total was far exceeded by the beds of the profit-motivated institutions. Attention should be called also to the situation in New York City, where there was some, but much less, proprietary growth. The great expansion in proprietary facilities in the City did not occur until the following decade.

Table 1. Growth of nursing-home-type facilities, New York State, mid-1930's to early 1950's

	Public		Voluntary		Proprietary	
	Homes	Beds	Homes	Beds	Homes	Beds
Mid 1930's						
Upstate	47	2,129	55	1,536	20	325
N.Y.C.	—ª	—	42	1,922	8	116
Early 1950's						
Upstate	44	4,191	109	2,579	603	11,027
N.Y.C.	2	1,311	66	3,785	76	2,801

Source. See Table IM, Appendix I.
ª Dashes indicate no facilities.

This difference in the historical development of upstate and downstate facilities suggests that public policies followed upstate were different from those in the city. In fact, there were strong historical differences in governmental support and regulation of proprietary nursing homes that do much to account for the two developmental patterns. Cleavages in political and social structure and in social welfare orientations have divided the state into upstate and New York City camps, and these cleavages have affected nursing home developments. The existence of other types of facilities in New York City, able to absorb some of the pressures that burst forth upstate as demands for nursing-home-type accommodations, was of great importance. This factor was closely related to the city's traditional and distinctive outlook on public medical services. The absence of these other types of facilities upstate was of considerable significance for the early and strong development of proprietary nursing homes there.

It may be that strong pressures developed earlier upstate than downstate. Table 6M[1] indicates that a somewhat larger proportion of the population was aged there than in the city until the 1950's, when that condition was reversed. This difference may have accounted, in part, for the different policies followed. There is some question, however, whether the relatively rural upstate society could not accommodate a greater proportion of aged in the population without resort to institutions than could New York City.[2]

Statutory Changes:
The Wake of the Social Security Act of 1935

During the session of the State legislature following the passage of the federal Social Security Act, the old-age relief legislation of 1930 was modified to bring in federal aid for assistance given pensionees within the state.[3] The age at which persons might become eligible for assistance was reduced from seventy to sixty-five years and the years of required residence in the state were cut. The amendments were necessary for the state to qualify for any aid whatsoever. Also, in its state plan— upon which federal aid was contingent—the state opted to include assistance to persons in private homes for the aged. This was a major policy change, because the 1930 legislation had barred state aid to institutional care and state aid, as well as federal, became available for such care under the 1936 law.

While making a resident of a "private home for the aged" (the law was specific) eligible to receive state-aided assistance

[1] See Appendix I.
[2] See Eli Ginzberg, *A Pattern for Hospital Care* (New York: Columbia University Press, 1949), p. 188.
[3] *Laws of New York, 1936*, chap. 693.

was a major change in policy, it did not constitute a broad endorsement of institutional care at government expense. The legislature did retain its 1930 provision that relief could include "medical and surgical care and nursing" which made it legally easier for the private homes to care for nursing home-type cases on public assistance. It also kept the clause allowing old-age assistance recipients to receive temporary medical or surgical treatment in a hospital[4] and added sanitariums as permissible dispensers of such short-term care,[5] but made reimbursement for such services contingent upon the specific approval of the State Department of Social Welfare. Assistance was otherwise still to be granted only to persons in their "own, or some other suitable family home," and could not be granted to anyone in a "public or private institution of a custodial, correctional or curative character," nor to anyone who was "because of his physical or mental condition in need of continued institutional care." The forthright ban of state aid for anyone who as an "inmate of a public home" was also left untouched.

Even more formidable barriers to institutional care of persons on home relief (generally, public assistance cases that could not qualify for any of the federal categorical aid programs established by the 1936 legislation—Old-Age Assistance, Aid to the Blind, Aid to Dependent Children) were applied as the state initiated a permanent policy of reimbursing localities for part of their expenditures for this purpose. Home relief, the original outdoor relief program, had been totally a local responsibility. But both the state and federal governments had injected funds into its operations during the deep depression years on an emergency basis, and in 1936 the State assumed the

---

[4] Despite its prohibition of federal aid for persons in public institutions, the Social Security Act was interpreted by its administrators to allow aid for persons who received temporary care in public hospitals. See U.S. Congress, Senate Committee on Finance, *Hearings on H.R. 6000, Social Security Act Amendments*, 81st Cong., 2nd Sess., 1950, p. 60.

[5] The reason for the addition of sanitariums is obscure, but probably was associated with the ambiguity of definitions of institutions.

responsibility for continuous contributions, at the rate of 40 per cent, adding home relief to the three federal categories to make four programs for which local governments could count on grants-in-aid. The Public Welfare Law of 1929 had provided that relief could be given in a hospital or other institution, but while the federal government was participating in home relief it rejected requests of the American Hospital Association to help pay for hospitalization of recipients.[6] As the state took on a permanent fiscal responsibility for home relief it excluded hospitalization as well as other institutional care from services that recipients could get, giving further force to the general trend that only outdoor relief received financial stimulation from higher levels of government. It did, however, allow medical and nursing care outside of institutions.[7]

The year 1937 brought further accommodations of the State law to the federal social security program and further limitations on institutional care that could receive state and federal aid. The existing aid to the blind program was reorganized and the finished product met the requirements for federal subsidization under Title X of the Social Security Act. The limitations imposed as to the kinds of establishments recipients could reside in or receive care in were similar to those already operating for the old-age assistance program.[8] A more significant limitation denied eligibility under the blind and old-age assistance programs to hospitalized persons who were not recipients before being admitted to the hospital.[9]

The impact of the latter change for the development of nursing homes was twofold. Obviously, it made placement of an individual in a hospital less financially desirable, from the standpoint of local government, than placement in some establishment where he could qualify for aided assistance. A second

6 State of New York, *Sixty-Eighth Annual Report of the State Board of Social Welfare, For the Year Ending June 30, 1934*, Leg. Doc. No. 22 (Albany, 1935), p. 108.

7 *Laws of New York, 1936*, chap. 873, sec. 4.

8 *Laws of New York, 1937*, chap. 15, art. 13.

9 *Laws of New York, 1937*, chap. 645.

consideration was that it made placement in a public home even less desirable than it already was because an inmate requiring hospitalization could not become eligible for aided assistance.[10]

Pressures and Accommodations: Public Homes

During the general period that official public policy was settling into the course described above, important developments were taking place among the body of patients and homes the policy was intended primarily to affect. The 1934 *Report* of the State Board of Social Welfare spoke of the public home census increasing by a third since 1929 and said it would have

[10] It has not been possible to determine clearly the motivation behind the 1937 denial of grants-in-aid for assistance to persons in hospitals who were not on relief prior to their admission. Some persons interviewed in regard to the matter have suggested, or argued, that New York City was lax about administering old-age assistance cases initiated in hospitals and consumed a disproportionate share of state money, causing the upstate-controlled legislature to bar such cases. Others have suggested that the 1937 change was simply a clarification of the law to guarantee that it would not be used, in individual cases, as a source of primarily indoor rather than outdoor assistance. What data have been found do little to resolve these conflicting interpretations, since they are for periods after the change had been made. During the period between August 1, 1937 and June 30, 1938, upstate New York spent $318,883 for old-age assistance hospitalization but New York City, with perhaps 20 per cent fewer aged, spent only $86,290. Letter of August 21, 1963, from Kathryn Miller, Senior Research Analyst, Office of Medical Economics, State Department of Social Welfare. The figure $309,323 was shown as the City's OAA hospital expenditure, and $496,385 as the comparable upstate figure for the year ending June 30, 1939. State of New York, *Report of the Department of Social Welfare for the Period July 1, 1936–June 30, 1939*, Leg. Doc. No. 75 (Albany, 1940), p. 34. There is reason to suppose that hospitalization became an increasingly important issue during 1937. On October 1, 1936, the eligible age for OAA had been reduced from seventy to sixty-five years; immediately before the change there were 60,822 OAA beneficiaries; a year later there were 100,377. Many of the additions had been previously on home relief—where no hospitalization was reimbursable—and had been transferred to take advantage of the federal aid available. *Report of the Department of Social Welfare, 1936–1939*, p. 27.

increased even more had there been more room.[11] There were bed shortages in private facilities as well.

Public Welfare Districts reported in 1935 that more than half the inmates of public homes were sick or infirm (and we may believe that the ratio was high), while the number of infirmary beds constituted considerably less than half the total beds. Facilities were most inadequate in small, rural counties; the proposal that the state establish district infirmaries to service several such counties was made.[12] The 1936–1939 *Report* clearly reflected the impact of the legislation described in the foregoing pages: "Generally speaking, only those clients are admitted to the public homes who require institutional care and who are not eligible for public assistance."[13]

Hardly any of the *Reports*, from the mid-1930's on through the 1940's, failed to speak of increasing proportions of aged, sick, and infirm people who made up the public home populations, but the lag in the provision of appropriate facilities was great. Though the 1935 figures indicated that over half the inmates were infirm, it was not until 1957—or 1959, depending on the definition of infirmary bed used—that the proportion of infirmary beds equaled that of the residential beds.[14] Some progress in improving public facilities was made, however. The 1938 *Report* tells of improvements or expansions in public infirmaries in six counties. The 1939 issue reported the construction of infirmaries for Genesee and Oneida County Homes. During the period between 1934 and 1943 some 1,300 infirmary beds were added—and we may safely assume that these additions represented improvements despite the fact that such improvements were purely local enterprises, made in the face of competition from private facilities boosted by state and federal

[11] P. 147. [12] P. 136. [13] P. 74.

[14] In 1958 the State Department of Social Welfare began counting as infirmary beds of public homes only those beds meeting its infirmary standards, which it had established in 1951. Consequently, the number of infirmary beds, equaling custodial beds in 1957, fell slightly below in 1958. Since 1959 infirmary beds meeting the standards have exceeded custodial beds.

policies. The Department of Social Welfare could offer nothing but advice and admonitions for public homes even though these institutions clearly constituted one of the most unsatisfactory welfare-medical problems in the state. The principle of local responsibility applied, and was to continue to apply, in this instance.

Pressures and Accommodations: Voluntary Institutions

PRIVATE HOMES FOR THE AGED

By 1936, when the law accepted private homes for the aged as places where recipients of old-age assistance and aid to the blind might get care, these institutions were already mature organizations operating in well-established paths. Their purposes, procedures, and economics as philanthropic agencies were set and limited by tradition—self expectation, public expectation, and governmental expectation—and by legalistic charters of incorporation. The relatively simple change in their complicated ecological setting represented by the amendment to the law did not increase quickly the importance of these institutions, or cause any abrupt change in their character.

Private homes for the aged are important to this study because some provide infirmary care as well as domiciliary services. Significant questions to examine are the extent to which these institutions expanded as a whole, the extent to which they increased their infirmary facilities, and a related matter, the extent to which they accepted persons on public assistance as their clientele.

The number of these homes had increased from 82 in the 1890's to 200 in 1934, but then had hovered at about that latter figure—where indeed it continues to hover even today. The total number of beds in 1934—14,675—grew by only about a thousand through 1943 and half again that much through 1952. The new law, then, produced no new, sudden growth. Nor did the legal opening of doors to private homes for the aged to persons on public welfare result in any quick increase of such persons among the residents of these facilities. In 1933, when public money being spent in such agencies could come only from local sources, a mere 915 of their thirteen-odd thousand population were public charges;[15] but by 1942 the number had grown only to 1,300.

The contributory reasons staying the involvement of the private homes with welfare cases were neither simple nor few in number. Two general and interrelated reasons may be properly described as most important, however: the traditional function of these institutions as "homes," or residences, rather than medical care facilities; and their images as philanthropic, nongovernmental agencies.

As to the primacy of the established function of providing residence—there was a general policy among the homes that only persons in fair health were to be admitted.[16] Of more than fourteen thousand beds extant in the state in 1934, only 1,656 were infirmary beds, equipped for the provision of nursing care, as Table 2 indicates. The expansion in infirmary facilities that did occur came about primarily to care for residents who became ill as they became older—virtually all were aged— rather than for the reception of infirm persons from the community. But even this kind of expansion did not occur soon. In fact, the figures of Table 2 show that there was a decline in infirmary beds between 1934 and 1943, and the number of homes maintaining infirmaries also shrank.

To be sure, in the nine years following 1943 the infirmaries and beds both more than doubled in number. But this particular kind of facility lagged considerably behind other nursing-home-type accommodations upstate. Private homes for the aged were, and remain, primarily living quarters for the relatively well. They have been subjected to many of the same

[15] New York State Department of Social Welfare, Division of Research and Division of Medical Care, "Statistics of the Care of the Aged in Private Institutions in the State of New York" (typescript), Albany, 1935, p. 43.
[16] *Report of the Board of Social Welfare For the Year Ending June 30, 1934,* p. 148.

Table 2. Private homes for the aged in New York State, domiciliary and infirmary beds, 1934–1952

Year	Total homes	Homes with domiciliary beds only	Homes with domiciliary and infirmary beds	Domiciliary beds	Infirmary beds	Total beds
1934	200	128	72	13,019	1,656	14,675
1943	200	144	56	14,321	1,576	15,897
1952	200	62	138	13,247	3,825	17,172

Source. Files, New York State Department of Social Welfare.

pressures to expand their medical care services that public homes have felt because of the increasing numbers of sick, aged persons. Accordingly, there has been—as with the public institutions—a secular increase in the proportion of infirmary beds to simple residential beds since the early forties. In 1963, however, the domiciliary beds in these private homes upstate still outnumbered infirmary beds by a ratio of better than three to one—and in New York City the ratio was almost two to one.[17]

The emphasis of private homes for the aged offering domiciliary quarters for the well brought to their doors people who, by and large, could be expected to be less destitute than those requiring infirmary care, because destitution is so often related to long-term illness. Other policies of selectivity produced similar results. Usually only those applicants who shared the religious, fraternal, or geographic orientations of the managing organization were admitted.[18] The operation of such standards tends to exclude persons on assistance—the priority of economic need is tempered by other considerations. And with waiting lists, which are common, there was, and is, ample opportunity for selectivity. Finally, some homes simply exclude welfare clients. Particularly upstate, there were still in the mid-1960's numerous homes that would not admit these people.

Probably the greatest single cause for the private homes not becoming deeply involved with public welfare cases was their image as philanthropic, nongovernmental, institutions. This was at the root of some of their disinclination to become entangled with the governmental procedures and regulations that the acceptance of public charges entailed. Further, it supported the assumption, shared most importantly by government welfare administrators operating under budgetary pressures, that when welfare recipients were accepted by private homes they

---

[17] Files, State Department of Social Welfare.
[18] New York State Department of Social Welfare, Division of Research and Division of Medical Care, "Statistics of the Care of the Aged in Private Institutions in the State of New York," p. 36.

could be cared for without responsibility for the full costs being passed on to government. Operations based on this assumption soon made it clear that philanthropy was going to lag behind the increasing costs of giving care.

There was not only a general governmental unwillingness to pay the full costs of caring for welfare recipients in voluntary institutions, there was also a great hesitancy to recognize that infirmary care costs more than other public support efforts, which naturally discouraged the development of infirmary facilities. The State Board of Social Welfare ruled that residents of private homes for the aged could be eligible for public assistance but refused reimbursement on grants that exceeded the average grant in the OAA district in which the institution was located.[19] Infirmary care of much quality would, of course, cost more than the average old-age assistance grant, since the vast majority of OAA recipients always lived outside of institutions and without continuous medical care. Moreover, prior to 1956, the reimbursement policies of the Department called for a flat rate for each home, whether the resident received infirmary or domiciliary care. There was no provision for the greater expense that infirmary care entailed, and therefore homes undertaking or expanding this kind of activity were obliged to find additional nongovernmental money to support it. Even after 1956, when a differential rate for infirmary care was first permitted, there was a ceiling beyond which reimbursement could not go, regardless of the actual cost of care, until 1966.[20]

Another tradition that impeded the evolution of the home for the aged was the requirement that residents pay admission fees. Only 64 of 193 private homes for the aged had no admission fee arrangement in 1933; in only about one-sixth of the remainder were the fees below $500. Public assistance was not available, of course, for such payments. The situation was complicated when the State Department of Social Welfare decided

---

[19] *Report of the Department of Social Welfare, 1936–1939*, p. 28.
[20] See p. 136, below.

that such fee arangements, constituting life-care contracts that obliged the institution paid to provide for the resident concerned until his death without any further compensation, ruled out the payment of any old-age assistance money to the institutions in such cases. The Department saw this development as a "serious administrative difficulty,"[21] and welfare officials at all levels of government began advising the private institutions to abandon the entrance fee system for income from public assistance recipients. The argument was that assistance could be counted upon to continue until the recipient's death, while the reliance upon lump-sum fees involved the increasing risk, as inflation became an important financial consideration and as the aged became more likely to live on rather than to die, that expenditures would far exceed income from fees. In 1946 the State Health Preparedness Commission was repeating the advice and adding that the private homes might attract recipients of Old Age and Survivors Insurance,[22] who had begun to collect benefits in 1940.

Memoranda issued by the Department of Social Welfare illustrate some of the difficulties that nonprofit homes for the aged had in extricating themselves from commitments to past procedures. For a home to have an admission fee patient become eligible to receive public assistance it was necessary to demonstrate that, despite sound management, its resources for the support of such persons had been exhausted. A lengthy memorandum of 1953 specified many complicated steps required for this process. A memorandum of November 12, 1952, pointed out that some homes for the aged and blind had charters allowing them to give free care only; residents could not, consequently, receive public assistance.

Of course the established character of private homes for the aged constituted distinct assets, in many respects, for the wel-

---

[21] *Report of the Department of Social Welfare, 1936–1939,* p. 27.
[22] New York State Health Preparedness Commission, *Planning for the Care of the Chronically Ill in New York State—Some Medical-Social and Institutional Aspects,* Leg. Doc. No. 66A (Albany, 1946), p. 36.

fare of the community. This should not be overlooked. In having given many years of service they had built up and tested the administrative mechanisms necessary for carrying on this work. They had also developed pride and traditions of service among their workers and respected reputations in the community at large that they were interested in maintaining. By and large they had, moreover, close ties of responsibility to the religious, fraternal, or other subcommunity that they served and by whom they had been established. Under these circumstances there existed sets of self-regulating mechanisms that assured that the care given residents and patients would not fall below minimal standards. An examination of the historical literature brings to light no grand scandal involving these homes or evidence of any major failure on their part to perform satisfactorily. What exhortation addressed to these institutions one finds in the literature of the forties is generally aimed at promoting their expansion to serve more people rather than manifesting any great concern with the quality of care they were giving.

There was in operation not only the self-regulating ties of responsibility between the homes and their special publics. The State Board of Social Welfare and its agent, the Department, had been exercising regulatory responsibilities over such institutions for many years. Charters of incorporation for all private homes for the aged had to be approved by the Board before any such institution could begin operating. In addition, the Board had responsibility for setting down rules to supervise such organizations, and the Department for conducting inspections to assure that the standards thus established were met. Although the standards were general rather than specific, and far from comprehensive, there was, and had been for years, state government supervision of these homes.

With such beginnings the Department of Social Welfare moved to strengthen its influence over these institutions quite early. Soon after the 1936 amendment it established "standards of suitability" which homes would have to meet before they could care for public assistance beneficiaries. In so doing it added to its statutory regulatory powers the leverage of being able to deny assistance payment to persons, otherwise eligible, in homes failing to meet the standards. (This new economic weapon proved, in time, to be far more important in dealing with proprietary nursing homes than with the voluntary institutions under consideration here.) By mid-1942, one hundred of the private homes for the aged had qualified by the standards. Some, of course, had no interest in admitting welfare recipients and therefore in being inspected for that purpose.

In review, one should say that the established character of the private homes for the aged made them, in some measure, unresponsive to the new work they were being asked to undertake. At least part of their unresponsiveness, however, lay in the inadequacy of their image as philanthropic agencies, able to bear continuing, financial responsibilities for substantial shares of the cost of giving care which was growing increasingly expensive. It lay too in established perceptions of duty and responsibility which are an inseparable part of any ongoing administrative structure. It lay, further, in the very regulatory mechanisms that assured satisfactory performance—in their absence there would have been possible more of the unrestrained, uncontrolled growth that occurred among proprietary nursing homes.

The net consequence of these factors in upstate New York was a relatively slow growth of infirmary facilities in private homes for the aged. Table 3 shows that there was actually a loss in the decade following 1934. The statutory changes incident to the establishment of the federal social security system were not sufficient to generate marked changes so far as these institutions were concerned. And, although growth did occur between 1943 and 1952 in this area, no legislative changes can account for it. That growth, it must be concluded, stemmed from the increasing demands upon the homes to provide nursing-home-type care, and for the image of the private home for the aged to undergo evolution.

Table 3. Infirmary facilities in private homes for the aged,
upstate, 1934–1952

Year	Homes	Beds
1934	40	443
1943	30	390
1952	80	934

Source. Files, New York State Department of Social Welfare. See Table 4M, Appendix I.

INCORPORATED NURSING AND CONVALESCENT HOMES

We have been speaking about private homes for the aged. It
is much more difficult to analyze the character and accommoda-
tive qualities of the other voluntary institutions with which we
are concerned, the nonprofit incorporated nursing homes and
convalescent homes. First, they were not clearly recognized as
a class of institutions by commentators and investigators during
the historical period with which we are dealing, and in the
literature they are often discussed along with other kinds of
institutions, such as proprietary nursing homes. Second, although by the mid-1930's the concept of a voluntary, nonprofit
service agency was well developed, the concept of a "nursing
home" was not, and these institutions combined elements of
both.

The nonprofit nursing and convalescent homes had much in
common with private homes for the aged in that they were, by
and large, supported by and responsible to some fraternal,
religious, or other community group. Although there appear to
have been no allegations that their administration was scan-
dalously poor or dishonest, critics did charge, at times, that
some of these homes were not prepared, in terms of either
skilled personnel or appropriate equipment, to give more than
the most rudimentary levels of care.[23] This, of course, was one
of the problems of "becoming" a nursing home in an era when

23 See n. 5, p. 12, above; and n. a, Table 5M, Appendix I.

the concept was, as yet, still ill-defined. But it was also related to problems of money and the reliance put upon philanthropy as a financial source in the face of rising demands. Again, as voluntary agencies their required charters of incorporation had to be approved by the State Board of Social Welfare (nonprofit convalescent homes were subjected to this requirement only in 1941) but as nursing homes they were largely ignored by the Board and the Department. No set of standards or rules was designed for their regulation until 1951, when a nursing home code covering them as well as proprietary institutions— prompted mostly by problems concerning the latter—was adopted.[24]

One distinction between the convalescent and nursing homes and the homes for the aged that is of some relevance for this study was the former's concern with sick people, compared to the emphasis of the latter upon residential services. Associated with these, we may speculate, was a greater involvement of the nursing homes with public assistance recipients. No data are available to afford much historical comparison. A 1962 study found, however, that 36.6 per cent of the patients in upstate voluntary nursing homes were bed-fast or chair-fast, compared to 11.4 per cent of those in homes for the aged;[25] and 33.3 per cent of the nursing home folk were public charges, as against 16.3 per cent of those in homes for the aged.[26]

It should be noted that voluntary convalescent and nursing homes were not specifically accepted by the law as institutions in which recipients of old-age assistance and aid to the blind might be cared for. They were, rather, in the category of in-

[24] See pp. 92–93, below.
[25] Milton Matz, *Nursing Homes and Related Facilities and their Patients in New York State, 1962*, Medical Economics Report No. 1, May 1964, Office of Medical Economics, State Department of Social Welfare, Table 16. The Comparison is made here with the total population of the homes for the aged—domiciliary and infirmary. Of the infirmary cases alone, 37.5 per cent were bed-fast or chair-fast.
[26] *Ibid.*, Table 15. Of the infirmary population of homes for the aged, 18.8 per cent were public charges.

stitutions with proprietary nursing homes to whom care of such welfare beneficiaries was, if not forthrightly prescribed by the law, at least of doubtful legality.

Voluntary convalescent and nursing homes, then, shared some of the limiting characteristics of private homes for the aged. They also shared some of their qualities of being responsible and regulated. Resembling the modern nursing home in, as a class, aiming primarily at the care of infirm and chronically ill persons, they also were burdened by some of the limitations in organizational concept and legal unclarities that bothered proprietary nursing homes. Being the kinds of institutions they were, in the kind of setting described, they did not multiply rapidly. Although, to judge by numbers, they were significant in upstate New York in the mid-1930's they had expanded only by about half upstate by the 1950's, as Table 4 shows. They did not have the grow-power of proprietary nursing homes.

Table 4. Incorporated convalescent and nursing homes, upstate, 1935–1950

Year	Homes	Beds
1935	15	1,093
1950	29	1,645

Source. Files, New York State Department of Social Welfare. See Table 5M, Appendix I.

Pressures and Accommodations: Proprietary Nursing Homes

IN THE SHADOW OF THE LAW

The private home for the aged was a mature institution by the mid-1930's, but the concept of the nursing home was still an extremely amorphous one. The first proprietary nursing homes seem typically to have begun when women with invalid husbands took in other invalids, for fees, to help pay the bills. Non-profit "nursing homes" were hardly recognized, and were evolving out of a variety of precursors. This amorphous quality was important for the boost proprietary facilities received from the grant-in-aid arrangements. Regarded as similar to hospital care, nursing home care had not been considered reimbursable by the Temporary Emergency Relief Administration and the Department of Social Welfare, as it assumed the responsibilities for public assistance administration in 1937, set out to continue that policy.

Local welfare departments circumvented the technicality, however, by issuing otherwise eligible clients separate grants for maintenance in a home and for medical and nursing care.[27] The law provided, it will be recalled, that home relief, aid to the blind and to the aged could include "medical and nursing care" and could be given in one's own, "or other suitable family home." The proscriptions of care in "institutions of a custodial, correctional or curative character," care to anyone "in need of continued institutional care," and the home relief general ban on institutional care presented some problems. But, then, no one was sure what an institution was, what a family home was, or especially what a nursing home was. The State Department of Social Welfare being of the opinion that there was a considerable need for care that would not be met if the nursing homes were not used, and recognizing that "things were very much in a state of flux," adopted a definition of an "institution" as an establishment that cared for more than eight people.[28] Thus, small nursing homes were recognized as family homes and reimbursement of assistance to their patients who were otherwise eligible was legitimized.

As early as 1940, we find the Department of Social Welfare reporting that

physical disabilities, loss of friends and relatives, inability to care for themselves, and loneliness may combine to lead many of the

[27] Health Preparedness Commission, *Planning for the Care of the Chronically Ill*, p. 107.

[28] Interview with Miss Margaret Barnard, Bureau of Public Assistance, New York State Department of Social Welfare, Feb. 20, 1963.

[OAA recipients] to seek care in an institution as they advance in years. Suitable living arrangements can be found for these elderly people only in institutions or in nursing homes.[29]

In its 1941–1942 and 1943 *Reports,* the Department of Social Welfare explained that there had been a rapid expansion of private nursing homes during the war because general hospitals, with diminished staffs and increased demands from a prosperous public, had found it necessary to discharge many long-term care cases. The Health Preparedness Commission, however, finding nursing home beds had increased 20 per cent in the ten-month period between July, 1945 and May, 1946, concluded that "the demand for nursing home beds is increasing and is not solely related to such war-wrought factors as family dislocations and shortages of nurses, physicians and hospital beds."[30]

Meanwhile, in 1943, local welfare departments were requesting greater freedom in making nursing home placements for which they could expect reimbursement.[31] The State Department was restive about its interpretation of the laws,[32] and wanting more information before it moved further, undertook a study of 109 nursing homes in selected public welfare districts throughout the State. The general tone of the findings was neither condemnatory nor commendatory[33]—but one specific finding was that the study had included neither the worst nor the best of the nursing homes. As a whole, it was reported, most of the homes studied kept their patients comfortable despite a general lack of equipment, but they were not judged to be appropriate facilities for sick people. Commonly they were negligent in keeping records and only a third had registered nurses on their staffs. An important conclusion of the study was

[29] State of New York, Board of Social Welfare, *Social Welfare, 1940, Annual-Report for the Year 1940,* Leg. Doc. No. 68 (Albany, 1941), p. 31.
[30] *Planning for the Care of the Chronically Ill,* p. 25.
[31] *Ibid.,* p. 24.   [32] *Ibid.,* p. 109.
[33] See "A Study of Nursing Homes in New York State (1943)," Health Preparedness Commission, *Planning for the Care of the Chronically Ill,* pp. 107–121.

that those districts with the weakest public home establishments were "more often than not" unable to find enough satisfactory nursing home beds to meet the demand. Half of the patients in the homes were assistance recipients. A sample of these showed 52 New York City and 270 upstate cases, which in turn were comprised of 223 OAA, 85 home relief, and 11 aid to the blind cases.

Private Care Legitimized

During the 1944 session of the legislature, action initiated by the Department of Social Welfare amended the Social Welfare Law, changing significant words that had clouded the eligibility of nursing home inmates. Specifically, "private nursing homes" were included as places where the blind and aged could be eligible for reimbursable assistance;[34] the phrase "in need of continued institutional care," which had threatened reimbursable assistance in nursing homes, was dropped, as were the modifiers "custodial" and "curative," which had limited the kind of institutional care offered by grant-in-aid relief.[35]

Because "nursing home" had in the past been confused with "sanitarium," and care in the latter kind of institution was limited to that of a temporary character (a Social Welfare Department regulation specified three months), mention of "sanitarium" was removed.[36]

Pending the Governor's signature, the amendments were endorsed by the State Charities Aid Association and the Syracuse Council of Social Agencies. The State Division of the Budget saw the changes as "merely a clarification of the law" and reported that they would not increase the state's cost, "because reimbursement is now being made on such cases."[37] No evidence of opposition to the modifications of the law has been

---

[34] *Laws of New York*, 1944, chaps. 398, 391.
[35] *Ibid.*, chaps. 392, 399.   [36] *Ibid.*, chap. 392.
[37] New York State Legislature, 1944, Bill Jacket, chaps. 392, 398, 399.

found, even though they represented the crystalization of major changes in public policy.[38]

The Department of Social Welfare followed up these legal changes by issuing later in the year its Bulletin 105, which stated unequivocally that care in private nursing homes was reimbursable with OAA, AB, and home relief funds. A nursing home was defined, for purposes of reimbursement, as a home that offered "board, room and bedside care for compensation," and its services were declared not to be "institutional care" within the meaning of the home relief provisions. Reimbursement required recommendation of nursing home care by a physician, medical supervision comprised of a minimum of physician visits at three-month intervals, and certification of the home concerned by the local government agency authorizing the care. The certificates issued were to require annual renewal and were to be revocable for cause; their validity was to be contingent upon the home's compliance with local government ordinances and the Public Health Law and upon maintaining nursing home standards established by the local agency. An appendix to the Bulletin recommended minimum standards that local agencies might adopt relating to buildings and equipment, personnel and records. No ceiling limited the costs for which reimbursement would be available, and no time limit on care in nursing homes was mentioned.

Proposals for Further State Involvement

The *Annual Report* of the Department that described these developments noted the Department's lack of statutory authority to regulate nursing homes and saw the local certification pro-

[38] It is noteworthy that the modifications were of grass-roots origin, that they grew out of pressures generated at the local government level that were transmitted up through the bureaucratic levels of the welfare administrative structure to the central political authorities of the State, the Governor and the Legislature. Writing about the 1941 session of New York's lawmaking body, Belle Zeller and Elisabeth Scott reported that "approximately half of all proposals enacted came from State administrative agencies and from agencies of local governments." "State Agencies and Lawmaking," *Public Administration Review*, II (Summer 1942), p. 206.

gram as a "temporary solution." It also said that any state-wide move to close nursing homes failing to meet acceptable standards would "create even more serious problems for the sick and aged who are now getting at least some measure of needed care."[39] The State Health Preparedness Commission, made up of state legislators, the State Commissioners of Health and Social Welfare, and private citizens—two of whom were physicians—took a remarkably similar position in its report on chronic illness care in 1946.[40]

The Commission surveyed a broad range of nursing-home-type facility problems and proposed immediate state regulation. Mount Vernon had been licensing nursing homes since 1922 and New York City since 1929; by 1945, five cities and one county had established procedures for annual licenses for these institutions. In four other localities nursing homes were included in broader classes of accommodations subject to regulation. Local regulation was found to be quite inadequate, however. The problem of incomplete geographical coverage, absence of consistent concern with medical, nursing, and dietary service, and lack of qualifications of local officials to make judgments about nursing home quality were among the reasons the Commission called for state action.

The Commission was hardly decisive about what it thought state regulation should consist of, however. It noted that at least twenty states licensed nursing homes, that the licenses expired either annually or biannually and generally could be revoked for cause, and that there were penalties for violations of the laws involved.[41] It described state "licensure" of all facilities caring for sick persons as a first policy choice. It posed the "regulation" of all nursing-home-type facilities as a second choice[42] and then went on, in its summary conclusions, to say that "if such licensure is not *advisable* or attainable at an early

---

[39] New York State Department of Social Welfare, *Public Social Services in 1944, 28th Annual Report, January 1, 1944–December 31, 1944*, Leg. Doc. No. 63 (Albany, 1945), p. 28.

[40] *Planning for the Care of the Chronically Ill.*

[41] *Ibid.*, p. 87 ff.   [42] *Ibid.*, p. 29.

date, *registration* of nursing homes should be established immediately."[43] After declaring licensure as the first choice, the
Commission seemingly found it to be perhaps unadvisable.
(The apparent inconsistency is quite probably attributable to
conflicting opinions within the Commission itself or within
the arena comprised by it and its advisory committee.)

By registration, the Commission had in mind a listing of
institutions and, in time, inspections by state authority to
determine whether each home was meeting state-established
standards. Once inspected, institutions could not operate without approval; but approval, once given, would last indefinitely.
New establishments, however, or expansion of old ones, would
require prior approval for both structural and operational plans
before they could be used. It is important to note that the
Commission saw as desirable the inclusion of all nursing-home-
type facilities—public, proprietary, and nonprofit—in any regulatory program.[44]

One further point—as much emphasis was put on teaching
and assisting the management and staff of institutions as upon
punitive enforcement. And the Commission advised: "Enforcement of regulations must be so executed as to preclude the
closing of nursing homes when alternate facilities do not exist
for placement of the patients who would thus be displaced."[45]
Scarcity of qualified personnel to serve as an inspection force
was also a consideration. For most nursing homes, regulation
was to consist of gentle persuasion; the official power of the
state would in fact be partially neutralized by the power that
the institutions had, the power growing out of the public's
dependency on them.

Meanwhile, the Commission paid considerable attention to
the problems of increasing nursing-home-type facilities, particularly those of voluntary and public sponsorship. It declared
that private homes for the aged should be encouraged to expand their infirmary accommodations.[46] It analyzed the views
of local public welfare officials throughout the state on care of

[43] *Ibid.*, p. 36. Italics added.   [44] *Ibid.*, pp. 29–30.
[45] *Ibid.*, p. 29.   [46] *Ibid.*, pp. 36, 37.

the chronically ill, making it clear that from the standpoint of these participants in the administrative process what was most needed was the inclusion of public homes, on the same terms as those for operating private homes, among the institutions where reimbursable care could be given.[47] Another proposal commanding support from the local administrative level—though not nearly so much—was one that the state supply financial aid for construction of local facilities.[48] The Commission itself showed much concern for the expansion of infirmary facilities in public homes, the fitting of such institutions into relationships with general hospitals, and their conversion to community facilities open to paying patients as well as to indigents. Most important, it suggested that state reimbursement be made available for patients in public homes meeting minimum standards.[49]

The 1946 Formula Change: Unbalance Compounded

At the very time these arguments were being pressed—though with less backing and less articulately than later on—steps were being taken to increase the difference between the state's policies toward public and private homes. The Temporary State Commission on Municipal Revenues and the Reduction of Real Estate Taxes was recommending that the reimbursement rates then in effect be raised and standardized. The Temporary State Commission, appointed in 1944, saw its proposals put into law in 1946. One of its major recommendations had been that state participation in OAA, AB, and HR be raised to where localities would carry only 20 per cent of the financial load of each of the three programs.[50]

[47] See *Ibid.*, pp. 32, 37, 46, 48, 58.

[48] *Ibid.*, p. 58. For a period the State Postwar Planning Commission was offering financial assistance for detailed construction plans for public homes.

[49] *Ibid.*, pp. 31–37.

[50] The amounts of federal aid available had been increased over the years and in 1946 were raised again; the federal payments for OAA and

Why were the policy differences distinguishing public from private homes being increased just as students of the problems of nursing homes were voicing opinion that such differences should be abolished? Once again, support for the public home was not the foremost policy problem up for consideration; it was vastly overshadowed by the fear of postwar depression and by state-local political cleavage. While an important reason for the establishment of the Temporary State Commission was to achieve greater order and clarity in state-local fiscal relations, the central purpose was to shore up local resources against what was commonly expected—a recurrence of such an economic crisis as had followed World War I.[51] Though welfare was not the only field in which adjustments were made, it was considered an extremely important one since the costs of its programs mount at precisely the times local tax systems weaken.[52] The main purpose of the Temporary Commission was reflected in its full title and in the character of its membership. The State Comptroller, Frank P. Moore, was its Chairman; the State Commissioner of Social Welfare was the only representative from the health or welfare fields; eight of the other fourteen members were financial officers or chairmen of finance

---

AB cases became two-thirds of the first $15 and one-half of the remainder up to $45 per month. The financial burden for the aged and blind programs had been shifted in 1936 from an equal division between the state and local governments to an apportionment under which the state contributed an amount sufficient that, when the federal aid was counted, the localities paid 25 per cent of the cost. See Laws of New York, 1936, chap. 693. There was no federal aid for home relief, but the state had been reimbursing local governments for 40 per cent of these costs since 1936.

[51] Interview with Joseph D. McGoldrick, former Comptroller of the City of New York, member of the Temporary Commission on Municipal Revenues and Reduction of Real Estate Taxes, Nov. 28, 1962. See also the New York Times, March 14, 1945, p. 1. Also, the final report of the Commission shows clearly the concern with depression. See the Report of the Commission on Municipal Revenues and Reduction of Real Estate Taxes (Albany, 1945).

[52] Ibid., p. 21.

committees of the State legislature. Also, local government was heavily represented.[53]

There were two intersecting political cleavages within the Temporary Commission's membership—upstate-downstate and state-local. New York City asked that the state assume all welfare costs. Upstate cities, towns, and counties wanted a high rate of reimbursement but feared the state control that would follow if it were 100 per cent. The State Comptroller agreed to reimbursement at 80 per cent for the four programs—OAA, AB, HR, and Aid to Dependent Children—for which there was currently reimbursement. This represented increases from 75 to 80 per cent for two programs, from 40 to 80 for a third, and from 50 to 80 for the fourth, and pleased the local government representatives. But when the Governor was informed of the agreement, he instructed the Comptroller (the Governor's political party subordinate, though independently elected) to reduce the rate, arguing that such state support would generate local irresponsibility in the management of funds.

The Comptroller's efforts to carry out these instructions met with intransigent resistance from the local government people, including at least one threat to resign from the Commission. Believing they had a chance to get the 80 per cent, even though it was almost more than they had dared hope for, the local representatives decided to devote all of their efforts to that goal. There was nothing left for them to bargain with for the reimbursement of additional programs. Public homes and other matters that might have been considered were left unmentioned when an unusual opportunity to make gains in another way presented itself. Faced with such dogged opposition, the Governor acceded to the 80 per cent formula and the local representatives went home victorious.[54]

53 *Ibid.*, p. 12. The Chairman had been one of the organizers of the Association of Towns in 1933 and its Executive Secretary from 1933 to 1943.

54 Although one can surely not argue that the Republican party dominated New York City during the LaGuardia Administration, the fact that the city's representatives were chosen by Mayor LaGuardia, rather than by a Democrat, probably helped persuade Republican Governor

The Temporary Commission's final report reflected the Governor's apprehension about local irresponsibility and the concern that reimbursement would affect placement. It advised that localities should establish integrated welfare systems "appropriate to the needs of the eligible individuals or family, regardless of the rate of reimbursement for the particular type of assistance and care" and warned against "abuses" of the high reimbursement rate.[55] Pronouncements such as these were not to ward off troubles related to reimbursement, however. The press was shortly to supply the Governor with support for his argument that the 80 per cent rate encouraged local irresponsibility. And the avoidance of placement in nonreimbursable institutions was to remain a problem for a number of years.

The Fur Coat Scandal

In 1947, elements of the local press charged the New York City Department of Welfare with looseness in its administrative practices, particularly in its determinations of whether clients actually needed relief. The "fur coat scandal," so called because a woman owning an allegedly valuable fur coat was receiving assistance, brought on an investigation by the State Board of Social Welfare. The City Commissioner of Welfare was summarily dismissed by the Mayor and an extensive reorganization of the City Department followed.[56]

It is worth noting that the Democrats had again taken over the stewardship of the city but that Governor Dewey was to remain in office through 1954. The New York Times reported, upon the Mayor's removal of the City Welfare Commissioner,

---

Thomas E. Dewey to meet the local demands. This account of the decision making on the 1946 reimbursement formula is drawn from an interview with Joseph D. McGoldrick, Nov. 28, 1962.

55 Report of the Commission on Municipal Revenues, p. 21.

56 See the New York Times, Oct. 26, 27, 1947; and March 12, June 15, July 23, 1948.

that "the Mayor's action in relieving Mr. Rhatigan of his command in the Welfare Department the day before the State Board of Social Welfare announced that hearings would begin on Wednesday was considered in official circles as a move to take the City administration 'off the spot.' "[57] On the following day, the same newspaper noted: "In official circles the consensus was that Mr. Rhatigan had been caught in a 'squeeze' of conflicting state and local political forces."[58] The cleavage was not only in the state-local dimension, but also the Republican-Democrat.[59]

Proposals for Change

The "fur coat scandal" not only raised questions in Albany about the wisdom of high reimbursement rates; it contributed considerably to attitudes of mutual disrespect and distrust held toward each other by many state and New York City officials. In addressing the opening of the legislature in 1948, Governor Dewey said:

[57] *Ibid.,* Oct. 26, 1947.   [58] *Ibid.,* Oct. 27, 1947.

[59] Democratic leadership has traditionally been identified with New York City, even to the point that large upstate cities are more likely to be Republican than is the case with their counterparts in other states. Therefore, the parallel between party identification and geographic location has been stronger in New York than has usually been the case elsewhere. See Ralph A. Straetz and Frank J. Munger, *New York Politics* (New York: New York University Press, 1960), pp. 40–41. It is quite conceivable that the future pattern may differ, however. Attention has been called to a shift on Democratic strength from the big city to its suburbs, which lie in upstate territory. See Marilyn Gittell, "Metropolitan Mayor—Political Dead End?" *Public Administration Review,* XXIII (March 1963), pp. 20–25.

The pattern of political influence was, in fact, much more complex than any account here can properly describe. One aspect, heretofore unmentioned, was the influence of employee unions in the City Department of Welfare in reducing the Commissioner's effectiveness. See New York State Department of Social Welfare, *Public Social Services in 1947, 81st Annual Report, January 1, 1947–December 31, 1947,* Leg. Doc. No. 78 (Albany, 1948), p. 34.

The State government has in recent years gone far—perhaps too far—in its expansion of local assistance. Apart from the effects on State finances and State government in the future, there is the progressively degenerative effect that excessive grants-in-aid produce upon aided units of government.[60]

In 1949 the Special Committee on Social Welfare of the Joint Legislative Committee on Interstate Corporation, comprised of state legislative and administrative personnel, echoed the Governor's sentiments. The Special Committee discussed the possibility of supplanting the 80 per cent reimbursement in four categories with a 50 per cent rate for all welfare activities, including public home and hospital care. This would have been tantamount to the complete abandonment of the old distinction between indoor and outdoor relief, which had by now become quite fictional. The Special Committee foresaw difficulties in operating under such a reimbursement formula, however. Among them were the need for greater local government security against economic depressions, the variety in quality of public home care, and (the real stumbling block) the lack of agreement upon criteria of indigency entitling clients to hospital care at public expense.[61] Again, a cleavage between New York City and upstate was at work. The city had had for years a tradition of liberality in providing free hospital care. In 1948 over $42 million in government funds was expended there for general hospital care; this amounted to $5.30 per capita. Upstate, for the same year, the comparable total figure was under $10 million and the per capita, $1.45.[62]

Local governments generally were opposed to any reduction of the reimbursement rates, but the prospect of aid for public

---

[60] Leg. Doc. No. 1, 1948, p. 12.

[61] See the Special Committee's *Report*, Leg. Doc. No. 62 (Albany, 1949), pp. 70–73.

[62] Eli Ginzberg, *A Pattern for Hospital Care* (New York: Columbia University Press, 1949), p. 160. In 1961 New York City spent $93 million for nonreimbursable hospital care, while upstate New York spent $8 million. Files, New York State Department of Welfare.

home and other care was attractive to them.[63] Cries for broader reimbursement were becoming louder and clearer. The Health Preparedness Commission, after its somewhat equivocal statement of 1946, had forthrightly said in 1947: "If the present system of state welfare reimbursement were expanded to include the care of all the publicly dependent and medically indigent chronically ill in the hospitals and in publicly operated facilities of the nursing home type which meet minimum standards, the localities would then be able to do their part in providing promptly the variety of care best suited to the patients' needs."[64] In 1948 a subcommittee of the Special Committee of the Joint Legislative Committee on Interstate Cooperation judged the shortage of nursing-home-type facilities to be acute and critical throughout the state.[65] The following year the parent body reported a tendency for clients to be assigned to assistance programs according to reimbursement considerations rather than to needs.[66] By 1951 the same group was telling of local welfare personnel frankly indicating that persons were not admitted to public homes unless placement in an institution where care was reimbursable was impossible.[67] Meanwhile, Eli Ginzberg, in a study done for the state, declared that the reimbursement formula had encouraged the growth of proprietary nursing homes while discouraging the modernization and improvement of county homes and infirmaries, even though some large counties had improved their public homes.

[63] Interview with Byron T. Hipple, Jr., former Deputy Commissioner for Administrative Finance and Statistics, State Department of Social Welfare, November 2, 1962. See also the *New York Times*, Jan. 12, 1951.

[64] *A Program for the Care of the Chronically Ill in New York State*, Leg. Doc. No. 69 (Albany, 1947), p. 35.

[65] *Report of the Special Committee on Social Welfare and Relief of the Joint Legislative Committee on Interstate Cooperation*, Leg. Doc. No. 51 (Albany, 1951), pp. 133–135.

[66] *Report*, Leg. Doc. No. 62, p. 70.

[67] *Report of the Special Committee on Social Welfare of the Joint Legislative Committee on Interstate Cooperation and the Final Staff Report to the Subcommittee on Fiscal and Administrative Problems*, Leg. Doc. No. 87 (Albany, 1951), p. 147.

Professor Ginzberg went farther, in fact, and suggested that the federal government re-examine its reasons for barring assistance grants to persons residing in public institutions.[68] As early as 1947, however, the American Public Welfare Association, the American Medical Association, the American Hospital Association, and the American Public Health Association had recommended in a joint policy statement that the Social Security Act should be amended to provide federal matching funds for care in public medical institutions, including nursing care in public homes.[69]

Reimbursement was not the only resource explored in the late 1940's that might possibly open the doors of public homes to more people. The Health Preparedness Commission had suggested in its 1946 report that paying patients be allowed to use these facilities, the idea being that the character of the home would be changed to that of a general community facility, such as schools or the post office, rather than remain limited in its conception as a service for the underprivileged or the unfortunate.[70] Other groups made similar proposals during the next two years and one reported that in fact upstate homes were taking paying patients. In 1948 the legislature legalized this *de facto* situation.[71] Data from the Annual Reports of the Department of Social Welfare show that the percentage of income of public homes from private sources increased 2 points from 1937 to 1947, and 10 points from 1947 to 1957. But private funds made up less than 14 per cent of the incomes of

[68] *A Pattern for Hospital Care*, p. 195.

[69] See "Planning for the Chronically Ill," *American Journal of Public Health*, XXXVII (Oct. 1947), p. 1263. Cf. also the following statement: "By 1947 both the Social Security Board and the American Public Welfare Association were urging elimination of the so-called 'institutional prohibition.'" Evaline M. Burns, *Social Security and Public Policy* (New York: McGraw-Hill, 1956), p. 7, n. 5.

[70] The interpretation here is more elaborate than that of the Commission. The APWA, AMA, AHA, and APHA, in their 1947 statement, saw a possibility that paying patients in the public home would help it to shed the almshouse tradition. "Planning for the Chronically Ill," p. 1263.

[71] *Laws of New York, 1948*, chap. 759.

the homes in 1957, which suggests that much of the problem has been related to the initial provision of appropriate facilities as well as paying current operating costs. Generally, the public home is still seen as a place for the unfortunate or under-privileged, with some promising exceptions such as Onandaga and Monroe counties.[72] In 1962 only 5.7 per cent—6.2 upstate and 3.9 in New York City—of the people in such institutions were not public charges.[73]

Conditions at the close of the 1940's may be observed through a Staff Report to the Special Committee of the Joint Committee on Interstate Cooperation. The staff recommended, among other things, that state aid should be extended to hospital and public home care.[74] The Special Committee, however, neither approved nor disapproved the recommendations of the staff because of disagreement among those responsible for admin-istering welfare throughout the state,[75] and hospital care was clearly an issue on which there was a major division. The staff report was generally critical of public home infirmaries though it saw them as possibly preferable to private nursing homes. It saw, as a major reason for the existing low level of development of these institutions, the lack of state involvement:

Very little has been provided in written state requirements con-cerning the operation of . . . city or county homes. In actual practice, state enforcement of standards through its inspection role has been limited to physical facilities and sanitary conditions of the public homes and infirmaries relying for requirements to a large extent on local safety regulations and pertinent sections of the Public Health Law. . . . Recommendations arising from state inspection of city and county homes have had to be mainly advisory and tend to be ignored if they call for increased local expenditures.

[72] A Broome County Public Institution with a rate structure indicating that public assistance recipients are "less than welcome" has had low-occupancy problems.
[73] Matz, *Nursing Homes and Related Facilities*, p. 47.
[74] *Report*, Leg. Doc. No. 87, 1951, pp. 27, 177.   [75] *Ibid.*, p. 3.

A conclusion was that the "absence of written minimum standards for public homes and infirmaries and absence of State financial participation in the program has tended to make the operation of public homes both a neglected and an independent function."[76]

By the time the staff report had found its way into print, a number of steps had been taken that were to influence considerably the issues concerning nursing-home-type facilities it had pointed out. The State Department of Social Welfare had conducted a study of upstate proprietary nursing homes that would lead to its statutory regulatory power over these facilities. The Social Security Act had been amended to add a new assistance category, and to make matching grants available for care in public medical institutions—involving the establishment of state standards for public infirmaries. And, the Governor had appointed a special group whose labors and negotiations would eventually bring about state aid for public infirmaries.

Statutory Power over Proprietary Nursing Homes, 1951

In 1950 the State Department of Social Welfare reported on a year-long study of 754 proprietary institutions offering nursing or related services in upstate New York.[77] Fourteen local governments had extended some kind of regulation over the institutions, covering about a third of the homes and slightly less than half the 9,611 beds involved.[78] The regulation related primarily to sanitation and fire protection, the study found; little was being done about qualifications or size of staff. The six nurses who conducted the survey thought that about a third of the homes could be rated as "reasonably adequate to

[76] *Ibid.*, p. 59.

[77] "A Survey of 754 Proprietary Nursing and Boarding Homes for Adults in New York State," Nov. 21, 1950 (mimeo).

[78] An undetermined proportion of the remainder of beds were subject to local certification for reimbursement purposes as Bulletin 105 had provided in 1944.

their purpose." They found approximately 80 per cent to be at least "fair." A very few were "excellent" or "bad." The great majority of places accepted public assistance cases, and usually the rates for these patients were appreciably lower than for those who paid their own way. The larger homes, it was judged, tended to have superior equipment and personnel. Limited budgets and "the necessity of operating at a profit" sometimes proved detrimental to patients, and "glaring health and safety hazards" were found in a "substantial number of establishments."

The report on the study recommended educational and consultation services as a first step in state supervision and the promulgation of minimum state standards as a second. The distinguishing of nursing from foster and boarding homes, surely a sound move, and the raising of rates for some public assistance patients were the other recommendations. Legislation was not specifically recommended by the study and therefore no pattern for it was described. Subsequently, however, the Department did request legislation,[79] and what was passed was clearly patterned on the sentiments of the Department and of the Health Preparedness Commission of 1944—gentle persuasion. Proprietary nursing homes had, during the 1940's, outstripped in numbers all voluntary and public facilities combined. The public was now more dependent upon them than ever.

Chapter 455 of the *Laws of New York, 1951* added to the Social Welfare Law definitions of proprietary nursing homes, convalescent homes, and homes for adults, and then included these three types of proprietary homes among the kinds of establishments over which the State Board of Social Welfare had its traditional visitation, inspection and rule-making power. (Though the law made no specific provision for such arrangement, an agreement was reached between New York City Hospitals Department officials and those of the State Depart-

79 See the *New York Times*, April 4, 1951, p. 33.

ment of Social Welfare that left the regulation of proprietary facilities in the City in the hands of the Hospitals Department.)[80] The regulatory principle adopted upstate was one of registration rather than licensure. No specific approval or disapproval procedure was provided through certification or other means. The rules of the Board implementing the legislation provided the registration feature by prescribing that each nursing home should submit to the Department information about its patients, facilities and operations.

Had licensing been adopted, presumably any nursing home would have been forbidden to operate until inspection had shown that it met specified standards and a license had been issued, and the Board or Department would presumably have been empowered to revoke the license if continued compliance with the regulations was not forthcoming. These administrative decisions would have been subject to review by the courts when, and insofar as, they were challenged by the nursing home concerned. Instead of adopting a licensing mechanism, however, Chapter 455 merely brought nursing homes under the coverage of some (approval of charters was not required of proprietaries) of the long-standing provisions of the Social Welfare Law to which the voluntary institutions had long been subject. Under these provisions, regulations and rules of the Department and Board could be enforced only by a court order.[81] Moreover, the Board and Department could not seek such an order themselves, directly, but had to rely upon the State Attorney General to present their case.

The 1951 Rules of the Board of Social Welfare for private nursing homes—except for definitions, there was no discrimination between proprietary and nonprofit homes—comprised two

[80] Interdepartmental memorandum from James M. Rosen, Chief, Division of Collections, New York City Department of Hospitals, to First Deputy Commissioner, New York City Department of Hospitals, April 5, 1951. The reader will recall that New York City had been regulating proprietary nursing homes, under a provision of the City Charter, since 1929.

[81] See sec. 21, 8.

pages of rather general statements. The regulations of the Department, the agent of the Board, were somewhat more specific and extended over four and one-half pages—but did not discriminate whatsoever between proprietary and nonprofit homes. The regulations required a registered professional nurse or licensed practical nurse to direct nursing services in each home. They prescribed an outside ratio of one attendant for each fifteen chronically ill patients; more staff could be required, depending upon the care necessary. They continued the requirement that nursing home care for public assistance cases could be given only upon the written order of a physician.

Beds were to be spaced three feet apart, bedrooms were to be "adequately" ventilated and lighted and above ground, toilet and bathing facilities were to be "suitable and adequate," and isolation rooms were to be "as needed." Facilities for sterilization were required, as were hospital beds, bedside tables, and call signals at each bed. The rules and regulations were consistent with the orientation that regulations should be educative and consultative but neither stern nor repressive. Yet they did establish some minimum state standards.

The budget had allowed the addition of eight persons to the inspection staff at about the time the study of proprietary institutions had begun in 1948.[82] These positions were continued on a permanent basis. However, proprietary nursing home inspection was not the only new responsibility given the bureau concerned during 1951. Proprietary convalescent homes were also added to their inspection tasks and inspections of public home infirmaries were made much more demanding by the establishment of a special set of standards for public home infirmaries. Under the circumstances, the inspection force could do little more than spread its efforts rather thinly, concentrating upon homes where the abuses were most flagrant. Nor were conditions to improve rapidly; only one new position was to be added before 1957.

[82] Files, State Department of Social Welfare.

The Social Security Act Amendments of 1950

CALLS FOR CHANGE

New York State had served somewhat as a model for the 1935 pattern of national social security in excluding persons in public institutions from public assistance benefits. It was not a model state when the important 1950 amendments were considered. Illinois was hailed for having converted at least fourteen of its public homes into institutions for the chronically ill under state standards. Some seven other states were cited as granting state-aided assistance to people in public institutions even though there was no federal participation.[83] New York State was hardly a front-line innovator, however.

Professional groups and state governments had more and more ardently been pressing to make persons living in public infirmaries eligible for federally aided assistance. In 1947 the Senate Finance Committee had appointed an Advisory Council, composed of business and professional people, to study public assistance and other aspects of the social security laws. In 1948 the United States Public Health Service, the Offices of Education and Vocational Rehabilitation, the Bureaus of Old Age and Survivors Insurance and of Public Assistance—all of the Federal Security Administration—and the Bureau of Employment Security of the Department of Labor, had joined together in a study of the problems of the aging and of federal and state programs for the aging.[84] Out of these efforts had grown specific recommendations affecting the future pattern of public policy regarding institutional care of chronic illness. In 1949 the House Ways and Means Committee began hearings on H.R. 2892, a draft bill submitted by the Truman administration, which proposed federal support for payments "to persons, agencies, or institutions furnishing [medical] services," includ-

---

[83] U.S. Congress, Senate, Committee on Finance, *Hearings on H.R. 6000, Social Security Administration*, 81st Cong., 2nd Sess., 1950, p. 186.
    [84] *Ibid.*, p. 136.

ing such services to "individuals living in public institutions
. . . as patients."[85]

In 1950 the Senate Finance Committee held hearings on the
measure, which had emerged from the House as H.R. 6000. A
major reference for the Committee was the report of its Advisory Council, *Recommendations for Social Security Legislation,* which carried the same two proposals that patients in
public medical institutions be eligible for federally aided assistance, and that payments for medical service could be made
directly to the person or agency performing the service.[86] A
concomitant of the proposed changes was a call for standards,
to be embodied in the state plans upon which federal aid was
contingent, that all medical institutions should meet before
they could participate in federally aided programs.[87]

STATE STANDARDS

The recommendations for state standards and "vendor" payments stemmed from the growing recognition that institutional
and medical care had grown in significance to where more
specific provisions were needed to manage them. It is noteworthy that proposals for federal standards were not yet part of
the picture. The policy of the federal offices involved was
definitely one of leaving the primary responsibility for initiative in the health, welfare, and related fields to the states. However, the requirement was imposed that states granting federally
aided assistance to persons in any institutions establish authorities responsible for setting standards for all such institutions.

VENDOR PAYMENTS

The vendor payment proposal was designed to give state and
local officials a more precise tool with which to provide medical
care for public assistance recipients. The 1935 Social Security

[85] U.S. House of Representatives, 81st Cong., 1st Sess., 1949, *H.R. 2892,
A Bill to Amend the Social Security Act,* sec. 1405. See also sec. 1404.

[86] U.S. Congress, Senate Finance Committee, 80th Cong., 2nd Sess.,
1948, Senate Doc. No. 208, pp. 112, 114.

[87] *Ibid.,* p. 116.

Act, with its grounding in the philosophy of outdoor relief, had required that federally aided assistance could consist only of "money payments" to aged and blind individuals.[88] Experience since 1935, coupled with the increasing amounts of assistance money being devoted to medical care, had convinced many that it was more important to have administrative control over the selection of and payment for medical care for recipients than to have recipients' freedom to spend their grants themselves. This was especially true because, under administrative interpretations, the recipient could not technically even be instructed to pay his medical bills.

Vendor medical payments were allowed by the 1950 amendments.[89] With a few minor exceptions, however, they do not appear to have been important in the development of nursing-home-type institutions. To begin with, usually they were not used; the billing of the welfare agency they required slowed the payment process down and since personal spending money commonly granted the recipient required a check to him, another check to the nursing home doubled the check writing that had to be done. Because patients' choices on nursing-home-type facilities had always been subject to the approval of the public welfare agency—indeed the welfare agency customarily found the accommodation for the patient—vendor payments for this purpose probably did not have the potential for improved quality control that they had in other areas of medical care. It should be added that the federal Medical Assistance to the Aged law of 1960 authorized only vendor payments, that most New York public assistance cases in nursing-home-type facilities were transferred to the MAA program, and that there was a consequent trend to vendor payments for nursing home cases.

REIMBURSEMENT FOR PUBLIC INSTITUTIONS:
NEW YORK STATE'S POSITION

More relevant for present purposes, over the years there had been increasing conviction that Paul H. Douglas had been right

[88] 49 *U.S. Statutes* 620, secs. 6, 1006.   [89] 64 *U.S. Statutes* 548–549.

in what he had said, upon the passage of the original Social Security Act, about making care in public medical institutions reimbursable. There was much opinion, by the late 1940's, that "the Social Security Act [had] been successful in accomplishing its immediate objective, . . . the abolition of the old-fashioned poorhouse."[90] The proposal to require standards, mentioned above, was intended to assure that the old almshouse would not return; Elizabeth Wickenden, of the American Public Welfare Association, a representative of the public assistance administration of Pennsylvania, and Jane Hoey, Director of the Federal Bureau of Public Assistance, as well as the Senate Finance Committee's Advisory Council, were among those supporting the establishment of standards for this reason, but these and many others favored federal support of care in public infirmaries. The Commissioner of Public Welfare of Massachusetts spoke particularly of the increasing financial pressures on public medical institutions.[91] The Deputy Secretary of Public Assistance for Pennslyvania said:

We missed a couple of bets . . . in the original Social Security Act. We were rather enthusiastic to empty the poorhouses and I guess it was a pretty good idea but in so doing we put in a provision that a person could not get assistance if he lived in a public institution. Now, the big need today is for nursing homes. . . . There is such a need for that that we are strongly in favor of giving assistance to the person whether he is able to live in his own home, a private nursing home or a public nursing home.[92]

Similar sentiments were heard in the House Committee hearings of 1949 from Illinois, Rhode Island, Indiana, South Carolina and Colorado; and the most forceful statement of all in this vein came from Jane Hoey. Miss Hoey reported that "some of the most acute want in the nation is to be found among persons needing long-time care in medical institutions" and that the effect of the original Social Security Act had been to foster

---

[90] U.S. House of Representatives, 81st Cong., 1st Sess., 1949, *Hearings on H.R. 2892*, p. 17. See also p. 228.
[91] *Ibid.*, p. 187.   [92] *Ibid.*, p. 199.

the growth of commercial homes that were operated for profit and often gave "very inferior care."[93]

The Senate hearings of 1950 added substantial support to testimony for federal aid to public homes, but New York's formal representative took no position on the matter. Spokesmen for Minnesota, California, the American Association of Social Workers, and the American Legion left clear tally marks for the federal support for public home care. New Jersey stood virtually alone in its fear of a recrudescence of the poorhouse—but would have extended the ban to operate against aid in private institutions too.[94] Although, as has already been pointed out, students of the problem were alarmed at conditions even in New York, the State Commissioner of the Department of Social Welfare made no reference to the matter as he spoke before the Senate Finance Committee. He addressed himself to the desirability of broadening the coverage of old-age and survivors insurance, to the likelihood that minimum federal indigency standards would reduce caseloads in other states, and to the need for increased flexibility in aid to dependent children programs—all important issues—but made no mention of aid to public homes.[95] No evidence has been found to indicate that New York should share much of the responsibility, or credit, for expanding the federal assistance program to include care in public infirmaries. Indeed, even though federal legislation did extend its aid to such care in 1950, New York State was to eschew responsibility, itself, for such program involvement until 1954.

The 1950 amendments to the Social Security Act provided for old-age assistance payments to persons in public medical institutions (but excluded aid to persons institutionalized because of mental diseases or tuberculosis).

---

[93] *Ibid.*, p. 400.
[94] U.S. Congress, Senate Committee on Finance, *Hearings on H.R. 6000, Social Security Administration*, 81st Cong., 2nd Sess., 1950, p. 2038.
[95] *Ibid.*, p. 362 ff.

AID TO DISABLED

Of particular importance for the development of nursing-home-type facilities in New York State was a third change in the law, the addition of assistance for a new category of persons, the permanently and totally disabled. States could grant assistance to persons between eighteen and sixty-five years of age who were disabled; the federal government would share in the expenses according to the same formula used for the OAA and AB programs.[96] The convolutions of opinion, organization, and influence that led to the creation of the assistance category for the disabled are of undoubted relevance to the stream of relationship between public policy and nursing home facility development that is being traced out here. But what is perhaps most interesting about it for present purposes is that, although it was surely not intended to influence any particular kind of facility, it led, as we shall see, to governmental stimulation of proprietary nursing homes in the early 1950's.

The 1950 Federal Amendments and State Policy

STALEMATE—ALMOST

The federal government's offer to encourage public infirmary development caught New York State in a difficult period. Despite years of study of the state's unsatisfactory reimbursement formula for aiding localities in public assistance programs by bodies for whom the matter had been a formal assignment, and years of concern by administrative and political leaders for whom the consequences of the formula were of importance, the state remained unable to resolve the many problems associated with revamping its formula. Local governments stoutly resisted suggestions that the state reduce its contributions to welfare costs, "such as Governor Dewey [was] reported to favor."[97] The alternative of lowering the state's financial participation in in-

[96] 64 U.S. Statutes 555–557.
[97] New York Times, Jan. 12, 1951, p. 19.

dividual programs while spreading state aid over a broader spectrum to include institutional care was impeded by the varying quality of services rendered among the public infirmaries (although a remedy for this problem was germinating). The same alternative was virtually precluded by the diversity of criteria employed at the local level for determining eligibility for government-supported hospital care. The magnitude of the hospital issue is indicated by a contemporaneous article discussing the upstate-downstate conflicts, by Douglas Dales, columnist for the *New York Times,* which interpreted the 1950 federal amendment as providing for the "hospitalization" of "certain categories of relief."[98] The change had not affected hospitalization in voluntary or other private hospitals and had only removed the "temporary" from hospitalization reimbursable in public establishments. A third factor complicating the reimbursement picture was the continuing need for stability of local finances and, indeed, the increasing demands of local budgets.

Caught in this impasse, the state could not be moved to add resources of its own to federal aid for care in government medical institutions. The 1951 session of the legislature made provision for the newly available federal aid to flow on to localities for public assistance recipients cared for in public home infirmaries;[99] but the maximum federal aid was $30.00 per month, while the rate for ordinary domiciliary care in New York City's public homes was $3.75 per day. Getting federal aid alone was a good bit different for the local governments from getting 80 per cent of their welfare bills paid by the state-federal combination, as was the case with care given in private institutions. The tenor of opinion of the local welfare administrators upon this state failure to shift its policy is revealed by a memorandum to the Governor from the New York Public Welfare Association in which this organization asked that he

[98] *Ibid.,* Jan. 12, 1951, p. 19.
[99] *Laws of New York, 1951,* chaps. 67, 77. The change became effective April 1, 1951.

have the bill amended to provide the 80 per cent for public infirmary care:

During the past few years local public welfare districts have encouraged the establishment of private nursing homes to care for recipients of relief who need nursing care, for the reason that they could receive 80 per cent reimbursement.

For the most part the private nursing homes which have been established are large, private, wood-structured houses which are not adaptable for nursing homes and which, to say the least, are fire traps.

The public welfare commissioners believe that persons needing nursing care can be taken care of more adequately and at a cheaper cost in county home infirmaries than is possible in private nursing homes. If local public welfare districts are to receive only the federal share of reimbursements, when they are able to receive 80 per cent reimbursement in nursing homes for this care, the County Boards of Supervisors are going to be reluctant to make any expenditure for the remodelling or enlargement of county home infirmaries.[100]

The legislature treated hospitalization reimbursement in essentially the same fashion as that for public infirmaries. The practice had been for people on the federal assistance category lists prior to being hospitalized "for medical or surgical care" to be continued under the 80 per cent arrangement "temporarily"—to wit, under administrative interpretation, six months. Where these conditions did not obtain, hospital cases had been completely local charges. The new law removed the "medical" and "surgical" qualifiers and changed the six months from an administrative to a statutory determination. It also provided that after the six months, when the state would withdraw its financial participation from the federal categorical assistance, federal money available would continue to flow on to the localities.[101]

The political cleavages—and the reference is not only to

100 New York State Legislature, 1951, Bill Jacket, chap. 67.
101 *Laws of New York, 1951*, chap. 67.

party politics but also to politics in its broadest sense—that resulted in these state decisions were not to be quickly dulled or harmonized. Charges and countercharges about New York City's fiscal responsibility in its welfare program on one hand, and rigid dictation from the state level on the other, were to be heard in the future.[102] And as the state benefited from new federal aid, particularly by transferring to the new disabled category many people who had been on home relief, the city's Welfare Commissioner charged the state with having passed on to localities only a "minute share of some $45 million that have accrued annually to the state through recent amendments to the Social Security Law."[103] Meanwhile, the Joint Legislative Committee on Interstate Cooperation, currently studying the reimbursement formula, had been joined by another group. In 1951 the Governor had appointed a Special Committee for the Revision of the Welfare Formula, headed by Frank P. Moore, who had chaired the 1946 Temporary Committee on Municipal Revenues, and who was now Lieutenant Governor. The other members of the new committee were chairmen of finance committees of the legislature, state fiscal officers and the State Commissioner of Social Welfare. But it was to be 1953 before a new allocation of fiscal responsibility for welfare could be agreed upon.

A CODE FOR PUBLIC INFIRMARIES

The availability of federal funds for care in public infirmaries, and the conditional requirement for standards, sparked the Board and Department of Social Welfare into writing and compiling a set of specifications for such institutions. The year was 1951, the same as that of the establishment of the rules and regulations, or code, for private nursing homes. Marked similarities between the two sets of requirements indicate they were simultaneously conceived, or that one grew from the other. However, Bulletin 139, which embodied the public home in-

---

[102] See the *New York Times*, Jan. 27, 1952, p. 62; Jan. 28, 1952, p. 19.
[103] *New York Times*, Nov. 7, 1952, p. 1.

firmary rules and regulations, rested upon the reimbursement power: cost of care could be reimbursed only after the infirmary had been inspected and approved as meeting the specified requirements. There were other differences. First, rules (that would have been inappropriate for nursing homes) required infirmaries to be physically and administratively separate from the domiciliary quarters of public homes. Second, infirmaries were to provide physician care, which led to other specific differences among the rules and regulations.

Examination of the two codes indicates that the provision of physician care in infirmaries tended to elevate requirements slightly in the public institutions. For example, medical policies were to be formulated by infirmary physicians—and approved by the commissioner of public welfare—while there was no similar requirement for nursing homes; head nurses in infirmaries had more responsibilities, pertaining to keeping records and other matters, than those in nursing homes; only a registered professional nurse could direct the nursing service of an infirmary while a licensed practical nurse could be charged with these duties in a nursing home; rehabilitation was urged for infirmaries but not mentioned in the nursing home code; office space and examining rooms for doctors, and utility rooms and arrangements to provide privacy where more than one person occupied a room, were required of infirmaries alone. Aside from the differences growing out of organic dissimilarities between the two kinds of institutions, however, similarity of the rules and regulations tended to prevail.

Bulletin 139 became effective on June 15, 1951. Out of some forty-six public infirmaries in the state, eleven were approved as meeting the marks it set. A year later the number had increased to twenty-three—and the number of approved beds stood at 3,701 compared to 1,801 unapproved beds—indicating that even federal reimbursement alone had spurred an upgrading of facilities. This change was a small thing, however, when seen in a perspective that includes the other kinds of facilities that were available.

Recapitulation

Because New York City has a story that deserves separate treatment, we should focus on the upstate setting in concluding this chapter. As Table 1 (p. 58) indicates, proprietary nursing home facilities had by 1952 increased far beyond the slower growing public and voluntary facilities. The number of public infirmary beds—approved and unapproved—plus the voluntary nursing-home-type beds in upstate New York was far below the number of proprietary nursing home beds. The public infirmary had been a well-recognized concept, if not a well-established institution, at the time of the hearings of the State Commission on Old Age Security in 1930. The private old-age home had long been a traditional facility by this time, even though it did not have extensive infirmary holdings upstate. The voluntary nursing or convalescent home, in the 1930's only an aggregate of rather disparate entities—which have been pressed under a single rubric for the purposes of this study—seemed still only to be crystallizing into a class by the early 1950's. The proprietary nursing home, a nascent concept in the 1930's, and barely extended standard legal recognition by 1952, had shown the most dynamic growth. But that growth had clearly been galvanized by public policy that had been in effect.

CHAPTER 5

Federal and State Policies and Upstate Development, 1953 through the Early 1960's

A Period of Policy Change

The decade following 1953 was one in which public policy relating to nursing-home-type facilities in New York State veered substantially, with some consequences for such facilities. In 1954 stimulation of care in public infirmaries through state aid was added to that of the federal government. In that year also federal financial support became available for the construction of public and voluntary facilities. And although federal loan guarantee arrangements began to excite the proprietary field at the end of the 1950's, the further development of standards for proprietary institutions, along with other factors, actually reversed the growth trend of such institutions for a period, though not permanently.

The decade's development can be seen in Table 5. Public infirmary beds grew modestly but quite steadily in number, as did those in voluntary institutions. What happened in the case of proprietary beds was different, however. Although growth was strong and quite steady through 1958, which culminated in a peak of over 14,000 beds, there followed a four-year period of halting decline. Recovery then occurred, during 1963, and in 1964 the number of proprietary beds rose above the former peak, seemingly influenced by rejuvenated growth forces. It should not be overlooked of course, that at the beginning of the decade, at the end of the decade, and even at the nadir of the four-year slump, the number of proprietary beds exceeded substantially those found in public and voluntary facilities combined.

Table 5. Growth of nursing-home-type facilities, upstate, 1952–1964[a]

	Public		Voluntary		Proprietary	
Year	Homes	Beds	Homes	Beds	Homes	Beds
1952	44	4,191			603	11,027
1954	44	4,545	123	2,833		
1955	43	4,708			632	12,810
1958	35	5,023	122	3,317	597	14,441
1959	35	5,268	120	3,337	564	14,326
1960	36	5,513	114	3,386	525	17,718
1961	37	6,110	112	3,365	496	13,995
1962	37	6,030	87	3,449	478	13,279
1963	37	6,200	94	3,859	455	14,170
1964	39	6,666	95	3,708	446	15,358

Source. Tables 2M, 3M, 4M, and 5M, Appendix I.

[a] Blank spaces indicate that no data have been found.

The changes were not exclusively in growth patterns, or all a result of public policy. The regulation of all three types of institutions improved somewhat during this period, and the legal requirements imposed upon proprietaries were brought substantially abreast of those on voluntary and public institutions. In some measure changes, in the proprietary field particularly, were evolutionary modifications in the character of the institutions. Voluntary homes began to de-emphasize philanthropy and to make greater claims on government. Larger, more stable and systematically run proprietary homes that required greater financial backing and promised more serious and skillful efforts to influence public policy, and possibly even greater growth in the proprietary field, began to appear on the scene.

State Reimbursement for Public Infirmary Care

In 1953 the Special Committee for the Revision of the Welfare Formula, capitalizing upon the study that had gone into the matter in the years before and in consultation with many concerned parties, was able to propose changes in the allocation of fiscal responsibility for welfare that could move New York out of its reimbursement-formula stalemate. One of the state officers who assisted in drafting the modifications has commented: "In 1953 everything worked about right—in other years it wouldn't have been possible."[1] One might add that compromise as well as auspicious circumstances promoted the change.

One of the features that made the new formula acceptable to localities was the state's agreement to extend its financial participation to institutional care, including that given in public homes and infirmaries, in municipal lodging houses and shelters, and to care given children not in their own homes. (The barriers against indoor relief were at last abolished from state policy. They had, of course, been sustained for some time only by community cleavage.) The state still balked at sharing the cost of all hospital care given at public expense because of New York City's liberal policy on free hospital care and the lack of any ready mechanism by which State control over criteria for eligibility for such care might be secured. State participation was extended to hospital care of home relief cases where the person had been receiving such relief for at least thirty days. Under the thirty-day provision, eligibility for relief was to be determined by the local welfare department, which was subject to the supervision of the State Department of Social

[1] Interview with Byron T. Hipple, Jr., former Deputy Commissioner for Administrative Finance and Statistics, State Department of Social Welfare, Nov. 2, 1962.

Welfare, and not by the New York City Hospitals Department. But no time limitation upon state contribution to hospitalization costs was imposed, and the six-month limit was removed from the OAA, AB, and AD categories.[2]

The *quid pro quo* for the broadened state participation was a diminution of the depth of its participation, as had been proposed earlier. Instead of financing enough of some programs that the localities paid only 20 per cent, after federal contributions were counted, the state agreed to participate in almost all programs to the extent of half the cost, after federal aid was counted. In effect, after a locality received the federal aid to which it was entitled, the state would share equally with it half the remaining cost of any program except hospital care of someone who had not been on home relief or one of the federal categorical aid programs before entering the hospital. The state was thus not so deeply involved in any program, and local governments would, the reasoning ran, act more responsibly when spending a greater proportion of their own money on any given program. At the same time, local welfare districts could expect an increase of some $6.4 million annually in state aid and, the Governor noted, they would no longer be operating under incentives to make placements according to reimbursement criteria.[3]

Two other impediments to the state's spreading its responsibility over a broader area and to a shallower depth had been articulated. One was the inconsistency in the quality of public home care. It had been mitigated by the establishment, in 1951, of standards for reimbursement for public infirmary care by Bulletin 139. The other impediment was the need for some

[2] When the Medical Assistance to the Aged program became effective April 1, 1961, it became possible for persons sixty-five years of age and over who had not been receiving reimbursable aid when admitted to a hospital to become eligible for such aid while hospitalized. The federal contribution to MAA costs was 50 per cent and the state's was 25 per cent.

[3] *McKinney's Consolidated Laws of New York, Annotated, Social Welfare Law*, (Brooklyn: Edward Thompson Co., 1940), Governor's memorandum on signing bill, sec. 153.

guarantee to local governments that they would not be rocked by soaring welfare expenses and shrinking revenues should a depression occur. The year 1953 saw relatively high employment, which assuaged local fears somewhat. However, the new formula provided for special increases in home relief, wherein lay the major threat, that would be granted in the event of economic reverses.[4]

The provision of state assistance for public infirmary cases was one of the major selling points in weaning local welfare districts away from the 80-per-cent formula, and as soon as the legislation went into effect, the State Commissioner of Social Welfare began a campaign to encourage the erection, improvement, and expansion of public home infirmaries. Data are not complete enough to give a precise picture of the growth rates for 1951 and 1952, but as Figure 1 indicates, from 1943 through 1952 upstate infirmary beds had grown at an average rate of 81 beds per year. During 1953 the growth, evidently stimulated by federal reimbursement alone, was 259 beds. Over the next four years, through 1957, growth averaged 198 beds per year. This was a steady increase; the addition of state aid evidently stabilized growth at a rate somewhat more accelerated than that of the 1940's.[5]

---

[4] The new formula, effective January 1, 1954, became law through chap. 562 of the *Laws of New York, 1953*.

[5] The expansion was larger if one counts only beds in approved infirmaries, which Table 2M (Appendix I) does not show prior to 1958. The total increase in all public infirmary beds from 1952 through 1957 was 851. But the increase in beds that met the standards of Bulletin 139 for the same period was 1,348. This occurred, of course, because a certain proportion of the existing beds that did not meet the standards for approval could be upgraded and thereby became classified as approved without expensive construction or reconstruction. The surgelike increase in the number of approved beds resulting from the upgrading of existing beds appears to have occurred within a limited period; i.e., it does not seem to have been a continuing phenomenon. Once those beds with the potential for the needed upgrading at a limited cost had been upgraded, which tended to happen soon after the establishment of reimbursement contingent upon the meeting of standards, getting beds approved involved new construction or extensive reconstruction, which is activity characterized by gradualism.

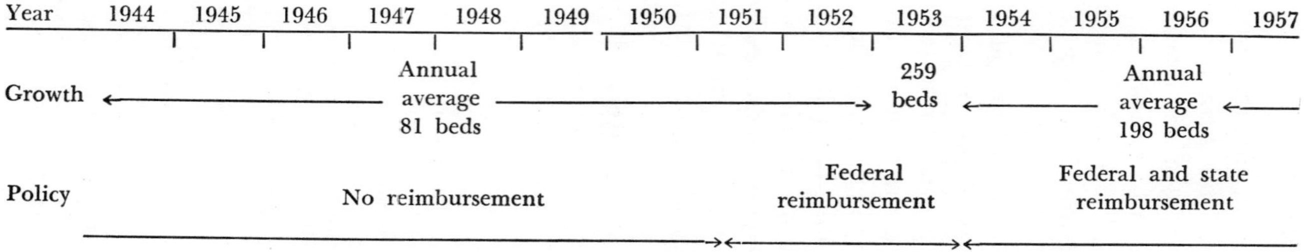

Year	1944	1945	1946	1947	1948	1949	1950	1951	1952	1953	1954	1955	1956	1957

Growth

Annual average 81 beds

259 beds

Annual average 198 beds

Policy

No reimbursement

Federal reimbursement

Federal and state reimbursement

Figure 1. Policy changes and growth in numbers of public infirmary beds, upstate New York, 1943–1958

Source. For bed data, see Table 2M, Appendix I. The figure does not extend beyond 1957 because the data available for 1958 artificially reflect a drop.

The Hill-Burton Program

THE PROPOSAL

During the early 1950's there had been fermenting concern at the national level with problems of chronic illness. In 1953 the Commission on Chronic Illness, representing an alliance between the national medical, public health, welfare, and hospital associations, joined with the United States Public Health Service and thirteen states to gather concrete information about nursing homes and their patients.[6] In January 1954, President Eisenhower delivered a special health message to Congress that reflected a desire of the Public Health Service to encourage the growth of public and voluntary nursing-home-type facilities.

The administration bill embodying the President's recommendations provided for the authorization of appropriations amounting to $10 million annually to be contributed to public and voluntary agencies to cover part of the costs of constructing or remodeling nursing home or infirmary quarters. The program was to be administered by the Public Health Service. Authorization for appropriations were also recommended for chronic disease hospitals, diagnostic or treatment centers for ambulatories, and for rehabilitation facilities. The measure was to be an amendment to the Hill-Burton Act, or Hospital Survey and Construction Act of 1944.

RESISTANCE FROM THE AMERICAN HOSPITAL ASSOCIATION

The American Hospital Association had been largely responsible for the drafting and passage of the original Hill-Burton Act.[7] However, the Association had serious reservations about the proposed amendments.

[6] Jerry Solon, Dean W. Roberts, Dean E. Krueger, and Anna Mae Baney, *Nursing Homes, Their Patients and Their Care: A Study of Nursing Homes and Similar Long-Term Care Facilities in 13 States*, Public Health Monograph No. 456 (Washington, U.S. Government Printing Office, 1957).

[7] *Hospital Management*, LIX (Feb. 1945), 39; *The Ohio State Medical Journal*, XLI (March 1945), 251.

Mr. George Bugbee, its Executive Director, testified before the Senate Committee on Education and Public Welfare that the categorization of appropriations "for the four kinds of facilities—and the separation of these appropriations" from that provided for hospitals generally—would introduce undesired rigidity into decisions about what functions new construction should serve and encourage the division of medical facilities from each other.[8] He also argued that the primary deterrent to increased numbers of long-term care beds was not a lack of funds for initial construction but an inadequacy of governmental contribution for operating costs.[9]

However, the federal bureaucracy and the administration were firmly of the opinion that a deliberate policy emphasis on nursing home facilities was needed, and that the categories should be adopted. Statistics were introduced to show that after six years of operation of the original Hill-Burton Act, which had been cast along the lines of flexibility, 86,000 general beds but only 3,000 chronic beds had been produced.[10] And Dr. John W. Cronin, Chief of the Public Health Service's Division of Hospital Facilities, pointed out that *no* nursing homes had been built with the $600 million in federal money and twice that amount in matching money that had been spent under the Hill-Burton provisions.[11] The Secretary of the Department of Health, Education and Welfare, Oveta Culp Hobby, stressed the expense being incurred because long-term patients, who had no other places to go, were crowding general hospitals, which are more costly to operate than nursing homes.[12]

[8] United States Congress, Senate Committee on Labor and Public Welfare, *Hearings on S. 2758 and H.R. 8149*, 83rd Cong., 2nd Sess., 1954, pp. 109–111.

[9] *Ibid.*, p. 106.   [10] *Hospital Progress*, March 1954, p. 62.

[11] Senate Committee on Labor and Public Welfare, *Hearings*, p. 59.

[12] U.S. Congress, House of Representatives, Committee on Interstate and Foreign Commerce, *Hearings on H.R. 7341*, 83rd Cong., 2nd Sess., 1954, p. 17.

It has been asserted by a spokesman of the American Hospital Association that the Republican Eisenhower administration wanted a clear political accomplishment of its own with which to garner public support, and therefore was unwilling to settle for legislation that would simply build on to the original Hill-Burton Act.[13] Under the Democratic Kennedy administration, however, the Public Health Service still resisted moves to undermine the categories,[14] which seems to indicate that the determination with which the position was held was not entirely attributable to the administration's desire for public attention. According to the legislative liaison officer for the Public Health Service the administration, looking for health issues, had selected the new Hill-Burton program and a program for training practical nurses from among alternatives presented by the Service.[15]

OPPOSITION BY PROPRIETARY NURSING HOME SPOKESMEN

Proprietary nursing home representatives appeared in force at the congressional hearings.[16] Their opposition to the proposed legislation was bitter. Robert F. Muse, speaking for the American Association of Nursing Homes, said the Eisenhower administration was "drifting toward socialism in the medical field at an unprecedented pace." He also spoke of the "cruel and ill-considered policy of fostering Federal grants for the purpose of competing with [proprietary] nursing homes, without first, or at least concurrently, allowing this private industry and profession the opportunity to fulfill whatever may be lack-

[13] Interview with Kenneth Williamson, Director, Washington Service Bureau of the American Hospital Association, Nov. 13, 1962.

[14] Jack C. Haldeman, Chief, Division of Hospital and Medical Facilities, U.S. Public Health Service, "Hill-Burton and the 'New Frontier,'" *Hospital Management*, May 1961, p. 41.

[15] Letter from Robert W. Barclay, staff member, Senate Committee on Labor and Public Welfare, Nov. 26, 1962.

[16] The American Association of Nursing Homes, for example, had representatives at the hearings from twenty-two states. House Committee on Interstate and Foreign Commerce, *Hearings*, p. 101.

ing in the public health program of America in those areas served by nursing homes."[17]

The nursing home operators found allies among some of the House Committee members, John V. Beamer and William L. Springer, Republicans of Indiana and Illinois, in particular. Mrs. Hobby had stressed that proprietary institutions were not being included because the proposals under consideration were for amendments to the Hill-Burton Act, which had limited its grants to public and nonprofit organizations. She had explained, however, that the $10 million proposed for nonprofit nursing homes was so small that it could not present a serious competitive threat to the proprietary homes. She was asked, then, if the proposed program might not include proprietary homes. She replied in the negative but added that "we hope they will live because as you know we need so many beds."[18] With grants to proprietaries disposed of, her questioners moved on to the matter of loans. Pressed rather far, she turned to Dr. Cronin and to Surgeon General Leonard A. Scheele for support. The three stood on the proposition that they could take no position on the question until after a nation-wide survey of facilities, which the new amendments were to provide for, was completed.[19]

One major threat of the proprietary nursing home people's strategy was to get Federal Housing Administration underwriting for loans. They had found the terms of the Small Business Administration unfavorable, they reported, principally because the loans available from that agency could extend over only ten years. Bank loans were difficult to get because nursing homes tended to be single-purpose buildings with little resale value to be realized in the event of a mortgage foreclosure.[20] Their purpose of securing more favorable loans for themselves was a companion to their purpose in attempting to prevent

[17] Senate Committee on Labor and Public Welfare, *Hearings,* pp. 178–179.

[18] House Committee on Interstate and Foreign Commerce, *Hearings,* p. 45.

[19] *Ibid.,* p. 52.   [20] *Ibid.,* pp. 106–107.

Hill-Burton grants from strengthening voluntary and public nursing home institutions. Their fear of competition was clear.[21]

SUPPORT FROM NEW YORK

Of course, there was support for, as well as opposition to, the 1954 Hill-Burton amendments. The most significant support came from the executive branch, which had initiated the proposals. It should be added that Dr. John J. Bourke, Executive Director of the New York State Joint Hospital Survey and Planning Commission—the agency responsible for the administration of Hill-Burton funds in the state—supported the bill in the Senate hearings. Dr. Bourke recommended that the four categories should be established in law. He stressed the preferability of nursing homes constructed as units of suitable general hospitals—an approach that tended to counter the American Hospital Association's opinion that the categories would impose a rigid pattern of compartmentalization upon community medical care. This approach was in line with Public Health Service thinking and a priority for such nursing home units was established in its regulations and in the New York State plan when the new amendments went into effect.[22]

THE LEGISLATION

Essentially unchanged, the administration's plan became the Medical Facilities Survey and Construction Act of 1954,[23] an amendment to the Hill-Burton Act. Appropriations lagged substantially behind the authorizing legislation as the new program moved into gear, however. As an addition to the original

---

[21] See, for example, the statement of Robert F. Muse, Executive Director of the Massachusetts Federation of Nursing Homes. *Ibid.*, p. 97.

[22] United States Public Health Service, Division of Hospital and Medical Facilities, *Public Health Service Regulations*, Part 53, Sec. 53.79(b). New York State's plan presents alternatives: (a) The unit is to be part of a general hospital; (b) the unit is independent but is formally affiliated with a general hospital. Hospital Council of Greater New York, *Bulletin*, Vol. XII, no. 2 (March–April 1957).

[23] 60 *U.S. Statutes* 1041.

Hill-Burton scheme, moreover, the new law inherited the formula by which its proceeds were to be allotted—a formula that emphasized rural, rather than urban, needs. The proportion of funds for each state varies directly with the population and inversely with the per capita income; while New York was the largest state, with many people to care for in nursing homes, it has also been one of the richest—in 1957 only Delaware and Connecticut had a higher per capita income. Through 1965 it had received only 4.6 per cent of the funds appropriated since the program became effective in 1948.[24] The amounts allocated to New York proved less than sufficient to meet the demand. The Hospital Council of Greater New York reported in late 1958 that it would have required over ten times as much federal money as the state received to finance all of the Hill-Burton applications filed in the state from 1956 through 1958 at the full level of federal participation, which was one-third in New York.[25]

Congress appropriated only $4 million for nursing homes each year through 1957; in 1958, for fiscal 1959, it raised the amount to $10 million. The economic recession that had begun to plague the country in 1957 was "undoubtedly" an important factor accounting for the increased appropriation.[26] In time the concern over the need for nursing homes grew greater and larger amounts of Hill-Burton money became available. For fiscal 1962 the Community Health Services and Facilities Act raised the authorization ceiling to $20 million[27] and $18.5 million were appropriated. The appropriation for the next two years was the full $20 million.

In 1964 the Hill-Burton program underwent substantial

[24] Files, Department of Health, Education, and Welfare, Public Health Service, Division of Hospital and Medical Facilities.

[25] Hospital Council of Greater New York, *Bulletin*, Vol. XIII, no. 5 (Nov.–Dec. 1958).

[26] *Ibid.*,

[27] Public Law 395, 87th Cong. It also established a $10 million per year grant program to develop and demonstrate better methods of care for chronically ill and aged outside of hospitals.

revamping, emerging from the process with a new name—
Hill-Harris. The Hill-Harris amendments provided aid for five
more years—through the fiscal year 1969. They also reflected
two important modifications in the rationale of federal aid to
medical facilities. First, they provided for some modernization
of obsolete facilities—this was intended particularly to help
urban areas. Second, and of greater relevance to this study, they
elevated the relative value attached to long-term facilities compared to the other kinds of institutions provided for; authorization ceilings for hospitals, diagnostic or treatment centers, and
rehabilitation facilities were continued at their former levels
but chronic disease hospitals and nursing homes, for which
there had been authorization of $20 million each under the
Community Health Services and Facilities Act, received an
authorization of $70 million between them.[28]

[28] Public Law 443, 88th Cong.
The amounts devoted by the New York State Hill-Burton agency to
nursing-home-type construction have been:

Fiscal year	Amount	Transfer in	Transfer out
1955	$ 460,561	*	
1956	230,352	*	
1957	414,222	*	
1958	697,077	*	
1959	542,254	*	
1960	471,157		
1961	475,366		
1962	731,599		*
1963	950,735		
1964	595,131		*
1965	2,257,309	*	
1966	3,523,176		

Figures from the records of T. E. Hynson, M.D., Hospital Program
Director, Regional Office II, United States Public Health Service, U.S.
Department of Health Education and Welfare, as of January 13, 1966.
   Under the law, funds in the categories for diagnostic or treatment
centers, chronic disease hospitals and nursing homes may be transferred
among the three categories insofar as applications do not absorb them
from the category to which they were assigned. 68 *U.S. Statutes* 464. Also,
sums not expended during the fiscal year may be carried over through one

IMPACT OF HILL-BURTON ON NURSING-HOME-TYPE FACILITIES
IN NEW YORK STATE

Through 1964 fifteen nursing home or infirmary projects, representing 1,561 beds, had been completed in New York State under this federal program. (By the end of 1965 the number of completed projects had increased to twenty and the beds to 1,849.)[29] These projects reflected the original rural emphasis of Hill-Burton purposes. Twelve of the fifteen projects and 1,148 of the beds had gone to upstate regions. New York City had been allotted only three projects involving 413 beds. The upstate bias was clear on the ratio of money granted to the total cost of the approved project, as well. Under the law, Hill-Burton construction grants for hospital and related facilities in New York State may go up to as much as one-third of the cost of the project approved under the program but they may be less. Eight of the upstate projects received grants comprising the full 33⅓ per cent; none received a grant of less than 20 per cent; the ratio of all grant money to total cost was 28.5 per cent. The three New York City plants had grants of 9, 16, and 27 per cent, and the grant money made up only 16.18 per cent of the costs of the approved projects. (A similar pattern is found for the projects completed after 1964.)

Nor were Hill-Burton resources large enough, or influential enough, to produce beds in quantities to meet the state's needs. An over-all assessment of needs conducted by the Division of Hospital Review and Planning in 1964 concluded there was a shortage of over 4,000 beds in New York City and a need for

---

more fiscal year (*ibid.*, p. 563). The figures in the "amount" column reflect transfers. The Hill-Harris amendments of 1964 made one change in this regard. Funds for nursing homes and chronic disease hospitals were combined under one category, the money to be divided among them as need dictates. The figures for fiscal 1965 and 1966 include money for both chronic diseases and nursing homes.

[29] Our concern here is primarily with data up through 1964, since the tables for this study, found in the appendix, do not include information beyond that date.

almost 12,000 new beds, largely as replacement for existing beds housed in unsatisfactory structures, in upstate regions. The Division declared that the state as a whole should have 17,040 new beds—including some geographically unassigned need—and estimated that the cost of construction would be $208,721,000. It went on to examine the possible future impact of Hill-Burton funds, noting that if all of the $1.9 million currently available on an annual basis to the state for long-term facilities were used for nursing home or infirmary construction on the one-third matching basis, construction expenditures of only $5,660,718 annually would result.[30] At this rate some thirty-seven years would be required to meet the state's plant needs of 1964.

Hill-Burton influence should not be judged only by bricks and mortar, however. In their study of the eight Blue Cross plans in New York, Dr. Ray E. Trussell and Frank van Dyke said: "Not only has the Hill-Burton program resulted in long range master planning activities and a wealth of data, but to the extent federal funds are needed for local building, the Hill-Burton agency can exercise some direction."[31] The state Hill-Burton agency wielded considerable influence in integrating the nursing home units it helped finance into administratively desirable working relationships with other kinds of facilities. For example, an affiliation with a general hospital, represented in a written agreement, was part of the agreement for every nursing home project approved in the state except six. In those six the projects were made integral parts of general hospitals.[32] Integration in the sense of fitting into community

[30] New York State Department of Health, Division of Hospital Review and Planning, "Evaluation of All Types of Nursing Home Facilities in New York State and Projection of Needs and Capital Construction Costs," October 1, 1964 (mimeo.), pp. 8–10. The $1.9 million figure was changed by later developments. The Division's point is still well taken, however.

[31] *Prepayment for Hospital Care in New York State,* School of Public Health and Administrative Medicine, Columbia University (New York, 1960), p. 255.

[32] Memorandum from Hildegarde Wagner, Chief, Hospital Planning Services, New York State Department of Health, July 12, 1962.

needs also has been promoted by the Hill-Burton machinery; grants are made according to priorities of county needs determined by a continuing inventory of nursing-home-type facilities throughout the state.

The Hill-Burton venture into the nursing home field also has provided leverage for boosting nursing home standards in non-Hill-Burton institutions. The Public Health Service standards for construction were established at a reasonably high level that set a mark for the Federal Housing Administration to consider as it inaugurated its loan guarantee program in 1959. The same standards were adopted by the State Department of Social Welfare for new nursing home construction not under Hill-Burton auspices. The state Hill-Burton agency required of its projects twenty-four-hour supervision by registered nurses, a provision later adopted by other government units concerned from the beginning of its operation.

Also the impact of Hill-Burton funds are not reflected closely in changes in the numbers of beds to be found in the state. New beds financed with the aid of the federal program may simply replace existing unsafe buildings, or even safe ones in cases where such considerations as the efficient use of space receive high priority. Moreover, in one New York project supportive facilities—a garage, conference room, and chaplain's quarters—but no beds were involved.

By the end of 1964 seven Hill-Burton projects for public nursing-home-type facilities had been completed in upstate New York. They involved the replacement of 454 beds and the addition of 162. (By the close of 1965 two additional projects, with 153 beds, had been completed.) Through 1964, four such undertakings for voluntary facilities were finished, representing the replacement of 208 beds, the addition of 324, and the provision of the supportive facilities mentioned above. (One further voluntary project, of 64 beds, was completed during 1965.)

The Public Works Acceleration Act of 1962

The significance of the federal government's concern for the nation's economy for nursing home development again became manifest with the passage of the Public Works Acceleration Act of 1962.[33] The measure had been sponsored by President Kennedy as a quick-acting counterpart of the Area Redevelopment Act of 1961, which had been designed to build up the economies of depressed areas of the country by developing new long-term employment in them.

The Area Redevelopment Administration had taken the position that, by and large, persons employed in nursing homes are technical people, already in short supply, and therefore had aided virtually no nursing homes in the 1961 law.[34] The purpose of the 1962 law, however, was to produce immediate impact—it was more of an emergency measure—rather than to undertake the slow processes of developing new industry that would put to work large numbers of idle persons. The construction of nursing-home-type facilities could fit within the purpose. The device chosen was that of accelerating public works for which the need had already been established and the plans laid.

The arrangement by which the public works were to be accelerated was one of pouring additional money, up to 75 per cent of the cost of each project, into pre-existing federal channels for providing federal grant-in-aid money for public works projects, using the established administrative mechanisms. The Public Health Service, as the agency responsible for managing the Hill-Burton program, was therefore an appropriate disburser of some of the new funds. As the operation was actually

[33] Public Law 658, 87th Cong.

[34] See the testimony of Harold W. Williams, Deputy Administrator, Area Redevelopment Administration, United States Congress, Senate, Joint Sub-Committee on Long Term Care of the Special Committee on Aging, *Hearings on Long Term Institutional Care for the Aged*, 85th Cong., 1st Sess., 1963, p. 81.

carried out the state Hill-Burton agencies designated to the Accelerated Public Works unit of the Area Redevelopment Administration what projects had been proposed to them by governmental or voluntary sponsors that met Hill-Burton requirements as to standards and as to community need. The federal agency responsible for making determinations as to what projects should get acceleration money encountered considerable difficulty in weighing proposals according to the two competing sets of criteria involved: needs for properly distributed health care facilities and needs for economic stimulation of the community.[35] In New York, however, the acceleration program did not work at cross-purposes with health care planning within the nursing-home-type field. Two projects for nursing home units, each in a voluntary hospital, were approved, and each was in the highest priority class of the five classes of need employed by the Health Department's Division of Hospital Review and Planning.[36]

The number of nursing-home-type beds growing out of the acceleration program was not great. One project, completed in 1965, involved 31 beds; the other, completed in January 1966,

[35] Interview with Dr. Johannes U. Hoeber, Acting Deputy Administrator for Public Works Acceleration, Area Redevelopment Administration, United States Department of Commerce. My conclusions after studying the matter (and I cannot attribute my conclusions to Dr. Hoeber) are that there was a strong pork-barrel quality to Accelerated Public Works, as there usually is to public works programs. Moreover, there is some evidence that priorities for medical care facilities were not clearly spelled out by the Hill-Burton agencies.

[36] However, one might question the appropriateness of the distribution of funds from the standpoint of relative need of nursing home facilities and hospitals. Seven hospital projects were approved with federal grants totaling $5,487,000. The two nursing home projects received a total of $1,577,000 in federal aid. See U.S. Department of Commerce, Area Redevelopment Administration, Accelerated Public Works Program, *Directory of Approved Projects as of July 1, 1964* (Washington: Area Redevelopment Administration, 1964), pp. 104–109. On October 1, 1964, the Division of Hospital Review and Planning of the State Health Department declared that "the greatest deficit in medical care facilities, including New York City, is in the field of nursing home care." "Evaluation of All Types of Nursing Home Facilities in New York State and Projection of Needs and Capital Construction Costs" (mimeo.), p. 1.

has 42 beds. Acceleration money paid half the cost of the former and 43 per cent of the latter. Congress, in the act, had authorized the appropriation of up to $900 million. Later in the year it had appropriated $850 million. Under the law the money was distributed according to the relative economic needs of the economically distressed areas, and of the economic strength of the state and local governments involved. Capacity of local resources also determined the proportion of each project that would be covered by federal money. A further factor was the wide range of public works competing for the money. Some 207 projects such as sewage plants, courthouses, and wildlife facilities, as well as the two nursing home projects, received acceleration money totaling $36.3 million in upstate New York. No money went to New York City.

The accelerated public works appropriation was exhausted within a year and was not renewed. Measures were introduced in Congress to provide additional money but the administration sponsored none. The program is of interest to this study as another example of policy not directly aimed at nursing homes yet exerting some influence upon them.

The Upstate Public Infirmary Picture

There are problems concerning upstate public infirmaries other than those of reimbursement and financing for construction that deserve passing mention. A few of these institutions, particularly those in urban counties, have outstanding reputations. No attempt to evaluate them can be made here. Even such a model as the Monroe County Infirmary, however, where substantial progress has been made in developing the facility as a center for the appropriate placement of patients and as a chronic treatment center with such specialties as physical therapy service and intensive nursing, has had inadequacies and critics.[37]

---

[37] See Bureau of Medical Services, Department of Social Welfare, County of Monroe, *Annual Report, 1961*, pp. 23–24. Miss Ollie Randall,

Moreover, county homes, particularly those in smaller counties, have often been managed by people without appropriate training. In upstate New York the operation of county homes and infirmaries is the responsibility of local Public Welfare Commissioners. A report by Greenleigh Associates to the Moreland Commission on Welfare in 1962 declared that the qualification of these commissioners were "on the average . . . the lowest of any state in the United States." The report also noted that New York was the only state where local welfare commissioners and deputy commissioners did not come under merit system requirements.[38] It can be added that at least seventeen wives of local welfare commissioners, and two wives of deputy commissioners, were holding posts as matrons of county homes or infirmaries in 1965. In that year, however, the law was changed to bring commissioners under the merit system.[39] In time, improvements of administration in this respect may be expected.

A pictorial representation of the development of upstate public nursing-home-type facilities in comparison to voluntaries and proprietaries is offered in Figure 2, which presents the relevant data of Tables 2M, 3M, 4M, and 5M in graph form. The most arresting feature of the figure is its indication of the extent to which proprietary holdings dominate the field. More germane to the matters immediately under discussion, the figure makes it clear that the long-range rate of public infirmary growth prevailing before the early 1950's was altered toward faster growth (the 1958 dip is artificial) by federal and state reimbursement and by the construction grants of the Hill-Burton program. It also makes it clear, however, that no

---

Vice-President of the Council on Aging, declared in 1963 that the Monroe County Infirmary suffered seriously from staffing problems and from being overinstitutionalized. Interview, June 11, 1963.

[38] *Report on the Moreland Commission on Welfare of Findings of the Study of Public Assistance Program and Operations of the State of N.Y.,* Nov. 1962, p. 62.

[39] See pp. 244–245, below.

strong or abrupt change occurred in public sector trends and that, if they continue unchanged, no great transformation will take place in the public sector, except perhaps over a very long period.

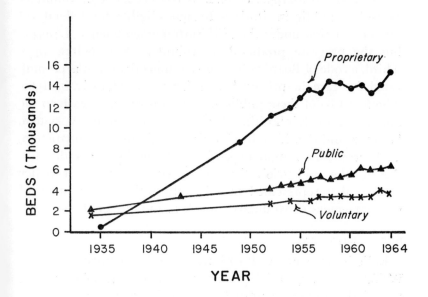

Figure 2. Growth in numbers of public, voluntary, and proprietary nursing-home-type beds in upstate New York, 1935 through 1964.

Note. The triangles, crosses, and dots indicate the points at which the lines are based on data. The smoothness of the lines is, to some extent, attributable to the absence of data.

The shrinkage in the number of public beds during 1958 is artificial, the consequence of the Department of Social Welfare's dropping all unapproved beds from its listing as of that year.

Source. Data in Tables 2M, 3M, 4M, and 5M, Appendix I.

Voluntary Nursing-Home-Type Institutions

Public policy did not stimulate greatly the growth of upstate voluntary nursing-home-type institutions during the dozen years that followed 1952. There were three policy changes that invite investigation into growth rates. First, a differentiation in reimbursement rates for private homes for the aged, providing for higher payments for infirmary than domiciliary beds, was provided for homes whose infirmaries met certain specifications by new rules and regulations of the Board and Department of Social Welfare in 1956. Second, as has been noted, voluntary as well as public institutions became eligible for federal aid for construction under the Hill-Burton amendments of 1954— but the program produced no voluntary beds before 1958. Third, a code of Board rules and recommendations was promulgated for care in private homes for the aged early in 1960. The first two of these public policy shifts did not reach to the essential growth-inhibiting factors in the voluntary system, however, and the third, by elevating standards for construction, made growth even more expensive and therefore more difficult. But in the mid-1960's there occurred a number of policy changes that represented promise, although no guarantee, of encouragement of voluntary growth in the nursing home field.

DIFFERENTIAL RATES

Bulletin 119a of the Board and State Department of Social Welfare was the official pronouncement of the policy of differentiating rates for private homes for the aged to make higher payments for infirmary care. One cannot be certain where the idea for the policy began. Differentiated rates had, in effect, been established for public homes by Bulletin 139 in 1951. Representatives of the old-age homes had raised the matter with the New York City Welfare Department some time after. In 1955, Governor Harriman convened a conference on the problems of the aging, composed of prominent social welfare and other community leaders. One recommendation growing out of the conference panel on group care of the aging called for "a review of the rate structure . . . for Homes for the Aged, based on a realistic review of the costs and the quality of service given."[40] In a special message to the legislature on the

---

[40] *Charter for the Aging: New York State Conference Convened by Governor Averell Harriman at the State Capitol in Albany, 1955*, p. 178.

problems of the aging the following January, the Governor reported that the State Department of Social Welfare would authorize differential rates for private homes for the aged. He saw advantages for improving services, since homes receiving the higher rates would have to meet stipulated infirmary standards, and for encouraging the development of needed infirmary facilities.[41]

Bulletin 119a, which stipulated the standards, was issued the following June. The format was different from that of the rules and regulations for public infirmaries and private nursing homes that had been issued in 1951. Many of the ideas were strikingly similar, however, particularly to those in the code for the public infirmaries. The scope of the provisions for the two kinds of infirmaries was approximately the same. The private infirmary code was slightly more specific than its predecessors in some matters and less so in others, probably reflecting the five years of experience with the earlier codes. It was similar to the public infirmary requirements in calling for separation of the infirmary from residential quarters.

The Bulletin required homes receiving the differentiated rate to "maintain financial records which make possible the identification of expenditures chargeable to operation of that part of the home providing domiciliary care and expenditures chargeable to that part of the home providing infirmary care," and thus the first steps were taken to provide solid accounting information in the nursing home field. The Bulletin went on to say that the costs of care in other kinds of institutions should be considered in setting the infirmary rates. It then admonished: "In comparing rates, it should be borne in mind that private homes for the aged and for the blind are charitable institutions and, as such, receive public subsidy in the form of tax exemptions, and may also receive contributions from community chests, churches and other private donors."

The differentiated rate did not spark any remarkable growth in infirmaries of private homes for the aged. Upstate, 64 beds

[41] *Ibid.,* p. 653.

were added during 1957, 28 the followng year, and 93 during 1959. There was a clear flush of enthusiasm over this development in New York City. Prior to the establishment of the differentiated rate in the city, the maximum monthly payment to an old-age home was $200. The new rate schedule, set up in 1957, allowed $240 a month or "actual cost," whichever was lower, for patients in infirmaries approved as meeting the requirements of Bulletin 119a. The City Department of Welfare received assurances that some 2,000 new infirmary beds would be created in 1957, and confidently stated in its *Annual Report* for that year that they were created.[42] In fact, most of the new beds failed to materialize. The 1957 increase in the city was 15 beds. For 1958 and 1959, the growth was 107 and 160 beds, respectively. At the end of 1965, only 22 of the 55 private homes for the aged in the city had approved infirmaries even though they could receive as high as $480 each month for a welfare patient in such facilities, as compared to $320 a month for a person in residential status. But three voluntary nursing homes had been brought under the preferred rate. Meanwhile, as of the end of 1964, for every two persons living in old-age homes there was one outside waiting to get in.[43] And lists are commonly longer for infirmary than for domiciliary beds.

A CODE FOR PRIVATE HOMES FOR THE AGED

A code of rules, recommendations and principles for private homes for the aged became effective on January 1, 1960.[44] It is significant that these institutions did not become subject to such a set of rules, aiming at comprehensive and systematic

---

[42] Pp. 13–14.

[43] Files, New York State Department of Social Welfare.

[44] In early 1957 a revised code of rules and regulations for proprietary and nonprofit nursing homes was issued by the State Department of Social Welfare, implementing statutory changes in the Board's and the Department's powers. By far the most significant change related to proprietary homes alone, however. For this reason a discussion of the matter will be presented in the section of this chapter that deals with proprietary nursing homes rather than here.

government regulation, until well after private nursing homes. (The reader will recall there had been a nursing home code since 1951.) Although Bulletin 119a had since 1956 prescribed conditions necessary for infirmary sections to receive differential rates, there had been no codification of standards applicable to all private homes for the aged, including those not caring for public assistance recipients. Historically the need for strengthened governmental regulation of homes for the aged had not seemed so urgent, and therefore the establishment of a code for these institutions followed precedent—the nursing home code—rather than setting one. Setting a precedent would have required greater concern on the part of government officials or others. But the supervision of homes for the aged by the various fraternal, religious, and other groupings that were responsible for them had been reasonably satisfactory. Indeed the evidence does not indicate that the 1960 code was drawn up because of unacceptable performance by these homes but because of a desire for more system in a field of growing importance.

The new code rested upon the traditional powers of the Board of Social Welfare and its agent, the Department of Social Welfare, rather than upon the power to withhold reimbursement as had been the case with Bulletin 119a of 1956. The big difference between the two was, of course, that one was designed to establish special criteria for the differentiated compensation of infirmaries and the other to regulate private homes whether they had infirmaries or not. But the 1960 provisions did have four subrules for homes caring for chronically ill persons. As was to be expected, the new code, including the subrules, was not as demanding as the Bulletin. For example, physically and administratively separate infirmaries were not required, nor were registered professional nurses, call signals for individual beds, nor specified medical and nursing equipment or qualifications to use such equipment. Nor were detailed duties of nurses spelled out.

The great gains in the code were in a requirement for prior

approval by the Department of Social Welfare for any new construction or reconstruction, and the application of the State Building Code plus Board Rules for all new building activity, and specific construction standards for new centralized nursing facilities. Specifications for the nursing institutions were pro-vided that were comparable to Hill-Burton requirements as to the level of what they demanded, although they were not so comprehensive as those pace-setting standards.

REPRESENTATION OF VOLUNTARIES IN PUBLIC POLICY FORMULATION

The process by which the code was drawn up is of signficance in that it illustrates the extremely important role that voluntary organizations have played in determining their relationship with government. That relationship is far from being one of government domination; it is far more one of reciprocity, bargaining, and balance.

An advisory committee, a body of sixteen "officials, board members, and specialists from representative institutions for the aged in New York State," was established for the drafting of the code. It consisted of four members of Roman Catholic organizations, four of Jewish and five of Protestant—fairly balanced representation from each of the major religious faiths in the state. Two other members were from nonsectarian institutions and one was from the National Committee on the Aging. The introduction to the code paid tribute to the committee, calling its cooperation indispensable.[45] Persons who participated in the project have, in interviews, emphasized the extent to which compromise and negotiation among the various institution's representatives, and among them and representatives of the Department and Board of Social Welfare, were important to the shaping of the code.

Voluntary organizations are effective on two fronts. Not only are they effective in maintaining lines of responsibility to

---

[45] *Rules, Recommendations, Principles: Private Homes for the Aged* (Article 16 of the Rules of the State Board of Social Welfare, effective January 1, 1960), p. 6.

themselves of the nursing-home-type institutions they sponsor, they are also effective in seeing to it that the terms on which they conduct their community affairs are not too inimical to their interests, as they interpret those interests. They can be extremely active in pressing their causes and asserting their independence, as any veteran of public administration knows. They have vigorously and concertedly pressed their claims for higher welfare rates for public assistance clients in their homes —perhaps more so in New York City than upstate because they carry a greater share of the welfare load in the city. In 1962, when the Anderson-Javits Bill, which would have provided nursing home care for the aged under Social Security Insurance, was amended in the United States Senate to make homes not affiliated with hospitals eligible to receive patients included under the program,[46] the American Nursing Home Association, as spokesman for proprietary nursing homes, took virtually sole credit for what it regarded as a victory. (And, rather ambivalently, simultaneously rejoiced in the defeat of the whole bill.)[47] However, nonprofit institutions, too, had communicated their opposition to the affiliation requirement to Senators, though not in the trumpeting style of the proprietary organization.[48] More recently, voluntary groups were instrumental in working out the language of the Medicare Act providing that a "transfer agreement" between a nursing-home-type institution and a hospital would satisfy the requirement for the home to participate and, moreover, that the requirement would be considered fulfilled if the facility had attempted "in good faith" to conclude such an agreement even though it had failed.[49]

[46] Senator Muskie's proposal, made on the floor of the Senate, that the Secretary of Health, Education and Welfare should have discretion to determine if homes without affiliation could constitute acceptable skilled nursing facilities, was adopted. U.S. *Congressional Record*, 88th Cong., 1st Sess., July 17, 1962, p. 12915.

[47] "Special Report," *Nursing Homes: Official Journal—American Nursing Home Association*, Sept., 1962, p. 2.

[48] Interview with Ollie Randall, Jan. 11, 1963.

[49] See p. 233, below.

They were also successful in arranging that homes for the aged able to provide skilled nursing care, as well as nursing homes per se, could participate.[50]

Through the strength of their organizational ability and their long establishment in the field of welfare, voluntary organizations had developed effective arrangements assuring their representation in the policies and activities of the Board and Department of Social Welfare. It is worth recalling that as early as 1881 the State Charities Aid Association had acquired a legislative mandate to conduct inspections of poorhouses and almshouses and make reports to the State Board of Charities, the predecessor to the State Board of Social Welfare.[51]

As time moved on, and the traditional custodial function of charity was more severely challenged, particularly by progress in health care offering more and more opportunities for positive, aggressive achievement as distinguished from caretaker activities, questions arose about the state welfare administration's orientation toward voluntary health care organizations. In 1963 a report of a State Moreland Act Commission found that although the State Board of Social Welfare was an "excellent vehicle for dealing with voluntary agencies," the welfare administration's top-level structure did not provide for constructive leadership.[52]

In essence, the Commission found that the Board emphasized "dealing with and representing private welfare agencies and

---

[50] Interview with Lester Davis, Executive Director, American Association of Homes for the Aged, Sept. 30, 1965. The American Association of Homes for the Aged, an offshoot of the National Council on the Aging, was established in November of 1961. It has undertaken, among other activities, the following: "[to] provide legislative information, serve as a spokesman for the non-profit Homes, and help shape public policy by providing a forum for discussion of needed legislative action." *Guidelines to Growth*, American Association of Homes for the Aging (New York, 1962), p. 2.

[51] See p. 26, above.

[52] New York State, the Moreland Commission on Welfare, *Public Welfare in the State of New York*, 1963, p. 8.

institutions" but did not fully meet its administrative responsibilities, such as inspection and approval of health care facilities. The Commission charged the Board with administrative shortcomings, among them being "derelict" in allowing the position of Deptuy Commissioner of Medical Affairs in the Department of Welfare to lie vacant for almost two years.[53]

The importance of the representative character of the welfare administration compared to its administrative effectiveness, expecially in its health-related aspects, had been sharpening as an issue for some time. As early as 1949 Eli Ginzberg had called for "effective leadership," the assignment of the broad problem of institutional health care to a single agency, and had concluded: "Neither the Board of Social Welfare nor the Department of Social Welfare is any more likely to be able to provide leadership for a hospital [and nursing home] group than it has in the past."[54] In 1961 the consultant firm of Cresap, McCormick, and Paget had leveled an extensive criticism at the Board and Department of Social Welfare and had proposed that the supervision of all adult institutions should be transferred to the State Department of Health.[55] It gave "inadequate administration and supervision to both the quantity and quality of medical . . . care provided within the framework of public welfare"[56] as one reason for its recommendation, and the lack of coordination in the collection and interpretation of "information on the use, suitability and services of hospitals, nursing homes and other facilities" as another.[57] The Board of Social Welfare responded by declaring that the Cresap, McCormick, and Paget report "almost totally ignores the vital policy role our state government has played in the affairs of

[53] *Ibid.*, pp. 82–85.
[54] Eli Ginzberg, *A Pattern for Hospital Care* (New York: Columbia University Press, 1949), pp. 357, 358.
[55] Cresap, McCormick and Paget, Management Consultants, *New York State Department of Social Welfare: Study of the Administration of Public Welfare in New York State*, 1961, Vol. I, chap. 3, pp. 9–10.
[56] *Ibid.*, chap. 4, pp. 19, 23.   [57] *Ibid.*, chap. 5, p. 56.

the hundreds of private nongovernmental welfare agencies and institutions spread across the state." It added: "No adequate account is taken either of the religious and philosophical motivations, which lie back of our government welfare activities and had their source—and have their continuing support—among groups and associations of private citizens."[58] Voluntary organizations supported the position of the Board. On the other hand, interestingly, the New York State Nursing Home Association—representing proprietary nursing homes—took a neutral stand.

The strength of the voluntary organizations in promoting their representational values was clearly manifested in the Metcalf-McCloskey Act, which was passed in 1964, and which implemented the principle of regional planning for hospitals, nursing homes, and related medical facilities in the state. This law provided that no new hospital or nursing home facilities, including expansions and major modification of existing facilities, could be constructed without the prior approval of the Board of Social Welfare, such approval following review of the proposed construction by a Regional Hospital Review and Planning Council and a similar council at the state level. Among the criteria stipulated for the approval of proposed new institutions is that of "public need." Senator George R. Metcalf, Chairman of the State Joint Legislative Committee on Health Insurance Plans, contended during Committee Hearings that the "regional planning bodies should make a determination as to whether a hospital [or nursing home] should be built solely on the basis of objectively determined need." However, Monsignor Patrick J. Frawley, representing the Archdiocese of New York of the Roman Catholic Church, wanted recognition to be "given to the imperatives imposed upon Catholic groups by their faith as a valid consideration in a decision to build a hospital."

The Monsignor defined "need" more broadly than the

58 *New York Times,* Feb. 6, 1961.

Senator and sought a supply of beds for any given community reflecting the religious identifications of the population. To include sponsorship of hospitals in this fashion in the determination of what beds a community should have may be expected to require a greater number of beds and result in a lower average occupancy rate. In this event, hospital prepayment plans such as Blue Cross must charge higher premium rates to maintain all of the beds. Such was the issue. "An apparently irreconcilable difference of opinion between Mr. Tobin [representative of the New York State Catholic Welfare Committee] and Monsignor Frawley, on the one hand, and Senator Metcalf, on the other, failed to be resolved." Monsignor Frawley warned that if consideration were not given to the imperatives mentioned above, "it might be necessary for these Catholic institutions to withdraw from all affiliation with hospital regulating authorities, including Blue Cross."[59] The legislation that was passed, and that governs these matters today, reads in part as follows: "The needs of members of the religious denomination concerned, for care or treatment in accordance with their religious or ethical convictions, shall be deemed to be public need."[60]

CAPITAL COSTS FOR VOLUNTARIES

At the end of 1965, voluntary organizations were still operating under the state's assumption that they should provide some financial responsibility for the care of the public charges they admitted. The ceiling to the amount the state would reimburse

[59] *Report of the Joint Legislative Committee on Health Insurance Plans*, Leg. Doc. No. 39 (Albany, 1964), p. 86. Mr. Robert Shulman, Deputy Commissioner of the Department of Social Welfare, reported that the Board of Social Welfare, prior to the passage of the Metcalf-McCloskey Act, took considerations of religion into account "all the time" in deciding whether or not to approve charters of incorporation for medical facilities (p. 82).

[60] New York Social Welfare Law, sec. 35(b)(i); New York Public Health Law, sec. 2802, 2(b). It should be noted, however, that Roman Catholic leaders have often been among the strongest supporters of community-wide planning and development of health facilities.

for the care of a patient was one important device reflecting this assumption. Several of the private homes spent well over the ceiling in giving infirmary care. In the event an institution spent less than the ceiling, however, it would still receive less than it spent; the "actual cost" never included the money necessary to provide plant and equipment, or to retire debt incurred for such purposes.[61]

In the opinion of the Assistant to the Commissioner for Finance and Statistics of the New York City Department of Welfare, it was precisely because the capital costs involved to meet the standards of Bulletin 119a were too great for the homes that the 2,000 new infirmary beds announced by the City Welfare Department's *Annual Report of 1957* did not materialize.

As the standards for new physical plant and equipment had risen, the costs of constructing and equipping new facilities had risen as well, and for voluntary institutions the need for money had become more and more pressing. Traditionally, voluntary health care agencies had not charged their patients for depreciation nor had they set money aside from current income for capital purposes—as for money received for the care of public charges, such funding was prohibited. Instead, they had met these expenses from fund-raising drives, bequests, or

[61] In New York City, at the time of the provision for the differential rate, the representatives of the three major religious faiths met and devised a model set of accounts. The model was tested by homes associated with religious organizations. On December 8, 1958, the Bureau of Special Services of the New York City Department of Welfare promulgated its Bulletin No. 58-1, an official set of instructions for the submitting of account statements by private homes for aged or for the blind and for voluntary nursing homes, derived from the tested model. It required annual statements prepared by certified public accountants. Leading off the instructions is a list of nonallowable items, among them "Payments of Accounts of Principal of Mortgages" and "Depreciation." The "Chart of Accounts" (as the set of instructions was titled) did provide, however, that "for purposes of computing allowable costs, *actual expenditures* of a capital nature will be allowed up to a ceiling of 3 per cent of the total allowable costs exclusive of capital expenditures." (Italics added.) On October 7, 1964, the ceiling was raised to 4 per cent.

other philanthropic resources. As the character of health care progressed from custodial to curative and restorative, however, and as it became possible for medical professions actually to remedy more and more conditions, the costs of training personnel and of providing them with the complex physical plant and equipment they needed to do their work grew higher and higher. Philanthropy proved unable to keep pace, and voluntary institutions fell farther and farther behind, financially.

A study of the finances of the Federation of Jewish Philanthropies is an excellent illustration of the problems voluntary organizations were facing.[62] The Federation was supplying funds to ten membership hospitals and four (later, five) long-term care institutions. Two of the long-term care facilities were homes for the aged, with infirmaries approved under Bulletin 119a, and two were nursing homes in 1957–1958. Philanthropy provided 17 per cent of the funds for the operating costs and all of the capital construction costs. Public funds supplied 47 per cent of the operating costs[63]—a high proportion of the patients and residents were welfare cases. It should be mentioned that the Federation was supporting programs in child care, family service, community service, camps, and religious education, and that the hospital and long-term care institutions received less of their support from Federation grants than any of the five other programs.[64]

Over the two decades ending in the late fifties, philanthropic grants to Federation hospitals virtually doubled, but the proportion of income such grants comprised dropped from 32.4 per cent to 10.8 per cent.[65] Over the same period the average cost per patient day in a Federation hospital quadrupled, rising from under $7 to almost $28.[66] And operating costs in nursing-home-type facilities were undoubtedly increasing as well. Such voluntary organizations were not only facing increasing con-

---

[62] Eli Ginzberg and Peter Rogatz, *Planning for Better Hospital Care* (New York: King's Crown Press, 1961).

[63] *Ibid.*, p. 90.   [64] *Ibid.*, p. 130.   [65] *Ibid.*, p. 63.

[66] *Ibid.*, p. 66.

struction costs for nursing-home-type facilities, they were swept up in a whole battery of rising costs that made desires to improve and expand nursing-home-type facilities difficult to achieve.

Further evidence of this kind of development is found in a 1959 study of voluntary convalescent homes, *Convalescence and Institutional Convalescent Care*:

> One of the . . . major problems for the homes is their lack of adequate financing. In former years, the substantial endowments of many homes paid for patient care and maintenance, but this is no longer true. Now, after years of rising costs, most seek payment for patient care, at least in part, and request voluntary, city, and agency contributions. . . . The City itself is a major source of support, since many "City cases" are referred to the homes.[67]

Facing rising operating costs, the voluntary organizations temporized with their plant needs, postponing even the replacement and modernization of their acute care hospital buildings, let alone the construction of new long-term care beds. By 1965 the problem had assumed monumental proportions in New York City, where so little Hill-Burton money had found its way. A survey of hospitals in the city by the Hospital Review and Planning Council of Southern New York, completed in 1965, concluded that 26 of the city's 78 voluntary hospitals should be replaced completely and estimated that the cost of such replacement and of the modification needed for the remaining 52 institutions would be over $389 million.[68]

Under this kind of mounting financial pressure, the traditional image of the voluntary health care agency as one emphasizing philanthropy began to change. Voluntary groups began to press government for higher rates of payment for

[67] Magda Gislaine Pendall, *Convalescence and Institutional Convalescent Care*, Columbia University School of Public Health and Administrative Medicine (New York, 1959), pp. 94–95.

[68] The report recommended that much of the total replacement of hospitals occur through the merging of institutions. Its estimate of the modernization costs for the city-owned hospitals was $267 million; of the proprietary hospitals, $48 million.

nursing-home-type cases, and some argued that capital construction costs as well as operating costs should come from public sources. Such pleas were heard increasingly during the 1950's and Hill-Burton provisions had already established some precedent for the use of government money for voluntary health agency construction; but social conventions such as those attending charitable institutions do not change rapidly, especially among budget-conscious welfare administrators. In 1960 the State Board of Social Welfare responded to queries of the Temporary State Commission on Coordination of State Activities with the following statement:

There is constant pressure from some of these agencies [not nursing-home-type institutions alone but a broad range of private organizations] to be paid for the full cost of the care of those assigned to them by the public departments. Indeed, a few of those agencies in the child welfare field now receive from public funds close to 100 per cent of their operating budgets. There is still a saving to the State in that it is spared the capital costs of the construction of the facilities. On the other hand, there is the view among some of these agencies that capital construction costs should also be provided from public funds. If the latter view should prevail, the whole structure of the private welfare system in this field may be forced to give way to a system of State-built and State-operated facilities with consequent public control.[69]

DOWNSTATE AND UPSTATE INSTITUTIONS:
CHARITY AND CONSERVATISM

In the matter of accommodating the image of the voluntary institution to new conditions, there is a noticeable tendency for many upstate organizations to reflect the persuasions of the communities of which they are a part. Although there are ex-

[69] This statement is an excerpt from a memorandum of the Board to the Temporary Commission reprinted in State Department of Social Welfare, *Public Welfare: A Community Responsibility, Social Welfare in New York State in 1960, 94th Annual Report*, Leg. Doc. No. 101 (Albany, 1961), p. 23. This is only a stronger presentation of a position taken earlier. See New York State Department of Social Welfare, *Public Social Services in 1948, 82nd Annual Report, January 1, 1948–December 31, 1948*, Leg. Doc. No. 76 (Albany, 1949), p. xii.

ceptions, by and large these persuasions are relatively conservative when compared to those found in New York City. As noted in Chapter 4, numerous upstate voluntaries—particularly private homes for the aged—do not accept public charges. Only one person out of every five in upstate homes was a public assistance recipient at the end of 1964, in contrast to homes in the city where the comparable ratio was one in every two. On the other hand, a much higher proportion of the clientele of the city homes was supported at the expense of the home— one in ten as compared to one in twenty-eight upstate. Further, upstate homes still had one of every three of their residents on a life care contract; in the city the ratio was only one to every fifteen.[70] Finally, the city had more voluntary nursing-home-type beds despite the fact that it had fewer aged.[71] The tradition and resources for charity are stronger in the city than upstate. Still, voluntaries downstate are less "traditional," in the sense that they are more willing to work with government, accepting public charges, government money, and the concomitant additional government regulation involved.

STEPS TOWARD STATE AID FOR VOLUNTARY CONSTRUCTION

An Aborted Effort

The problem of voluntary agencies acquiring capital funds for medical facilities was the subject of a series of meetings held under the auspices of the State Joint Legislative Committee on Health Insurance during 1963 and 1964. Senator George R. Metcalf, Chairman of the Joint Committee, called the meetings, which were attended by spokesmen of hospital groups, religious organizations, experts in hospital affairs and representatives of interested state government departments and of Blue Cross plans.[72]

---

[70] Files, New York State Department of Social Welfare.

[71] Table 6M, Appendix I.

[72] The source for the material of this section is chapter 6 of the *Report of the Joint Legislative Committee on Health Insurance Plans, 1964* Leg. Doc. No. 39 (Albany, 1964).

The meetings revealed early a consensus among those attending that state money should be made available for the construction of voluntary health care facilities. Matching grants
following the Hill-Burton model, but with a government contribution of about half rather than a third, were definitely considered preferable to loans; but loans were seriously discussed.
Dr. George J. Graham, of Ellis Hospital in Schenectady, ac-
knowledging that his position was unique, reported that his
Board of Trustees "would probably prefer loans to grants." Dr.
Graham explained that "I think our board is reluctant to have
government funds because of concern as to possible government
control over operation."[73]

There was a consciousness that voluntary organizations would
have difficulty in meeting operating, as well as construction,
costs, and that grants should be generous in order to compen-
sate for the deterrent to their undertaking greater nursing
home responsibilities that this would constitute. Mr. J. Douglas
Colman, of New York's largest—in fact, of the country's largest
—Blue Cross plan put the matter thus: "If we were members
of the Board of Trustees of a voluntary hospital and we were
facing the usual problem of accumulated obsolescence, and
someone were to ask us to take on another burden like [the
cost of operating] an affiliated nursing home, we would certainly say 'No, thanks.' This is perhaps an oversimplification."[74]
He went on to suggest that grants of 100 per cent of the construction cost should be available to encourage voluntary institutions to expand their activities in this area. Monsignor
Christopher G. Kane, of Catholic Charities, thought that grants
of a lesser proportion would be useful. He did report that the
New York Archdiocese "feels that it would be unwise to commit ourselves to the financing of such activity on the basis of
long-term loans. We reluctantly have been unable to move in
this direction." He also said, however, that "as far as the grants
[for nursing home construction] are concerned, if they were

---

[73] *Ibid.*, p. 57.   [74] *Ibid.*, p. 55.

available in amounts of fifty per cent or more in State funds this would be a most welcome development for hospitals. Catholic organizations in New York City have been anxious to assume this responsibility."[75]

Although there was agreement that there should be legislation providing for state grants for the construction of voluntary medical institutions, a major barrier to such legislation lay in a specific prohibition in the State Constitution to such grants.[76] A spokesman for the State Division of the Budget was of the opinion that loans to private bodies were also prohibited. The decision was made, and carried out, to draft two proposed constitutional amendments, one providing for grants and one for loans, and also to draft bills for introduction to the legislature to implement grant and loan programs.

The legislation drafted provided that the State Commissioner of Health would administer grants and loans for the "establishment and construction of new non-profit hospitals and nursing homes and for the expansion, modernization, renovation and replacement of land, buildings and building fixtures of existing non-profit hospitals and nursing homes."[77] The measure contained no formula for the grants, and no terms as to interest or duration of the loans. These were left completely to the discretion of the Commissioner. The loans and grants were to be allocated among voluntary hospitals, and voluntary nursing homes "affiliated and operated in conjunction with" general hospitals, either voluntary or governmental. The allocation was to be made after the Commissioner had received the advice of

[75] *Ibid.*, p. 56.
[76] Sec. 8 of art. VII of the Constitution reads, in part: "The money of the state shall not be given or loaned to or in aid of any private corporation or association, or private undertaking; nor shall the credit of the state be given or loaned to or in aid of any individual, or public or private corporation or association, or private undertaking." This provision has been construed to prohibit only "lump sum" grants and does not, of course, forbid the state to pay private organizations for the rendering of care to public charges.
[77] The proposed amendments and laws are to be found in the *Report of the Joint Committee, 1964*, pp. 64–71.

the state hospital planning mechanism, the Regional and State Hospital Review and Planning Councils, as to public need for the particular project under consideration.

The legislation drafted constituted an attempt to maneuver voluntary hospitals into following orderly financial practices to assure appropriate replenishment of their capital plant. It provided for rates of reimbursement for hospital care of public charges that included "an allowance, approved by the department of social welfare, for capital expenditures." Such allowance was not to be paid to a hospital unless a similar charge was levied by it against other purchasers of the institution's services and unless the institution regularly set the money thus acquired aside, in a funding arrangement, for future capital needs. The aim, to systematize the financing of plant needs, was clear. But the impact could not have been expected to be great. For these provisions were to apply to hospitals alone, and not to nursing homes, and although they would have required upstate governments to reimburse at a rate determined by the Department of Social Welfare that presumably would have been at cost, they would not have required New York City, where the problem of hospital plant obsolescence is greatest, to do so.

The two proposed constitutional amendments and the two implementing bills were introduced in the State Senate by Mr. Metcalf in February 1964. They were not passed, however.

A Successful Effort

Meanwhile a separate train of events had begun that was to eventuate in state financial support for the construction of voluntary nursing homes. A 1962 study by Herbert E. Klarman concluded that from 13,000 to 15,000 new long-term care beds would be needed in New York City over the next decade.[78] This report galvanized the concern of the city government about the shortage of suitable nursing home facilities and the City

[78] "Backgrounds, Issues and Policies in Health Services for the Aged in New York City," A Report to the New York City Interdepartmental Health Council and the New York City Health Council (mimeo.), p. 41.

Administrator's Office, an administrative arm of the Mayor, began devoting substantial attention to the problem.

In January 1963, Mayor Robert Wagner wrote to Governor Rockefeller, soliciting his aid and proposing two procedures by which construction of voluntary nursing homes could be encouraged by government. One would have involved government construction of nursing homes that would then be leased to voluntary organizations, which would operate the institutions. Payments for the use of the buildings by the voluntary organization would be used to retire the debt the government had incurred to finance the construction. The other would have construed nursing homes as being a kind of housing and thereby eligible for long-term loans from government at low interest rates under an amendment to the State Constitution that had been passed in 1938. The amendment provided that the state and localities may sell bonds and turn the money realized over to private agencies for the construction of housing that meets needs that could not be met otherwise. The bond debt must be retired by payments of the private agencies that include interest rates no higher than are necessary to sell the bonds, and administrative costs. As the arrangement has worked for housing, the life of the loan extends over as many as fifty years, and the amount of the loan may be as much as 95 per cent of the cost of construction. Thus worthy private endeavor can be financed with low-cost, long-term, government borrowing.

Both proposals encountered objections to their constitutionality. Although the city was following a procedure similar to the first one for financing docks, it was decided that docks enjoyed a privileged position under the Constitution not shared by nursing homes. At the behest of the City Administrator's Office, the city agency administering the low-cost loans for housing, the Housing and Redevelopment Board, drafted a bill for introduction into the state legislature that would include nursing homes in the existing law providing low cost loans for housing. (It is interesting that the Board, considering itself a housing agency, was reluctant to become involved with nursing homes and did so only under pressure from above.) The bill was introduced and passed the lower house, but not the upper. In the following year, 1964, the Mayor renewed his plea to the Governor. The bill was redrafted in the Governor's office, undergoing conversion to a proposed Constitutional amendment. There had been doubts as to the appropriateness of the inclusion of nursing homes as a class of housing; it was thought necessary to include the words "nursing homes" in the authorizing language of the Constitution.

The amendment was adopted, being passed by the legislature in 1964, again in 1965, and by the voters of the state in the general election of the fall of 1965.[79] It undoubtedly constitutes a significant step in the development of public policy concerning nursing homes. The doubts expressed as to the efficacy of loans as encouragement to voluntary organizations to expand their nursing home responsibilities must be remembered, of course. Also, the amendment and implementing legislation alone does not make loans economically feasible for voluntaries if the reimbursement rate for public charges does not cover the full cost of caring for public charge patients—including the cost of providing buildings. Legislation passed in 1965, however, directs that reimbursement be at rates "reasonably related to cost," as determined by the State Commissioner of Health. That legislative provision and others related to it will be described in the penultimate chapter of this study.

The choice of arrangements by which nonfederal govern-

---

[79] Constitution art. XVIII, secs. 1, 2. This may be some kind of speed record for the adoption of a constitutional amendment in the state. Amendments require passage by two successive legislatures and then by referendum. Legislatures are chosen at general elections and referenda are usually conducted as parts of general elections; legislatures ordinarily have a life-span of two years; general elections are usually held biennially. Ordinarily action in at least three different years is required to amend the Constitution. Because of reapportionment exigencies stemming from the 1962 United States Supreme Court decision in the case of *Baker* v. *Carr* (369 U.S. 186, 82 Sup. Ct. 691), however, the life of the legislature elected in 1964 was only one year, a new legislature was selected in 1964 which could vote on the measure in 1965, and a general election was held in 1965 in which the proposal could be submitted to a referendum. The whole procedure could thus be completed within two years.

ment aid for the construction of voluntary nursing homes was to be provided represented a response to a specific, alarming, condition. It did not represent the unfolding of broad-perspective planning. It utilized, for purposes of expedition, an existing legal mechanism for housing rather than linking the administration of its new policy to the state's planning mechanism for medical care. It ignored the inextricably related need for restoration of hospital plants, a crucial problem in New York City, the seat of the movement to provide the financial aid. No sooner was the constitutional amendment passed to provide loans to voluntary nursing homes than it became clear that hospitals had to have help too. In fact, it had been clear for some time. Governor Rockefeller announced in March of 1966 that he was asking for a constitutional amendment to allow the state to provide loans for the construction of voluntary hospitals.[80]

SPECIAL PROBLEMS OF CONVALESCENT HOMES

Incorporated convalescent and nursing homes have not received much specific mention in the immediately foregoing pages. They shared many of the problems of the private homes for the aged and bore others as well. As has been noted in Chapter 4, the voluntary nursing homes had in common many of the difficulties faced by not only homes for the aged, but also by proprietary nursing homes. And during the 1950's, a special problem began to plague the voluntary convalescent home. This kind of facility, although well intended, has found itself more and more in search of a purpose in recent years. Traditionally aimed at recuperation and consisting of comfortable living quarters in a scenic setting, such places were found to be increasingly challenged by the demand for, and possibility of rendering, more positive curative and restorative care. This condition created considerable instability among institutions classed here as "incorporated nursing and convalescent homes."

[80] *New York Times*, March 13, 1966.

Many conversions to other types of institutions, and many closings—and some openings—occurred. The instability is reflected in the figures of Table 6 and in the words of a study completed a few years ago:

The recent history of convalescent homes in the area [Greater New York] has been one of steady reduction in the number of beds and continuous opening and closing of facilities. . . . Since this study began in 1955, three more homes have closed, although no final disposition of their endowments has been made, and six others are known to be seriously contemplating relocating their facilities, changing to a nonconvalescent care program or closing permanently. The losses of convalescent beds cut across all types and sizes of facilities.[81]

Table 6. Incorporated convalescent and nursing homes, upstate, 1950–1964

Year	Homes	Beds
1950	29	1,645
1954	28	1,594
1956	31	1,645
1957	34	2,064
1958	33	1,941
1959	31	1,868
1960	30	1,896
1961	28	1,693
1962	31	1,843
1963	30	1,968
1964	27	1,797

Source. Table 5M, Appendix I.

In 1964 there remained upstate only four incorporated convalescent homes.[82]

[81] Pendall, p. 2.

[82] New York State Department of Social Welfare, "Incorporated Non-Profit Nursing Homes, Convalescent Homes and Homes for Adults in New York City and Upstate New York," March 1, 1964.

THE VOLUNTARY PICTURE UPSTATE:
UNCERTAINTY AND SLOW GROWTH

This section opened with the observation that public policy did not stimulate greatly the growth of upstate voluntary nursing-home-type institutions during the dozen years that followed 1952. The traditional image of the voluntary organizations as philanthropic agencies, found to a lessening degree among the organizations themselves but still prominently in public policy, inhibited the development of these institutions. Moreover, the evolutionary course of the facilities classed as incorporated convalescent and nursing homes was erratic and uncertain.

Table 6 and Figure 2 (p. 125, above) contain no evidence that public policy stimulated voluntary organizations to expand in the nursing home field. Hill-Burton influence was a "drop in the bucket" from an over-all viewpoint. The differential rate for infirmaries of private homes for the aged was disappointing.[83] And the code for these institutions, although representing a step forward, made expansion more difficult. Even cumulatively, the policy changes did not evoke strong growth.

If the new image of the voluntary institution consolidates— an image emphasizing the organized and systematic provision of comprehensive care in the face of greater and greater challenges—fewer elements of the responsibilities of these institutions will be left to providence or good will—to philanthropy. Such consolidation will also give voluntary organizations an improved base from which to press concertedly their claims for government support—in unity there is strength. One can reasonably look for more regularized and predictable financing for voluntary nursing-home-type institutions. The promise for growth of such facilities is better than it has been in decades.

[83] The increase during 1957 indicated by Figure 2 consisted of only 64 new beds in private homes for the aged, at which the differential rate was aimed. The bulk consisted of 419 additional beds among the erratic convalescent and nursing homes.

Proprietary Nursing Homes

The two most arresting features of the data on the number of proprietary nursing home beds in upstate New York during the period from 1952 through the early 1960's are, first, that the number continued to expand with the same rapidity of the 1940's through 1958, and second, that a trend of decreasing numbers of beds set in after 1958. The picture, with the beds reaching a peak of 14,441 in 1958, is most clearly seen in Figure 2 (p. 125) and in Table 3M in Appendix I. The change in the growth pattern is attributable to a number of factors, among them being some increase in the effectiveness of government regulation; the requirement of better physical plant for nursing home facilities; and the reaching of a market condition in which supply, at the rates being charged, tended to exceed demand. The change was accompanied by important changes in the character of the proprietary nursing home as an institution, and the proprietary sector burst into new growth in 1963, soon surpassing its old high-water mark. The average annual increase in beds from 1949 through 1958 had been 632. During the two years, 1963 and 1964, the growth was over two thousand beds.

REGULATION BY THE WELFARE ADMINISTRATION

State regulation of proprietary nursing homes, it will be recalled, began in 1951 with the adoption of a code for private nursing homes and the requirement that such institutions register with the Department of Social Welfare. It had been a system of registration, rather than of licensing, that had been established, and, moreover, important elements of the registration system, as conceived by the Health Preparedness Commission back in 1946, had not been adopted. The Commission had proposed that operating and structural plans for all new proprietary facilities should be required to have approval before they could open for business. Nonprofit organizations, including nursing homes, could not operate without the State Board of Social Welfare approving their charters. But proprietary homes had no charters and no other provision for prior approval had been made.

Governor Harriman called this to the legislature's attention in his special message on problems of the aging in January 1956. He asked for legislation empowering the Department of Social Welfare to require approval of new proprietary nursing homes before they admitted patients.[84] The panel on group care of the aging of the Governor's Conference on the Problems of the Aging had recommended in 1955 that further study of the advantages of a licensing program for the state be undertaken.[85] There was, however, no immediate follow-up of the recommendation. Licensing was to be delayed another decade. There was some opinion in the Department of Social Welfare that licensing was considered too ambitious a program to be undertaken with the limited number of inspection personnel the Department could realistically expect to have.

The 1956 session of the state legislature did give the Department of Social Welfare the power to require prior approval. Although this move fell short of licensing, it was nevertheless of substantial significance. Experience had shown that it was extremely difficult to get homes to elevate their quality after they were in business and patients and local welfare administrators had become dependent upon them. There was a chronic shortage of inspectors and the procedures for closing unsatisfactory institutions were extremely cumbersome. For the Welfare Administration to determine whether a proposed facility would be suited to perform nursing home functions and to prohibit the opening of those found wanting was a much more effective way to assure that at least minimal standards would be met. The implementation of the prior approval requirement was certainly an important factor contributing to the reduction of the number of proprietary beds after 1958.[86] In drawing this

[84] *Charter for the Aging*, p. 652.   [85] *Ibid.*, p. 178.

[86] The importance of strengthened enforcement of regulations as an element discouraging growth in proprietary beds appeared with dramatic clarity in New York City after 1958, as Chapter 6 will show.

conclusion, one properly allows some months for the new legislation to become administered and have an impact.

Another change made by the 1956 legislature, one made at the request of the Department of Social Welfare, was the establishment of special enforcement provisions applicable to proprietary nursing homes beyond the traditional powers under which such homes had been included in 1951. The new Section 35a of the Social Welfare Law, in which appeared most of the relevant 1956 legislative changes, provided that violations of the rules, regulations, or law by proprietary nursing homes would constitute a misdemeanor and that violations or threatened violations could be enjoined by the Supreme Court upon action of the Attorney General. However, resort to ultimate legal recourse remained an awkward and time-consuming process. There was still a great tendency for the administrator involved to use other techniques to secure compliance wherever possible. The withdrawal or threatened withdrawal of public welfare cases was among those most often relied upon, despite the fact that it was frequently difficult to find satisfactory beds to which patients could be transferred.

There were other significant provisions in the new law and in the revision of the code for private nursing homes that followed, appearing in early 1957. Section 35a provided that corporations could not operate or conduct proprietary nursing homes. It also provided that the Board or Department could leave the prior approval responsibility to local jurisdictions having requirements at least as stringent as those needed for state approval. For the most part, the code content was not new; additions tended to spell out what had been more generally stated in the 1951 code. Interestingly, the numerical minimum ratio of nurses or attendants to patients was replaced by the requirement that there be "adequate" nursing and other personnel. Twenty-four-hour licensed nurse coverage was mandated. Generally the rules and regulations applied to both proprietary and voluntary nursing homes. One exception attracts attention—proprietary homes alone were forbidden to provide medical care as a service of the home. The code required that nursing homes meet requirements of the Multiple Residence Law and the State Building Construction Code, that new homes have automatic sprinkler or fire detection systems and central heating systems; standards for fire stairs were raised. The elevation of standards for physical plants was decreasing the feasibility of converting dwellings and other kinds of structures into nursing homes, and increasing the amount of capital needed to go into the nursing home business.

The Bureau of Adult Institutions of the Department of Social Welfare was the administrative unit responsible for the supervision of nursing homes and, accordingly, the unit whose powers were augmented by the 1956 amendments. This added legal power met only part of the need, however. The Bureau was responsible for carrying out the Department's visitation and inspection function in a variety of public and private institutions in the state, including hospitals, dispensaries, health centers, and shelters as well as in the nursing-home-type facilities under discussion here. There is evidence to indicate that it did not get the support needed to do its work effectively. For example, an internal memorandum from the Deputy Commissioner to the Commissioner of Welfare dated April 23, 1962, cited a number of undesirable conditions in hospitals, some of which had resulted in deaths, to which the staff had not been able to devote sufficient attention because of personnel shortages. The memorandum reported that some upstate hospitals had not been inspected in twenty years.[87]

In the early 1960's the central staff of the Bureau spent well over a year drafting a new uniform code for all types of nursing home facilities, holding many meetings and consulting with representatives of voluntary and other institutions, and experts and spokesmen from other governmental agencies. A year after it was drafted, the Board of Social Welfare had not acted upon it, however, and it never went into effect; the responsibilities for regulating hospitals and nursing homes in the state were

[87] Memorandum of Robert Shulman, Deputy Commissioner of Welfare, to Raymond Houston, Commissioner of Welfare.

transferred from Social Welfare to the State Health Department in 1965.[88] The draft did serve as one starting point from which the Health Department drew up a code, however.

In considering whether the transfer of functions from the welfare administration should take place, the Governor's Committee on Hospital Costs (Folsom Committee)—which recommended the transfer—had the following to say about the Bureau of Adult Institutions:

In an environment predominantly oriented toward welfare administration, . . . the Bureau finds it difficult to shape program content along health and medical care administration lines. With the exception of the Bureau, the Department has tended to regard the Bureau's functions as an aspect of welfare administration. For long periods, no one in the Department's leadership has been qualified in the field of medical institution administration. At no time has there been in the Department what could be called a leadership corps in this field. Efforts within the Bureau to raise the level of medical and hospital administration have met with only limited success. Employment within a welfare department is almost never attractive to people with medical administration skills. The Bureau can keep itself on a policy track of this kind only by main force, for there is little in the climate of a welfare department to back its leadership up in such endeavor.[89]

REGULATION BY LOCAL GOVERNMENT

As noted, the responsibility for prior approval of proprietary nursing homes could be delegated to local governments provided the requirements imposed were at least as stringent as those needed for the approval of the Department of Social Welfare. No analysis has been made of the nursing home codes in effect in upstate areas but it is clear that local regulation was concentrated in relatively narrow areas. And it appears that local standards were, by and large, not much more demanding

[88] *Laws of New York, 1965,* chap. 795. The effective date of the transfer was February 1, 1966.

[89] Governor's Committee on Hospital Costs, *Report* (New York, 1965), p. 84.

than those of the state and not as demanding so far as structural standards were concerned. Of the state's sixty-three cities, twelve had nursing home codes in 1961. There were codes in six of the fifty-seven counties upstate. Although the codes usually were found where they were most likely to be needed, that is, in the areas where there were concentrations of proprietary nursing homes, still only 53 per cent of the upstate proprietary beds were covered by them.

It is of passing interest not only that the codes tended to be found where the beds were most dense, but also that the beds tended to be most dense in urban areas. Of the twelve cities the ratio of beds to each thousand aged persons was higher in eleven than it was in the remainder of the respective counties in which the cities were situated. One might conclude that proprietary nursing homes, and codes, were most typically urban phenomena. In fact, of the five counties with codes, four were among the one-third most urbanized in the state. And, all of the cities in the state with populations of 100,000 or over except Niagara Falls and Albany were covered by either a city or a county code. However, the generalization that homes and codes are most typically urban is one with interesting exceptions. For example, in 1961 Nassau County had a code and ranked as the most urbanized upstate county, yet fell sixteenth from the bottom in the ratio of proprietary nursing home beds per thousand aged. And Rockland County had no code, ranked as the eighth most urbanized of the fifty-seven upstate counties, and yet was fourth from the top in the ratio of proprietary beds per thousand aged.[90] The explanation for these two deviations from the general pattern was not to be found in consideration relating directly to health care facilities but to the zoning practices of the two counties. Nassau, being geographically close to New York City, being subject to suburban influences early, and for other reasons, had followed rather

---

[90] If voluntary and public infirmary type beds are counted as well as beds in proprietary nursing homes, Rockland County had the highest ratio of beds per thousand aged in the state and Nassau was ninth from the lowest.

restrictive zoning policies during the period of proprietary home growth. Rockland County, on the other hand, although on the rim of the metropolitan area, remained relatively rural until recently.[91] Zoning restrictions were comparatively casual during the period of proprietary growth and those wanting to build nursing homes found them receptive.

PRIOR APPROVAL OF CONSTRUCTION REQUIRED

Effective July 1, 1959, a new rule of the Board of Social Welfare required that all construction plans for nursing homes, whether for setting up new buildings or expanding old ones, be approved in advance by the Department.[92] Thus another step was taken in carrying out the recommendations made by the Health Preparedness Commission in 1946.[93] In July 1961 the new rule was stiffened considerably by its incorporation of the Hill-Burton construction and equipment standards and the stipulation that all plans must be in "substantial compliance" with those requirements and the State Building Construction Code in order to receive approval. In addressing the New York State Nursing Home Association in 1962, Robert Shulman, Deputy Commissioner of the Department, said that the adoption of the new rule "in effect wiped out the practice of adopting old buildings for use as nursing homes."[94]

CHANGES IN THE CHARACTER OF PROPRIETARY NURSING HOMES

A Changing Market

Meanwhile evidence was accumulating that the supply of nursing-home-type beds was overtaking the number that con-

[91] The 1950 census reported that 51.2 per cent of the population of Rockland County resided in rural areas. According to the 1960 census, however, this was true of only 24 per cent.

[92] State Department of Social Welfare, *Children in Need: Social Welfare in New York State in 1959, 93rd Annual Report*, Leg. Doc. No. 101 (Albany, 1960), p. 2.

[93] See *Planning for the Care of the Chronically Ill*, p. 30.

[94] "Proprietary Nursing Homes in Upstate New York—Past, Present and Future," address given at the 13th Annual Convention of the Association, June 12, 1962.

sumers were willing to pay for at the going rates, which were constantly increasing. One large institution was established in Albany county in the late 1950's which offered to care for public charges at rates lower than those the county was paying to proprietary institutions. The offer was accepted, patients were transferred from a number of small proprietary institutions to the new large one, and several of the small homes then went out of business. The Hill-Burton priority schedule for the allocation of federal grants for nursing home facilities effective July 1, 1961, showed an excess of 3,974 nursing-home-type beds —including public and voluntary beds—over the estimated need in upstate New York. Forty-six counties had more existing beds than their estimated need. Almost 16,000 of the 25,000 beds existing upstate were classed as "unsuitable" by the Health Department's Division of Hospital Review and Planning, but their services were still on the market. A transition was beginning through which eventually the nursing home industry, in the words of one authority on the subject, "Will change from a cannot-fail type of activity to a highly speculative investment field."[95]

A Trend toward Larger Homes

Demands by the state for improvement in plant and equipment, coupled with growing competition, accelerated trends in the proprietary nursing home industry that had long since been important.

Although there was an increase, evidently constant, in the number of proprietary beds in upstate New York through 1958, the number of homes reached a peak around 1955 and then began steadily to diminish. An increase in the average size of homes, as Table 7 shows, had begun even earlier.

Organization for Efficiency

A central factor involved in the increasing size of homes was the advantage for efficiency found in large-scale operations.

[95] Harold Baumgarten, Jr., *Concepts of Nursing Home Administration* (New York: Macmillan, 1965), p. 302.

Table 7. Average number of beds per proprietary nursing
home, upstate, 1949–1963

Year	Average number of beds
1949	14
1955	20
1958	24
1964	34

Source. Table 3M, Appendix I.

Note. The number of homes with less than ten beds
dropped tenfold in the decade following the early 1950's.
From 1961 through 1964, a period during which the trend
to larger facilities intensified, homes with 100 beds or over
grew from six to twenty.

Deputy Commissioner Shulman, in his address to the Nursing
Home Association cited earlier, noted that a small home cannot provide the required services at competitive prices, and a
nursing home administrator has asserted that it takes no more
gas to cook 100 pounds of stew than 60.[96] The appearance of
the first proprietary homes was not attributable to any generally
recognized demand for nursing home services but as isolated,
specific instances of placement of aged, ill persons. There had
appeared a proliferation of proprietary institutions, small and
primitive by today's standards because, in the absence of a
general recognition of the existing and future demand, the
industry attracted mainly people with leanings toward caring
for others and without substantial capital to invest. That proliferation, constituting clear evidence of demand, had attracted
persons with capital to invest and skills to manage the capital
and to promote its productivity. Size was not the only dimension of increased efficiency appearing in the newer homes. Increasingly they were in buildings designed for nursing home

[96] "You can cook 100 pounds of stew for roughly the same amount of
gas as 60 pounds. This sort of thing is responsible for our expansion
which will add about 30 beds to our home." Lawrence A. Kluger, Ramapo
Nursing Center, Suffern, New York, quoted in the Wall Street Journal,
Nov. 1, 1960.

use, rather than in converted dwellings—an enormous advantage.

On November 1, 1961, the *Wall Street Journal* quoted the president of a corporation in the nursing home business in Alabama as follows: "The new nursing homes are no longer heart-of-gold operations run by sweet old ladies. It's a highly efficient business."[97] Such observations had much more relevance for the future than for the present because, despite the marked tendencies toward larger homes, there remained a large residue of middle-sized and smaller homes. The average number of beds for all upstate homes at the end of 1964 was still only thirty-four. The author of the leading textbook on nursing home management has observed that certain factors attendant to the urbanization of American life plus our extended life expectancy "together generate an almost insatiable market for nursing home facilities except in a few areas which are overbuilt." He has said, further, that soon "clean, new, safe buildings will be the rule, not the exception, and at that point the building boom will develop into a management boom."[98] Attention to management, as well as large, new structures, increasingly characterizes the nursing home field.

Transformation of Proprietary Nursing Home Administrators

The responses of eighty-one members of the New York State Nursing Home Association to a questionnaire circulated by that organization in July 1962 corroborate the theme of this discussion in regard to the transformation of administrators of proprietary nursing homes.

Although any picture drawn from these data must be rather shadowy, from them emerges the impression that the upstate proprietary nursing home administrator generally has been female, has had a nurse's orientation and training, has not had a broad educational background, and has been well into middle age, if not late middle age. Such a picture is not incompatible with the characterization "sweet old lady."

[97] November 1, 1961.   [98] Baumgarten, p. 201.

Yet when looked at more closely the responses allow a more discriminatory conclusion, one with portent for the future. It has been possible to identify sixty homes with which respondent administrators were associated. A classification of these homes by number of beds indicates that the "sweet old ladies," forty-six in all, managed the smaller—and therefore older—homes.[99] The remaining fourteen administrators had no formal medical or nursing background. They were found to be associated, generally, with larger homes and much higher proportions of them had been to college and done graduate work. As the nursing home business became bigger, its managerial cadre with special nursing orientation tended to be supplanted by people who in some cases had higher levels of education but who did not have health care education.

An interesting parallel is found between this information about upstate administrators and that pertaining to management personnel in New York City proprietary nursing homes reported by the Steinle study of 1959. In the city, it was found that the smaller nursing home, the more likely it was that management personnel had health care or related backgrounds.

Moreover, the smaller the home the longer the administrators tended to have been in the nursing home business.[100] In a striking respect, however, the implications of the upstate and downstate figures are not in harmony. Though it is difficult to make precise comparisons as to job-relatedness, a considerably smaller proportion of New York City people apparently had backgrounds pertinent to nursing home administration than was true of upstate managers.[101] Of 115 City administrators,

[99] See Appendix II.
[100] John G. Steinle and Associates, *A Comprehensive Study of Proprietary Nursing Homes in New York City*, chap. 3, pp. 12, 13.
[101] *Ibid.*, pp. 11, 12. The specific enumeration upon which this statement is based is by the author of the present study. But on p. 13 the Steinle study says: "The majority of administrators were completely unprepared and unsuited by virtue of vocational background, education or experience to undertake administration of a patient-care facility at the time they entered the field."

almost exactly one-third had been engaged in medical, nursing or other health-related work prior to their assuming management responsibilities in nursing homes. But, there is one further consideration that brings all the figures into a consistent pattern. The average size, in beds, of New York City proprietary homes in 1958 was 76.5; upstate the average at the time the respondents sent in their questionnaires was probably still under thirty. The generalization that the larger the home the less likely the administrator would have a health care background is not inconsistent with, but only supported by, the differences between homes and administrators that were found in upstate and downstate New York.

COMPENSATION OF PROPRIETARY NURSING HOMES BY GOVERNMENT

The assertion has been made repeatedly throughout the historical development of proprietary nursing homes in the state that these institutions were not being adequately reimbursed for the public charges they cared for. The proposition that proprietary homes should accept welfare patients at rates below cost never was tenable, as an articulated policy, as it was in the case of the voluntary hospitals. The problem, historically, was that the rates at which proprietary homes were paid were not based upon any thorough determination of the cost of rendering care but upon negotiation. At the heart of the rate determination was the question of how badly the local welfare district needed the services of the nursing home and how badly the home needed the money forthcoming for the care of public charges. Mostly, a seller's market prevailed.

Although figures on the cost of giving care in proprietary homes upstate remained almost nonexistent through 1965, the argument was frequently advanced that proprietary institutions should receive rates comparable to the money allocated for the care of patients in public home infirmaries, where the care was rendered by a government agency. Public infirmaries cannot be equated with proprietary nursing homes, however. On the one hand, proprietary institutions pay taxes and public institutions do not. But on the other, public institutions provide, within the allotted funds, physician care, drugs, and other services that proprietaries do not provide. A schedule comparing rates paid in New York to the commercial, proprietary homes with the allotments for public infirmary care was recently offered by a representative of proprietary homes to a United States Senate Subcommittee as evidence that proprietaries were underpaid. Quite possibly the most important thing about the schedule, however, was not that among the forty-four local welfare districts using both public and commercial facilities, and thus affording comparisons, the public infirmary rate was in most instances higher, but that in a full 25 per cent of the cases the proprietaries were paid more than was alloted to the infirmary for a day's care of a patient.[102]

There can be no doubt that in the practical process of negotiating rates proprietary homes were often bargained into accepting rates so low that patient care suffered and that, in instances, non-welfare patients were charged more than they otherwise would have been to make up the difference. However, there were also cases where the homes prospered. The figures of Table 5M and the proprietary curve of Figure 2 showing the growth of proprietary beds are a rather persuasive indication that, in the main, prosperity was theirs.

THE NEW YORK STATE NURSING HOME ASSOCIATION

The New York State Association of Nursing Homes was organized in 1950. Some months later it became affiliated with the interstate alliance, the National Association of Registered Nursing Homes. In 1956 this latter group amalgamated with the American Association of Nursing Homes to become the American Nursing Home Association,[103] the most prominent organization representing proprietary nursing homes today. The State Association has never embraced a majority of the state's

---

102 U.S. Congress, Senate Joint Subcommittee on Long-Term Care of the Special Committee on Aging, *Nursing Homes and Related Long-Term Care Services.* Part I, 88th Cong., 2nd. Sess., 1964, pp. 29–31.

103 Margie S. Davis, *History of the American Nursing Home Association* (American Nursing Home Association, 1962), part 2, p. 23: part 1, p. 30.

homes within its membership. At the close of 1965, its membership of 213 comprised only 40 per cent of the 533 proprietary homes in the state. Nor has the membership it has embraced been a cohesive and well-disciplined group.[104] The New York City wing was in and out of the state organization until September, 1963, when a more stable union began. It is an indication of improved cohesion that the presidency of the State Association was, in 1966, held by the administrator of a New York City home.

Although the state nursing home group has been shot through with many fissures of opinion and interest, it seems to have been more homogeneous than its spokesmen have believed. According to its president, its membership has been broadly representative of large and small homes alike. However, a state membership list gleaned from the Spring 1958 issue of the *Westchester Calling Card*, a publication of the Westchester County Nursing Home Association, indicates that larger homes tended to be overrepresented.[105] The organization's membership also tended to overrepresent urban homes.[106]

[104] In part, this interpretation of the character of the State Association is based upon interviews on February 6, 1963, with Mr. Frederick Pfisterer, Mrs. Ruth Kruger, Mrs. Margaret McKinney, and Mr. Russell Price, all of whom are officers or past officers of District No. 3 of the state organization; and an interview with Mr. Austin J. Barrett, president of the state organization and Mr. Lawrence A. Kluger, an officer of District 3 on January 21, 1963. A review of the interpretation was conducted on April 20, 1966 with Mr. Sander Kolitch, President of the Association for 1965–1966.

[105] The list indicates that the total membership consisted of 179 homes, 30 per cent of the 597 proprietary upstate homes in 1958. (New York City homes were not in the organization at the time.) But the member homes had 36 per cent of the proprietary beds. From homes of 59 beds down to those with less than 10 beds, the smaller the home the less likely it was to be a member. Of the 57 homes with less than 10 beds, only two were members; of the 222 with from 20 to 29 beds, 68 were members; four of the seven with 50 to 59 beds held membership as did nine of the nineteen ranging at 69 beds and over.

[106] The existence of overrepresentation is substantiated by a comparison of the distribution of the 1958 membership list with that of all proprietary homes in upstate New York. There were members in 40 of

The New York State Nursing Home Association has among its avowed purposes those of promoting legislation; educating professional associations, governmental agencies, and the public at large; and protecting "nursing homes from the establishment of unreasonable or impractical rules and regulations."[107] It has been particularly interested in improving its public image. Its leaders believed that the upstate industry suffered greatly upon the exposure of misconduct of proprietary homes in New York City in 1958 and 1959. They explained part of the drop in the number of proprietary beds occurring after 1958 as public reaction to that exposure. There were, however, press exposés of conditions in proprietary nursing homes in upstate areas as well as in the city, though they were not so hard-hitting.

In pursuing these purposes, the Association in 1960 redoubled its efforts, engaging an executive director and professional public relations services, launching radio programs and an official journal, establishing or cooperating with government agencies and universities in establishing courses for training nursing home administrators. (In order for these steps to be taken it was necessary to raise the membership dues and a substantial loss in membership resulted.) It has since 1960 had a committee on legislation chaired by the wife of a New York Assemblyman.

The Association has not been notably powerful in shaping public policy. The closest cooperation of upstate homes has historically been at the local level where they negotiated for rates with the welfare districts. Even in this respect there was often a notable lack of success. In Westchester County, where the Association was unusually well organized, the local repre-

---

the 56 counties having homes, but 47 per cent of the member homes and 55 per cent of the beds in such homes were concentrated in the five urban counties of Westchester, Suffolk, Onondaga, Monroe, and Erie. Only 31 per cent of all homes and 38 per cent of the upstate beds were to be found in these counties.

107 Letter from Austin J. Barrett, President, Feb. 7, 1963.

sentatives attempted to negotiate on rates for fifty-seven homes on the basis of cost information but could persuade the administrators of only eleven homes to submit data. The welfare officials chose to ignore the fragmentary cost data.[108] The group apparently had an occasional success at the state level. For example, it claimed to have influenced the decision in 1956, as the code for private nursing homes was being revised, to replace the requirement that there be a specific minimum ratio of nurses or attendants to patients with the proviso that there be "adequate" personnel.[109] When the new code was being drafted by the State Health Department in 1965–1966 officials of the Department met extensively with spokesmen designated by the Association. The proprietary home representatives were of the opinion that they had an adequate hearing and that the new code was "one they could live with." In the opinion of the Department officials, the proprietary people were reasonable even though they clearly acted to protect their own interests. One should bear in mind, however, that the Association tends to represent the larger, urban homes; also the leadership comes from a somewhat more sophisticated level than that constituted by the general membership. Further, in part the agreement between the parties was rooted more in attempts of Health Department officials to be realistic about what could be required in staffing patterns in some areas of the state where there are undeniable shortages of skilled personnel than in power wielded by Association spokesmen.

The Association has kept no records of the number of employees of its member homes who have completed the special courses set up in universities for the training of nursing home administrators—which is one of the kinds of things the organization might have been expected to do had it been more effective, since the implications for the improvement of the public image of the proprietary home are patent. However, its presi-

[108] Interview with Frederick Pfisterer, President, District No. 3, New York State Nursing Home Association, Feb. 6, 1963.
[109] See p. 151.

dent in 1966 estimated that people from between two-thirds and three-fourths of the upstate member homes, or between 95 and 107, had completed the courses. This would comprise representation from between 22 and 25 per cent of the 433 proprietary homes extant in upstate New York.[110]

During the past what influence proprietary nursing homes had upon public policy in the state tended strongly to have been the result of their sheer mass, as individual operations without planning, rather than the result of coordinated effort on their part. As the trend to larger and better designed homes —representing larger business stakes and keener business orientation and more sophistication about organization—continues, it is quite likely that coordinated efforts will play a far more important role. It is possible that the Association, emphasizing its already present tendency to represent larger homes, will be the vehicle for the new coordination. If the Association lags behind the trend—or, indeed, does not stay ahead of it—it is not inconceivable that a splinter group or new organization will take up the new function.

Federal Financial Aid for Proprietary and Voluntary Homes

IMPACT OF FHA LOAN GUARANTEES

In late September 1959, Congress directed the Federal Housing Administration to include proprietary nursing homes among the kinds of investments for which that agency extended mortgage insurance. This was a development of considerable importance for expanded construction of these institutions and for recognizing and promoting them as business enterprises. Although the impact was somewhat slower in emerging in New York State than observers had expected, by early 1966 it had arrived: thirteen upstate projects had been constructed and

110 The new code requires administrators of all upstate homes after July 1, 1967, to have "successfully completed courses of training in hospital, nursing home, medical care, or other health service administration approved by the department."

two reconstructed for nursing home purposes through FHA financing; the total mortgage amount was $13,143,887; the new beds created numbered 1,658.[111] This is to be compared with 1,849 voluntary and public beds built in upstate areas from the mid-1950's through 1965 with Hill-Burton financial support. Eight of the FHA projects produced 100 or more beds each; the largest produced 246 beds. The mortgages on six were over a million dollars each.

POLICY OF FHA PROGRAM

Construction standards required for the FHA homes are substantially comparable to those applying to Hill-Burton projects[112] and therefore met the specifications for prior approval by the State Department of Social Welfare. Further, the statute establishing the program required that any applicant for an FHA guaranteed loan must secure a certificate from the state Hill-Burton agency that additional beds are needed in the locality where he intends to build. Beyond this prescription, however, builders were left free, so far as the federal legislation was concerned, of the powers of the medical facility planners of the state. (A similar situation prevailed in regard to Small Business Administration loans to proprietary nursing homes, which began in 1956. But the SBA has not specified construction standards.) These kinds of conditions prompted some objections from state medical facility planning agencies, evoking comment about a "series of loan programs," a "disjointed approach" to nursing home development and a conclusion that "in the light of this background it is hardly the obligation or the prerogative of this state to resolve the impasse between the several federal administrations."[113]

The primary difference between administration of a con-

---

[111] Files, New York Office, Federal Housing Administration.

[112] For a comparison of the two, see U.S. Congress, Senate Subcommittee on Problems of the Aged and Aging of the Committee on Labor and Public Welfare, *The Condition of American Nursing Homes*, 86th Cong. 2nd Sess., 1960, pp. 23–25.

[113] "Iowa Hospital Plan, 1963 Revision," pursuant to Hospital Survey and Construction Act, pp. 101–102.

struction program in nursing homes as conducted in the FHA style and in the Hill-Burton style is that FHA administrators view the nursing home as a business while Hill-Burton administrators, for which the United States Public Health Service is a focal point, see it as a medical care facility. For the former, the most important considerations are fiscal soundness and the promotion of economic strength.[114] For the latter the most important considerations are the quality of medical care given and the appropriate relationship of the institution to allied purveyors of care such as hospitals and physicians. This is not to say that the FHA people give no thought to the things the Hill-Burton administrators consider of prime importance, or that Hill-Burton workers do not care about financial soundness, but only that each operates according to a different set of priorities—and the differences in consequences are substantial.

In the disbursing of Hill-Burton grants, the selection of grantees with experience and demonstrated competence in the rendering of care has been a perhaps subtle, but nevertheless important, factor. A more managerial competence is stressed by FHA. There has been no policy statement establishing a priority in the FHA system for homes affiliated with hospitals, or encouraging such affiliation. This is quite in contrast to the Hill-Burton approach. Of some 32,000 nursing home beds constructed with Hill-Burton help throughout the United States by June 30, 1964, over 40 per cent were integral parts of hospitals and many others had medical affiliations with hospitals.[115] (Of course, in New York State all Hill-Burton nursing home

---

[114] As an interesting illustration, one administrator in FHA told the writer there is a local policy of encouraging the homes to be built under the guaranteed loans to be close to hospitals in order that, in the event of financial failure of a home, there might be some chance of selling the building to the hospital.

[115] Of the medical affiliations: "These affiliations vary greatly in extent and scope, but each one constitutes more than a 'working agreement' between a hospital and a nursing home to transfer patients from one institution to the other when the need arises." Department of Health, Education and Welfare, Public Health Service, Bureau of State Service, "Special Tabulation, Nursing Home Projects and Hospital Affiliation," Dec. 28, 1964.

projects are affiliated with hospitals.) It is impossible to compare these figures with those of FHA projects, for the information on the latter is not gathered. However, the typical proprietary nursing home has had no such ties. Moreover, with most general hospitals being voluntary organizations, there are built-in conflicts that continue to limit such associations.[116]

ENACTMENT OF FHA PROGRAM

FHA, Reluctant Administrator

The Federal Housing Administration did not want the responsibility for running a nursing home program. Norman P. Mason, Federal Housing Administrator, told the Subcommittee on Housing of the House of Representatives Committee on Banking and Currency:

"We are opposed to such an activity in FHA operations, believing that nursing homes are appropriately financed as business ventures rather than housing facilities. *FHA supervision of their financing would also involve supervision and evaluation of technical and administrative work in a field in which it has no background.*"[117]

On the other hand the state Hill-Burton agencies were themselves ambivalent about whether they should take on the new responsibility. A study done during the time that the loan guarantee provision was under consideration indicated that there was substantial support among the state units for loans for nursing homes and general hospitals. However, it found these administrators divided as to whether the approval power over such loans should be vested with them.[118]

[116] The transfer agreement provisions of the Social Security Amendments of 1965 constitute a new incentive for establishing some suitable arrangement with a hospital and some proprietary homes have done so. see p. 233, below.

[117] Statement of Norman P. Mason, Federal Housing Administrator, before the Subcommittee on Housing of the House of Representatives Committee on Banking and Currency, *Hearings on S. 57, Housing Act of 1959,* 86th Cong., 1st Sess., 1959, pp. 351, 359.

[118] Alan E. Treloar and Don Chill, *Patient Care Facilities: Construction Needs and Hill-Burton Accomplishments* (Chicago: American Hospital Association, 1961), pp. 179, 187.

AHA Call for Coordination

There was further division on the issue. The American
Hospital Association testimony during hearings of 1958 supported the idea of loan guarantees for proprietary nursing
homes but called for a substantial role in the direction of such
a program by the Hill-Burton administrative machinery. It
asked for a requirement that no mortgage insurance be extended without a certificate by the Surgeon General of the
Public Health Service that the nursing home project was in
conformity with the applicable state plan established under
Hill-Burton provisions.[119]

AMA Disagrees

The American Medical Association took a rather different
point of view. Part of its statement to the Senate Subcommittee
in 1959 reads as follows:

In the administration of a grant program under the Hill-Burton
system and a loan guarantee program under the Federal Housing
Administration, we recognize the desirability of cooperation; however, we believe that the loan-guarantee program proposed under
Title II of the pending bill *should be administered by the Federal
Housing Administration without mandatory supervision or coordination with the Department of Health, Education and Welfare.*[120]

Compromise

The legislation ultimately adopted was a compromise between these two latter positions. It did require the previously
mentioned certification by the state Hill-Burton agency that
there was a need for such nursing home facilities as the applicant proposed to build before the mortgage could be insured by
the FHA. State Hill-Burton certification that any nursing home

[119] U.S. Congress, House, Subcommittee on Banking and Currency,
Hearings on S. 57, Housing Act of 1959, 86th Cong., 1st Sess., 1959, p. 282.
[120] U.S. Congress, Senate, Subcommittee on Housing of the Committee
on Banking and Currency, *Hearings on S. 57, Housing Act of 1959,* 86th
Cong., 1st Sess., 1959, p. 364. Italics added.

included in the program would be subject to "reasonably minimum standards of licensure and methods of operation" was also made prerequisite to the insuring of loans.[121]

There were, of course, obvious reasons for considering the FHA, an agency with extensive experience at extending mortgage guarantees, as a prime agent for the new program. Proprietary nursing home representatives had most ardently pled for "FHA type loans" during the 1954 Hill-Burton hearings. In 1958 and 1959 they and the American Medical Association were noting that FHA assistance had been given to housing for the aged that included some infirmary facilities.[122] There were persuasive reasons also for taking the position of the Hospital Association, that coordination of federal nursing home programs was of paramount importance.

The Effect of Congressional Committee Structure

Despite the fact that there were the two opposing points of view, one should not conclude that the outcome was merely a resultant of the forces of reason and other influence from the two sides. Congressional committee structure should not be left out of consideration. Legislative proposals for FHA administration came out of the Senate Committee on Banking and Currency, a finance-oriented unit, and had been introduced in the Senate by the Chairman of its Subcommittee on Housing, Senator John J. Sparkman, of Alabama, who had long been interested in housing legislation. Senator Sparkman made it clear during the 1959 hearings, in another connection, that he was concerned about "jurisdictional troubles" relating to "the Hill-Burton program over which we have no jurisdiction."[123] Jurisdiction over Hill-Burton affairs has always been within

---

[121] Public Law 372, sec. 115, 86th Cong.

[122] U.S. Congress, Senate, Subcommittee on Housing of the Committee on Banking and Currency, *Hearings on S. 57, Housing Act of 1959,* 86th Cong., 1st Sess., 1959, pp. 351, 359.

[123] U.S. Congress, Senate, Subcommittee on Housing of the Committee on Banking and Currency, *Hearings on S. 57, Housing Act of 1959,* 86th Cong., 1st Sess., 1959, p. 351.

the province of the Committee on Labor and Public Welfare, chaired by Senator Lister Hill, also of Alabama, who had co-sponsored the original legislation in 1946. One of the aspects of the jurisdictional problem was whether a change that might affect significantly the functions of the Hill-Burton machinery —and indeed, FHA loans have proven to be significant in the nursing home field—should be initiated by a committee not schooled in, and intimately acquainted with, the Hill-Burton program. It also seems clear that the problem was not over-come—though it was probably lessened somewhat—by the fact that Senators Sparkman and Hill and Congressman Albert L. Raines, who introduced the related 1959 measure in the House of Representatives, were all Democrats from the State of Alabama. Another aspect of the problem was the question of what kind of facilities nursing homes are. During the 1958 hearings by the Subcommittee on Housing of the House Bank-ing and Currency Committee, Congressman Raines remarked that "it is my opinion that that particular phase of the housing bill [that deals with nursing homes] would be better considered by the committee that considers hospitals" because he saw nurs-ing homes as "business ventures" rather than housing![124] The original Hill-Burton legislation had gone through the House Committee on Interstate and Foreign Commerce.

After their failure to secure federal support under the 1954 amendments to the Hill-Burton Act, the proprietary nursing home operators had concentrated their efforts for federal legis-lation upon securing loan guarantees. Such a measure, proposing mortgage insurance for both voluntary and proprietary institu-tions, had been introduced by Percy Priest, Chairman of the House Committee on Interstate and Foreign Commerce in 1955;[125] but it had not become law. By 1958 the nursing home

124 Subcommittee on Housing of the House Committee on Banking and Currency, *Hearings, Housing Act of 1958*, 85th Cong., 2nd Sess., 1958, p. 283.
125 "Wire from Washington," *Modern Hospital*, LXXXV (September, 1955), 48.

people had interested Senator Sparkman in their cause and, with his help, loan-guarantee legislation passed the Senate but failed to get through the House. In 1959 the Eisenhower administration had a housing bill, S. 612, introduced; it contained no provision for nursing homes. Senator Sparkman introduced S. 57, which provided loan guarantees for proprietary homes. "Although they were not home," as a member of the Senator's staff put it, "they were at least on first base once the Chairman was on their side."[126] As a matter of fact, S. 57 was vetoed by the President after it passed Congress, and the measure that became law in September, 1959, was a redraft—but it preserved the nursing home provisions intact. The thorny problem of committee jurisdiction and the fact that the Chairman of the Subcommittee on Housing of the Senate Banking and Currency Committee was among those who took up the nursing home cause and were undoubtedly influential in determining that the Federal Housing Administration would have almost exclusive responsibility for administering the new nursing home program.

FHA Loan Guarantees for Voluntary Institutions

Committee jurisdiction appears to be related also to the exclusion of voluntary nursing-home-type organizations from the provisions of the 1959 law, although opposition to their inclusion by the American Hospital Association was probably more important. The 1958 Senate measure provided mortgage insurance for both proprietary and nonprofit nursing-home-type institutions. The Hospital Association expressed objections in the House hearings to loans at commercial rates, or bearing mortgage insurance costs, for nonprofit health facilities—revealing a rather exclusive predisposition toward grants for voluntary institutions as provided under the Hill-Burton program. The Association's argument was that such loans would

126 Interview with Lewis G. Odom, Staff Director and General Counsel, Senate Small Business Committee, Nov. 15, 1962.

increase substantially the cost of care to sick persons.[127] In
1959 Senator Sparkman took special recognition of the Hospital
Association's opposition and of the fact that voluntary nursing-
home-type facilities were eligible for Hill-Burton grants, "and
because of the conflict, if you call it a conflict, between this
program and the program of the Hill-Burton program over
which we have no jurisdiction," thought it advisable to limit
the loan guarantees to proprietary nursing homes.[128] It should
be added that the American Medical Association supported
loan guarantees for both nonprofit and voluntary nursing
homes.[129] And the American Nursing Home Association did not
oppose the inclusion of voluntary homes.[130] Legislation was
introduced, though not passed, in the eighty-seventh Congress
that would have extended 100 per cent FHA guarantees for
mortgages for voluntary homes.[131] Finally, however, voluntary
organizations were included, by the Housing Act of 1964,
among those to whom FHA loan guarantees would be extended
for the construction of nursing home facilities. The terms are
the same as those for proprietary homes.[132] But, as of early
1966, not one voluntary organization had submitted an application to the New York FHA office.

FHA TERMS

The Housing Act of 1959 provided for insurance of mortgages for proprietary nursing homes up to $12.5 million in the
proportion of 75 per cent of the estimated value of the property
involved.[133] The insurable proportion was raised to 90 per cent

[127] Subcommittee on Housing of the House Committee on Banking and
Currency, *Hearings, Housing Act of 1958*, 85th Cong., 2nd Sess., 1958,
p. 281.
[128] Subcommittee on Housing of the Senate Committee on Banking and
Currency, *Hearings, Housing Act of 1959*, 86th Cong., 1st Sess., 1959,
p. 351.
[129] *Ibid.*, pp. 351, 363.   [130] *Ibid.*, pp. 350–351.
[131] S. 3712, introduced September 11, 1962, by Senator Clark.
[132] Public Law 560, 88th Cong.
[133] Public Law 372, sec. 115, 86th Cong.

in 1961.[134] The statutory ceiling for interest rates for the mortgages was set at 6 per cent; the administratively determined ceiling has varied below the statutory limit and the maximum mortgage period, also administratively determined, has been fixed at twenty years. There are additional application, commitment and inspection fees and a service charge.[135] Nationally, lenders and operators have found these terms advantageous, judging by the business done under them. At least, this has been true since the raise of loan guarantees from 75 to 90 per cent of the value of the property. The program lagged somewhat until this change.[136]

Small Business Administration Loans

Small Business Administration loans have been of much less significance to the development of nursing homes in New York State than FHA guaranteed loans. Though the SBA has since 1956 granted direct loans to small profit-making organizations, or participates with commercial lenders in granting loans, its terms have not generally allowed enough scope for nursing home purposes. The statutory limit on SBA loan amounts is $350,000 and loans must be repaid within ten years.[137] From 1956 through 1965 the SBA made four loans to nursing homes in New York State, averaging $72,375. During the same period it participated with other lenders in two loans involving a total of $284,000.[138] Its impact cannot be measured in terms of beds because, as is permissible, the loans were used for working capital as well as for construction.

---

[134] Public Law 70, subsec. (d), 87th Cong.

[135] Federal Housing Administration, *Nursing Home Mortgage Insurance*, FHA No. 696, revised, June 1963.

[136] Robert G. Boucher, "Fundamentals in Financing Nursing Home Loans," *Nursing Homes*, July 1962, p. 6.

[137] Small Business Administration, *SBA Business Loans for Small Firms*, Sept., 1962, p. 9.

[138] Small Business Administration, *Semi-Annual Reports*, July 1, 1956–December 31, 1956, through July 1, 1961–December 31, 1965.

Business on Borrowed Money

There is strong feeling among some proprietary nursing home administrators that doing business on money that is 90 per cent borrowed is unjustifiably precarious. And administrators have been warned that the cost of doing business on borrowed money may run to a third or more of the income nursing homes may expect to receive, even in the more wealthy areas of the country.[139] A sober consideration of the dollars and cents involved clarifies somewhat the rationale behind the American Hospital Association's opposition to a loan program at commercial rates for voluntary institutions.

Notwithstanding, as of December 31, 1965, the FHA was committed to extend mortgage insurance to three more proprietary nursing homes in upstate New York; the prospective mortgages ranged from $1 million to $2.3 million and the numbers of beds to be provided from 140 to 238. And applications for mortgage insurance for seven more upstate homes were in process.[140]

Proprietary Nursing Homes: Recapitulation

During the approximate decade following the early 1950's the proprietary nursing home field in upstate New York underwent significant change. Would-be proprietors found that, under slowly strengthened regulations and more demanding standards for construction, they could no longer open homes as casually as they once had. And competition removed a number of economically marginal homes from the scene, reducing the numbers of beds available. Meanwhile, trends crystallized that had been in process for some time toward larger homes, involving large-scale financing and an emphasis upon manage-

[139] Baumgarten, pp. 304, 305.

[140] Federal Housing Administration, Research and Statistics Section, "Title II, Section 232, Nursing Home Program, Cumulative as of December 31, 1965."

ment. Federal Housing Administration loan guarantees encouraged this development, but did not guide homes toward
integrated health care service, as had the Hill-Burton program.
Concomitant with this change in the character in the large
segment of the field was a call for a more effective trade association. The net consequence was a consolidation of the proprietary sector upstate and, after four years, growth in the
numbers of beds resumed at a pace at least comparable to that
of earlier years.

CHAPTER 6

The New York City Story

An Overview

The story of the relationship of public policy and nursing-home-type facilities in New York City has two primary elements. The numerical dimensions are shown in Table 8. First, and most significant, after a relatively slow development during the 1930's and 1940's, proprietary nursing homes underwent an explosive growth during the early 1950's, displacing voluntary beds as the dominant kind of facility in the field. But when a program of vigorous government regulation began, their growth ceased. Second, and most innovative, after a history in which infirmaries as part of public homes had been of little or no significance, infirmaries in large, well-equipped public hospitals evolved and began to be of practical importance during the 1950's. Concurrently with these two developments and, indeed, from the 1930's through to the present, there continued a modest increase in voluntary facilities; though they had been outnumbered by proprietary beds, they still stood substantially ahead of public accommodations in the mid-1960's.

This historical pattern stands in sharp contrast to that of upstate New York, where proprietary growth had boomed during the 1940's, and where public facilities have consistently been of greater significance than voluntary. The strength of voluntary institutions in the city, compared to their upstate counterparts, appears to be not so much related to public policy, however, as to the greater importance that charity has played generally in the provision of medical care in the city.

Table 8. Growth of nursing-home-type facilities, New York City

Year	Public		Voluntary		Proprietary	
	Homes	Beds	Homes	Beds	Homes	Beds
1929	—ª	—			12	148
1934	—	—	25ᵇ	1,922ᵇ		
1935	—	—			8	116
1940	—	—			44	884
1944	—	—			51	1,449
1949	—	—			70	2,317
1951	—	—			73	2,503
1952	2	1,311	66ᶜ	3,830ᶜ	76	2,801
1954	2	1,610	64	3,667	95	4,699
1955	2	1,290			106	5,737
1956	2	1,290	65	3,997	113	7,195
1957	4	1,784	65	4,027	121	8,218
1958	4	1,784	65	4,214	124	9,489
1959	6	1,902	64	4,522	119	9,392
1960	6	1,918	62	4,514	113	9,354
1961	6	1,918	61	4,599	107	9,420
1962	6	2,124	57	4,803	91	8,704
1963	6	2,381	58	4,864	87	8,551
1964	6	2,465	54	5,060	87	8,805
1965					89	8,900

Source. Tables 2M, 3M, 4M, and 5M, Appendix A.
ª Dashes indicate no facilities. Blank spaces indicate that no data have been found.
ᵇ Sum of 1934 figure for private homes and 1935 figure for convalescent nursing homes.
ᶜ Sum of 1952 figure for private homes and in mid-point between 1950 and 1954 figures for convalescent and nursing homes.

Policies and Growing Pressures: The 1930's to the Early 1950's

REGULATORY POWERS OVER PROPRIETARY INSTITUTIONS

New York City consistently had firmer legal powers of regulation over proprietary nursing homes than the State Department of Social Welfare had over upstate proprietary homes. Local Law No. 2 of 1929, which established the City Department of Hospitals, charged the new department with the inspecting and licensing of proprietary hospitals, homes for the aged and homes for chronic patients. By 1936 the Department had experienced some enforcement difficulties and sought a stronger licensing law.[1] After March 1936 the City Charter provided that the licenses expire annually, unless revoked earlier, and that the operation of a proprietary home or hospital without a license was a misdemeanor punishable by a fine of up to $500 and a year of imprisonment.[2] In 1937 the Department secured its first conviction under the new law.[3] State regulation of proprietary homes did not begin until 1951.

Moreover, the codes promulgated for the regulation of proprietary homes by the City Hospitals Department had consistently higher minimum standards than those of the State Welfare Department for upstate homes and were more specific. The city code revised to 1936 required, among other things, that registered nurses be in charge of nursing or custodial care of patients; that each home have a mortuary, an isolation room, and a laboratory; that there be at least one toilet for every eight patients; and that new buildings over twenty feet high be of fireproof construction.[4] The code was revised again in 1942, 1949, 1954, 1956, 1960, and 1963. By 1956 it consisted of some twelve pages of fine print and was relatively detailed, specific and comprehensive.

A RELIANCE UPON MUNICIPAL HOSPITALS

The availability of city hospital facilities undoubtedly played a part in retarding the growth of proprietary nursing homes until the 1950's. In a 1939 study, the New York State Commis-

[1] New York City Department of Hospitals, *Annual Report, 1936*, p. 19.
[2] Section 692-a. The provision has remained unchanged, except for numbering, through the two Charter revisions since 1936.
[3] Department of Hospitals, *Annual Report, 1937*, p. 53.
[4] The City of New York, Department of Hospitals, *Regulations Concerning the Establishment and Maintenance of Private Proprietary Nursing Homes, Convalescent Homes, and Homes for the Aged or Chronic Patients, Revised to May, 1936.*

sion to Formulate a Long Range Health Program found that New York City, with over 55 per cent of the state's population, had less than 13 per cent of the first admissions to public homes. The Commission deduced that a possible explanation was that

New York City, possessing adequate hospital and clinic facilities, is hesitant in sending cases needing medical attention to public homes. On the other hand, since upstate counties do not have the elaborate medical facilities available in New York City, they are more prone to send cases requiring medical attention to public homes because of the expense involved in hospital care.[5]

This suggestion that such cases as were referred to nursing-home-type facilities upstate were absorbed in part by hospitals in New York City is reinforced by general conclusions drawn by Eli Ginzberg pertaining to the late 1940's. He reported that of thirty upstate municipal hospitals, four (in Erie, Westchester, Monroe, and Nassau Counties) resembled "the large municipal hospital system of New York City in that they provide not only general hospital care but also care for patients suffering from long-term illness."[6]

Professor Ginzberg also reported that "Municipal Hospitals in the City of New York are overcrowded because they are unable to transfer chronic patients to other suitable facilities."[7] But the determination of the "suitability" of other facilities was influenced by the tradition of availability of municipal hospital beds for the poor in the City. While upstate, in accordance with established pattern of medical care in institutions at public expense, the strong tendency was for people to receive such institutional care in public infirmaries or proprietary nursing homes, in the city a major alternative was receiving care in a

---

[5] New York State Commission to Formulate a Long Range Health Program, *Planning for the Care of the Chronically Ill in New York State —Regional Aspects*, Leg. Doc. No. 78A (Albany, 1945), pp. 15–16.

[6] Eli Ginzberg, *A Pattern for Hospital Care* (New York: Columbia University Press, 1949), p. 144. He also said: "Certain classes of patients such as those suffering from long-term illness could, with few exceptions, be cared for only in municipal hospitals in New York City" (p. 156).

[7] *Ibid.*, p. 144.

municipal hospital. Thus, during the late 1940's, some 60 per cent of upstate proprietary nursing home patients were public assistance cases;[8] in January 1950 there were over two thousand proprietary beds in New York City, but only thirty-eight of them were occupied by public welare recipients.[9]

THE CITY'S TRADITION OF CHARITY

A second resource of importance in New York City for long-term care were the nursing-home-type facilities maintained by voluntary institutions. Even before 1952, when the city began to receive state and federal reimbursement for the nursing home care of persons eligible under the public assistance provisions —as will be explained presently—voluntary institutions were caring for city charges and being reimbursed by the city. The 1935 *Annual Report* of the City Department of Hospitals spoke of maintaining the aged and infirm in ten private institutions. By 1951 the list had expanded to twenty-one institutions.

Philanthropy has been stronger in the city, with its many great fortunes, than upstate, as has been noted earlier in this study.[10] Table 9 shows the differences in the numbers of voluntary nursing-home-type beds at three historical periods. It takes some account of differences in demand for such services by comparing the numbers of beds available to each thousand persons aged sixty-five or over in the upstate and city populations.

[8] *Ibid.*, p. 187.
[9] Files, New York State Department of Social Welfare, through an interview June 6, 1963, with Marie Eichelberger, Supervisor of Adult Institutions. The number had always been modest, though not always as low as 38. In 1945 there had been 93 public assistance cases in proprietary homes. Welfare Council of the City of New York, Research Bureau, "Survey of Proprietary Nursing Homes in New York City," 1946, p. 40. In 1946 there had been 105. Welfare Council of New York City, Committee on Nursing Homes, *Report*, 1947, p. 21.
[10] Compare Eli Ginzberg's conclusion that charity plays a more important part in the financing of hospitals in New York City than upstate. *A Pattern for Hospital care*, pp. 65–70, 161.

Table 9. Voluntary nursing-home-type beds and ratios to thousands of aged patients, upstate and New York City, mid-1930's–1964

Period	Upstate		New York City	
	Beds	Beds per 1,000 aged	Beds	Beds per 1,000 aged
Mid-1930's	1,536	3.37	1,922	5.66
Early 1950's	2,579	3.95	3,785	6.25
Early 1960's	3,365	3.85	4,559	5.65

Source. Table 6M, Appendix I.

The difficulties of financing voluntary undertakings while philanthropic contributions were not growing at the pace of demand and cost of services have presented a problem in the city, as they have elsewhere. Nevertheless, the charitable underpinnings of the city's resources provided important resources in the 1930's and 1940's and are the base upon which the modest growth in voluntary nursing-home-type beds has occurred.

The voluntaries were important not only in representing numbers of nursing-home-type beds in the community. The relative willingness of these nonprofit institutions in the city to accept public charges, among whom much of the increasing demand occurred, helped the city delay the day when it would turn to massive use of proprietary nursing homes.

ANTI–PROPRIETARY HOME POLICY

The New York City Welfare Council

The availability of alternatives to the use of proprietary homes, then, allowed the city some latitude in the use of such homes for welfare cases. That latitude was used as discrimination about the quality of care proprietaries in the city afforded, and about the charges by the homes compared to the services rendered. In 1946 it was reported that while many upstate Welfare Commissioners used proprietary homes not because they were satisfactory, but only because no other resources were

available, in New York City proprietary homes were eschewed
because the rates were considered too high and the control of
standards inadequate.[11] Some of the conclusions of a 1947 study
of homes in the city undertaken by the New York City Welfare Council, a service agency for private and public welfare
organizations, were that three of the homes in the city rendered
"excellent" care, seven "good," eighteen "fair," and twenty
"poor."[12] Another study, covering 55 homes and conducted
by the Counseling Service of the United Hospital Fund of New
York in 1946, characterized the care given as follows:[13]

	Excellent	Good	Fair	Poor
Nursing care	3	7	18	20
Physical facilities	2	18	18	10
Interest in patients	6	16	18	8

And the committee of the Welfare Council concluded that
the inspection staff of the Department of Hospitals was inadequate, that the regulations should be changed to raise
standards, and that, in any event, proprietary nursing homes
were of limited usefulness as resources for public dependents
and low-income families.[14] The city's governmental health and
welfare agencies are represented on the Welfare Council. That
its conclusions were not in conflict with the City Welfare Department is evidenced by a letter of 1949 from the City Welfare
Commissioner to the State Department of Social Welfare indicating that proprietary nursing homes were considered too
expensive for expanded City Welfare use.[15]

The New York City Welfare Department

To turn to the explicit expression of the City Welfare Department's policy on nursing homes, we may look to its pro-

[11] New York State Health Preparedness Commission, *Planning for the
Care of the Chronically Ill in New York State*, Leg. Doc. No. 66A
(Albany, 1946), p. 42.
[12] Committee on Nursing Homes, *Report*, 1947, p. 30.
[13] "Proprietary Nursing Homes in New York City: September, 1946."
[14] Committee on Nursing Homes, *Report*, pp. 2, 3, 28.
[15] Files, State Department of Social Welfare, through interview June
6, 1963, with Eichelberger.

cedural manuals for 1941 and 1949. The 1941 regulations provided that OAA recipients could be in a nursing home licensed by the Department of Hospitals and that the rates could not exceed $35 per month, including nursing care, without special approval of the case supervisor. Most important was the following: "Residence in a nursing home should generally be limited to recipients in need of post-hospital or convalescent care for a period of not more than three months."[16] The 1949 version allowed the placement of OAA, AB, and home relief cases in licensed proprietary homes; the maximum rate not requiring special approval had risen to $100 per month. The policy was still one of limited use: "Nursing home care is not to be used as a substitute for custodial care or as a permanent living arrangement for persons suffering from chronic disabilities, except in individual situations where continued care may be necessary because no other resource is available." The need for nursing home care required certification by a physician at periods not to exceed three months.[17] The significance of the essential similarity between the 1941 and 1949 regulations is that the city chose not to go along with the liberalized use of nursing homes in 1944 when new state legislation and the issuance of Bulletin 105 by the State Department of Social Welfare removed all legal doubt that state and federal reimbursed payments for continued nursing home care was permissible.[18] Despite increasing pressures for greater nursing home use, a tight rein was kept. After the "fur coat scandal," there were additional reasons. As one employee of the Department of Welfare put it, "The department was walking on egg shells after 1947."

[16] City of New York, Department of Welfare, *Manual of Policies, Division of OAA, February, 1941,* sec. 44.

[17] City of New York, Department of Welfare, *Policies Governing the Administration of Public Assistance, March, 1949,* sec. 108. The $100 rate was set by an amendment effective November 1949. See *ibid.*, p. 173.

[18] See p. 77, above.

A GROWING BED SHORTAGE

But pressures in the city had been building up for many years for the expansion of facilities for the chronically ill. The 1930 Annual Report of the Department of Hospitals had stressed, but had not enumerated, the proportions of inmates of the City Home for Dependents suffering from long-term ailments. It said that many ". . . should be considered chronic institutional patients rather than merely inmates of a home for the aged who need nothing more than food and clothing."[19] Most of the thirty-nine buildings making up the home were close to a hundred years old. In 1933, Mary C. Jarrett, in her book *Chronic Illness in New York City*, had documented the need for more long-term institutional care.[20] In 1939, Goldwater Memorial Hospital had been added to the municipal facilities as a specialized institution for the active treatment of long-term illness, but by 1943 it was already crowded with custodial cases—persons no longer requiring the services of a hospital but needing continuous nursing and other care—because there was no other place they could be sent.[21] Plans had been begun in 1939 for the replacement of the City Home for Dependents by a new home and hospital, but World War II and other factors delayed the replacement so that it was not actually realized until 1952. The nursing home committee of the Welfare Council recommended in 1947 that there should be expansion of proprietary nursing home facilities, under proper safeguards, as a temporary expedient to meet "an emergent need" until the Hospital Department's postwar building program could be mapped out and completed.[22]

Meanwhile, the average occupancy rate of the city hospitals mounted from 81.2 per cent in 1945 to 99.2 per cent in 1948. In 1948 the average rate for Harlem Hospital was 141.7 per

[19] P. 108.   [20] Two vols.; New York: Columbia University Press.
[21] Department of Hospitals, *Annual Report, 1943*, p. 3.
[22] *Report*, pp. 1–5.

cent.[23] The hospitals were so crowded that conditions were inhumane. It was extremely difficult for doctors to make rounds. Beds were in corridors, blocking off elevators; food carts could not be taken around.[24] The Hospitals Department took remedial action, inaugurating a home care program in 1948 and reorganizing laboratory and X-ray services so that more of their work could be done on an out-patient basis. But the occupancy rate rose to 100.8 in 1949 and stood at 100.3 in 1950. The rate at Goldwater Memorial Hospital for 1950 was 119.1 per cent.

The City Welfare Department was finding it virtually impossible to place its clients who were candidates for nursing-home-type care. The Welfare Commissioner inquired of the State Department of Social Welfare as to the possibility of providing such care, with reimbursement, in nonprofit homes. However, voluntary institutions as nursing homes did not come under the jurisdiction of the Department of Hospitals and no certification procedure had been established so that they might provide such reimbursable care. The Hospitals Department was maintaining patients in a number of long-term care institutions with funds from local revenue. The Welfare Commissioner was advised that if his department would certify specified homes annually as nursing homes, in accordance with Bulletin 105 of 1944, state and federal reimbursement would be available.[25] However, the City Department did not establish the required certification procedures immediately. In 1952 the

[23] Figures are from the *Annual Reports* of the Department of Hospitals. The 1952 report makes the point: "An average occupancy of 141.7 per cent, it should be realized, means theoretically that, distributed over the year, three patients are accommodated in a space normally designed for two patients. Practically, it means that during weeks or even months, four patients are accommodated where there is normally space for two" (p. 11`

[24] Interview with Dr. Marcus D. Kogel, Commissioner of Hospitals (Feb. 1, 1949–May 4, 1954), Jan. 22, 1963.

[25] Letter of June 6, 1949, from George J. Clarke, Acting Executive Officer, New York State Department of Social Welfare, to Raymond M. Hilliard, Commissioner, New York City Department of Welfare. Files, City Department of Welfare.

three nonprofit nursing homes in the city that accept welfare cases became eligible to give care to patients on reimbursable public assistance. Employees of the City Department were elated at the prospects of placing a few more of their clients.[26] This development, however, was subsequent to important changes in city policy.

The Policy Change of 1951–1952

PRO–NURSING HOME (INCLUDING PROPRIETARY) POLICY

An abrupt reversal in the city's philosophy concerning the use of nursing homes grew out of the social security amendments of 1950 and the implementing state legislation of 1951. Stimulated by the provision of the new reimbursable welfare category "aid to the disabled," which became effective April 1, 1951, the City Commissioner of Hospitals appointed a task force on April 3 to develop the maximum benefits from the revised legislation for his department. The City Department of Welfare cooperated in the venture. Though it had been quite possible, at least since 1944, for the city to receive reimbursement for continued nursing-home-type care given old-age assistance and aid to the blind cases in nonpublic homes, it was only in 1951–1952 that the policy on the utilization of such institutions was changed from limited, restorative, or convalescent use to purposes of long-term, custodial care.

As part of a "pilot study" phase of the policy change, the Office of Institutional Inspection of the Hospitals Department conducted a search for vacancies in suitable nursing homes. By March 1952 some 250 patients had been transferred from municipal hospitals to such institutions. After the pilot study phase the Medical Superintendents of all the city general hospitals were alerted of the possibilities of such placement and urged to make use of these possibilities. The Home Care Office

[26] Interview with Miss Loretta G. O'Leary and Mrs. Ruth Snyder, Bureau of Special Services of the New York City Department of Welfare, Jan. 17, 1963.

of each hospital processed prospective candidates for nursing home care and their findings were reviewed by the City Welfare Department.[27] By the end of 1952 the number of transferees from city hospitals to nursing homes had reached 823. Moreover, 337 persons who had sought admission to city hospitals had been referred to proprietary nursing homes—most of these were people of independent financial means.[28] In 1953 the number of persons referred to nursing homes by the Hospitals Department—a majority of whom were referred through the Welfare Department—dropped to 880, but then the figure rose steadily each year through 1957, when it reached 2,340.[29]

Curiously, memoranda and reports of the Department of Hospitals seem to indicate that a change in state welfare policy during 1951 made possible the placement of OAA and AB cases in nursing homes as well as cases under the new category, aid to the disabled. For example, an inter–Hospital Department memorandum of April 5, 1951, reads, in part: "The State Department of Social Welfare Law and its Amended Rules and Regulations provide for the admission of recipients of grants in the [OAA, AB and AD] categories into private proprietary and non-profit nursing and convalescent homes."[30] Similarly, the *Annual Report* of the Department for 1952 says: "Liberalization of the State Department of Social Welfare's policy in utilization of the proprietary nursing home for the care of patients who no longer require active hospital care has relieved the City of a share of the financial responsibility in caring for this segment of our population."[31] In fact, as has been mentioned earlier, state policy had provided for continuous nursing home care for those on assistance since 1944; only the imple-

[27] Memorandum of Dr. Marcus D. Kogel, Commissioner, to the Board of Hospitals, March 1, 1952.

[28] Department of Hospitals, *Annual Report, 1952*, p. 17.

[29] Data from Department of Hospitals *Annual Reports*, and files, Division of Social Services of the Department.

[30] James M. Rosen, Chief, Division of Collections, to Maurice H. Matzkin, First Deputy Commissioner.

[31] P. 47.

menting laws, rules, and regulations pertaining to the AD category were new. The task force set up in 1951 worked closely with representatives of the City Welfare Department; it is quite possible that the increased integration heightened the awareness of the Hospitals Department administration to possibilities that had lain in the public assistance provisions and in nursing-home-type facilities for years. It should be noted that the desire to use such facilities for persons eligible for reimbursable assistance was one thing and that the knowledge that such an alternative was possible was quite another. It does not appear that the Department of Hospitals had had the knowledge.

The critical change in legal provisions was made not by the State Department of Social Welfare but by the City Welfare Department. The following statement from its *Annual Report, July 1, 1951–June 30, 1952,* describes the modification:

The Department of Welfare's policy in regard to eligibility for placement of patients in nursing homes was liberalized in order to meet the dire need for beds in the various municipal and voluntary hospitals throughout the city. . . . After the patient has been medically approved as suitable for this type of care and eligibility for public assistance has been determined, a review of the medical factors relating to the need for continued nursing home care is required at intervals of not more than six months.[32]

The crucial elements in the "liberalization" were the orientation of the policy to "continued" rather than limited nursing home care and medical review of the need in each case at least once every six months rather than every three months.

The change in philosophy was doubly motivated. First, there was great pressure to relieve the overcrowded city hospitals. Second, there was considerable recognition of the financial implications of the move.[33] The care of eligible patients in nursing-home-type facilities was reimbursable from state and federal

[32] P. 2.

[33] Inter-Hospital Department memoranda: Dr. James M. Rosen, Chief, Division of Collections, to First Deputy Commissioner Maurice H. Matzkin, April 5, 1951; Dr. James M. Rosen to Commissioner Marcus D. Kogel, Aug. 9, 1951; Dr. Marcus D. Kogel, Chairman, to Board of Hospitals, March 1, 1952.

funds at the rate of 80 per cent. The care of those in hospitals who had been on federal categorical aid before entering the hospital was reimbursable with state aid for only six months of the calendar year and hospital care of those not previously receiving such assistance, including home relief cases, was completely at city expense. The Department of Welfare stated, in its *Annual Report, January 1, 1952–December 31, 1952*, that the "program is yielding the City about $1,500,000 a year in additional revenues besides providing these folks with a more suitable type of care. It has also released hospital beds for acutely sick people."[34]

Voluntary Facilities

The policy change was double also in the sense that it looked toward the placement of persons in nonprofit as well as proprietary nursing-home-type institutions. It was the momentum of this campaign that brought about the certification of the three voluntary nursing homes mentioned above as qualified to accept public assistance patients. The opening of these facilities and a number of infirmaries of private homes for the aged to reimbursable welfare recipients was a complicated matter. Also, it may have been directed more toward saving the city money than toward relieving hospitals. For the city already had a number of patients in such institutions, for whose care it was paying without any reimbursement.[35]

The complications arose primarily from the fact that the State Department of Social Welfare and the City Welfare and

[34] P. 5.

[35] "It appears that most of the Department of Hospitals charges in the Homes for Aged and in the Welfare Department's reclassified Nursing Homes should rightfully be turned over to the Department of Welfare as their responsibility. The City should not be burdened with 100% reimbursement on cases where it should only assume a 20% share of the cost." Inter-Hospitals Department memorandum from James M. Rosen to Commissioner Marcus D. Kogel, Aug. 9, 1951. The number of patients being supported solely at city expense in these homes was apparently 2,140; but the memorandum does not definitely make it clear that reimbursement was not being received for any of them.

Hospitals Departments had not classified the institutions uniformly. Some were considered hospitals by the state while
designated nursing homes by the City Welfare Department
and not recognized as hospitals by the Hospitals Department.
As hospitals they would be reimbursed by the Hospitals Department by a hospital care rate that would be significantly higher
than a nursing home rate—and for which there would be less,
or no, state and federal reimbursement—and therefore many
resisted classification as nursing-home-type facilities. Moreover,
the rates set by the Department of Welfare, which would administer the public assistance programs, excluded certain items
from cost determination included for the rate set by the City
Controller for the Hospitals Department and "practically always [were] found to be lower."[36] This also undoubtedly raised
barriers to the common designation of the institutions as
nursing-home-type facilities that was necessary for their acceptance of 80 per cent reimbursable welfare patients.

It was 1952 before any nonprofit, long-term care facility
was transferred from the Hospitals Department to the Welfare
Department budget. By early 1963 there were 566 welfare
patients in the three voluntary nursing homes and 1,660 in
seventeen infirmaries of private homes for the aged that met
the infirmary standards established by the State Department of
Social Welfare's Bulletin 119A of 1956. The impact of the
differential infirmary rate established by that Bulletin has been
discussed in Chapter 5.[37]

The concerted efforts of the Departments of Welfare and
Hospitals to uncover vacancies undoubtedly helped in some
measure to relieve the pressure on city hospitals in the troublesome days of the early 1950's. By six weeks after the task force
had begun its operations, it was reported that 508 vacancies
in voluntary and proprietary homes had been found.[38] While
no evidence has come to light revealing what proportion of
these were in voluntary institutions, one newly available non-

36 *Ibid.*   37 See p. 128, above.
38 Memorandum of Dr. Marcus D. Kogel, Commissioner of Hospitals, to
the Board of Hospitals, May 11, 1951.

profit nursing home had not previously been used by the Hospitals Department.

LIMITED VOLUNTARY GROWTH

But the opening of voluntary nursing-home-type institutions to categorical aid welfare patients does not appear to have generated any expansion of such facilities. Table 4M (Appendix I) indicates, in fact, that there was a drop of 517 beds in infirmaries of private homes for the aged from 1952 to 1953. It was 1955 before these beds approached their 1952 number again. Unfortunately the whole picture cannot be examined in detail since no figures on voluntary nursing and convalescent homes are available for the years between 1950 and 1954. However, the general trend is revealed by Figure 3, an adaptation of data from tables in Appendix I; the absence of impact on voluntary institutions is clear, particularly in comparison to the obvious impact on proprietaries. Some of the lack of expansion is attributable to the fact that, in New York City, making voluntaries eligible to give care for which the city would be reimbursed in part represented merely a bookkeeping change —a transfer of patients from one kind of governmental support to another, the second of which was not quite so remunerative to the institution.

Of course, there was actually a mélange of factors related to the numbers of voluntary beds in the city of which the policy change of 1951 and the differential rate of 1956 were only parts. Hill-Burton grants aided in the construction of 211 new beds that appeared in 1958, 122 in 1959, 80 in 1963, and 40 in 1965—a total of 453 beds. Although their influence must have been slight, one might regard it as discernible in Figure 3.

Proprietary Facilities

GROWTH

It was for proprietary nursing homes that the policy change of 1951–1952 made a great difference. In 1954 the Department of Hospitals reported that it had "exerted every effort to en-

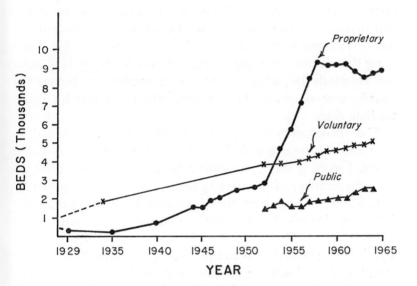

Figure 3. Growth in numbers of public, voluntary, and proprietary nursing-home-type beds in New York City, 1929 through 1964.

Note. The triangles, crosses, and dots indicate the points at which the lines are based on data. The smoothness of the lines is, to some extent, attributable to the absence of data.

Source. Data in Tables 2M, 3M, 4M, and 5M, Appendix I.

courage an expansion of the nursing home facilities in the City and also to force a raising of standards so that the patients will be assured the best possible nursing and custodial care."[39] Since it was thought to be unrealistic to expect proprietary homes to expand their facilities and render desirable care at the current rates, a series of conferences was held with Department of Welfare representatives during the latter part of 1952 on rates the homes received for the care of welfare patients and development of a classification scheme by which compensation would be according to the level of care required by such patients. By 1952 the maximum rate paid by the Welfare Department had crept up to $140 monthly. The Department of Hospitals set

[39] *Annual Report, 1953,* p. 7.

standards that homes would have to meet to qualify to provide each of three different levels of care—minimum, intermediate, and maximum. The City Welfare Department set the rates at $150, $180, and $200 and accepted the responsibility for classifying the clients according to the care needed.[40] By May 1953 the Hospitals Department had recommended ten homes for classification as maximum care institutions and one for intermediate care.

The encouragement offered the proprietary homes had at least some of the effects desired. Proprietary facilities, as Table 8 and Figure 3 show, expanded. In the three years prior to 1953 the number of proprietary beds in the city had grown by 484. From 1952 to 1955 they increased by 2,936 and in the following three-year period they increased by an even greater number, 3,752. Their total rose from 2,801 in 1952 to 9,489 in 1958. And, although the completion of the Hospitals Department's postwar building program and its decompression measures such as home care had also been important, the expansion of proprietary facilities had helped reduce the crowding of city hospitals.[41] The annual average occupancy rate had gone down to 93.1 per cent for 1953 and had dropped to 83.6 per cent for 1958.

CRISIS

It was also expected, however, that the classification of types of welfare care in nursing homes and the higher rates available would elevate the quality of care rendered. The Commissioner

[40] Department of Hospitals, *Annual Report, 1952*, p. 17; letter from Virginia O'Neil, Director, Bureau of Special Services, Department of Welfare, to Miss Minnie Mark, Chief, Division of Institutional Inspection, Department of Hospitals, March 9, 1959.

[41] There were probably better than 5,000 welfare patients in nursing homes in 1958. The City Department of Welfare kept no figures on living arrangements prior to 1959, but in April of that year 5,364 of its clients lived in nursing homes. Letter from Dr. James G. Haughton, Assistant Director, Bureau of Medical Services, New York City Department of Welfare, March 7, 1963.

of Hospitals, Dr. Marcus Kogel, was gravely concerned about the matter. He had made a tour of proprietary nursing homes before ever embarking upon the policy change and had found their services wanting. He had reorganized laboratory and X-ray services and established home care as measures to ease hospital crowding. He thought it imperative to take further measures, however, and so turned to proprietary nursing homes. He made budgetary requests for an enlarged inspection force to the Mayor and the Board of Estimate, but his requests were denied. The budget had made provision for no new positions since 1930; the force consisted of one general inspector and fourteen inspectors of lower grades—when all the posts were filled, which was usually not the case. And no new positions were to be added until mid-1955, after Dr. Kogel had left the Department, when lines for seven more employees were added.[42] Dr. Kogel recognized that there was little public awareness of the problems involved in nursing home regulation; formal statements notwithstanding, he received little support from community groups for strengthened enforcement machinery. Concluding that he could not augment regulation through governmental activity, he asked the proprietary nursing home operators to organize and institute self-regulatory procedures. Self-policing had proved effective in the restaurant, milk producing, and other industries; he was hopeful it would be effective in the nursing home industry.[43]

[42] The City of New York, *Annual Budgets*, 1930 to 1955–1956. The period during which the policy change concerning nursing homes took place was characterized by particularly weak leadership at the highest level. Wallace S. Sayre and Herbert Kaufman have said of Mayor Vincent R. Impellitteri, who was the city's chief executive from September 1950 through 1953: "Impellitteri, elected by chance, retreated into his self-described role as presiding officer of the Board of Estimates, sharing initiative and responsibility generously with any who would ease his burdens of accountability." *Governing New York City* (New York: Russell Sage Foundation, 1960), p. 697.

[43] Except for the budget data, the material in this paragraph is based upon an interview with Dr. Marcus D. Kogel, Dean, Albert Einstein Medical College, Yeshiva University, Jan. 22, 1963.

Public awareness of the problems of nursing home regulation was heightened by press coverage of the events of 1958 and 1959. In March 1958 the Department of Hospitals detected that records submitted by two different nursing homes, as required by the proprietary nursing home code, listed one nurse as working in both homes simultaneously. This led to an investigation of eleven homes by the Department of Hospitals. Specifically at issue was the question of whether the homes were rendering the services they had contracted to render to welfare patients, and that the code required of them. The code required of all homes at least one registered nurse for every sixty patients, or fraction of sixty patients, an additional registered or practical nurse for each twenty patients or fraction of twenty patients, and an attendant for each five patients or fraction of five. Homes giving intermediate or maximum care to welfare patients were to have registered nurses on the night tour of duty. In June 1958 the City Department of Investigation undertook broadening the probe to include all eighty-eight proprietary homes that cared for welfare patients. There ensued a struggle between the city and the homes over the right of the government to examine the accounts of the homes; the homes eventually capitulated. In an interim report to the Mayor in January of 1959, the Commissioner of Investigation charged that homes had defrauded the City by "padding payrolls, failing to provide the facilities required by the City's hospital code, and practicing other irregularities." He said that a majority of the 88 homes had admitted falsifying the employment schedules on nursing care that they submitted to the Department of Hospitals.[44] Shortly afterward, Ollie Randall, Vice Chairman of the National Council on the Aged, testified before a state joint legislative subcommittee that some nursing home buildings were unsafe and that conditions in some homes were shocking.[45]

[44] *New York Times,* Jan. 29, 1959, p. 1.
[45] *Ibid.,* Feb. 6, 1959, p. 27.

REFORM

In January 1959 the Mayor announced the institution of a reform program. It was to include a study of proprietary nursing homes in the city by John G. Steinle and Associates, the costs to be borne by the homes themselves; restitution to the Department of Welfare of overpayments resulting from nursing care reported but not actually given; and revision of the code governing proprietary nursing homes.[46] In response to representations made by private citizens, the mayor appointed, in February, a temporary citizen body on health services—known as the Heyman Commission, after its chairman, Mr. David Heyman—with a broad charge to review any of the health services in the city.[47] Its executive director was Dr. Ray E. Trussell, Director of the School of Public Health and Administrative Medicine of Columbia University, who soon after the Commission had submitted its final report, became the city's Commissioner of Hospitals and implemented much of the reform proposed.

Steinle and Associates submitted their 234-page report to the Commissioner of Investigation on December 1, 1959. It found nursing homes and their administration inadequate or improper in a number of respects, but recommended a rate increase for the welfare patients and was sharply critical of the code and found its enforcement arbitrary.[48]

The Hospitals Department had moved to strengthen its regulation in 1958, reorganizing its Division of Institutional Inspection. (Seven positions had been added by the 1955–1956 budget.) Simultaneously, the Board of Hospitals, which had acquired the quasi-legislative responsibility for amending or replacing the code upon its establishment in 1950, had increased the frequency of required reports to the Department

[46] *Ibid.,* Jan. 25, 1959, p. 1.
[47] "Report of the Commission on Health Services of the City of New York," adopted July 20, 1960 (mimeo.).
[48] John G. Steinle and Associates, *A Comprehensive Study of Proprietary Nursing Homes in New York City, 1959.*

from once every third month to once each month. Further, the policy had been adopted of issuing sixty- or ninety-day provisional licenses. In 1960 structural requirements for homes were stiffened through bringing to bear upon all homes standards that had been set in 1954, but from which homes existing in 1954 had been exempted. Regulation carried on at arm's length must invariably have some elements of rigidity. Some variances were granted upon administrative review; most significantly, three-year, nonrenewable variances were granted for some structural requirements. From 1958 through 1961 as many as twenty-five homes were unlicensed at one time. The Department of Welfare was not usually able to withdraw its patients when a home failed to be relicensed; bed shortages were acute.

The Heyman Commission made proprietary nursing homes one of the focal points of its survey, sponsoring a study of the care given a 3 per cent sample of the patients found in a representative sample of the sixty-nine homes in the city classified to give maximum care. Its findings helped to galvanize further the Mayor's reform program. It stressed the attitudes and lack of training of the administrators of the homes as probably the greatest problem. Its report on nursing homes carried the following comment of one investigating physician:

The striking thing to me about the homes, was the philosophy of care which was exhibited—custodial quality to it, and failure to appreciate human individuality and dignity. If only this philosophy could be changed, already a great improvement would occur.[49]

The homes were scored as to physical inadequacies of plant, safety hazards, uncleanliness, absence of recreation and physical therapy programs, and lack of attention to such matters as patients' needs for eyeglasses. Nursing care was judged as "poor" in 37 per cent of homes, "fair" in 40 per cent, and "good" in 33 per cent. Difficulties with hospitals in such respects as long

---

[49] "Medical Care for Welfare Patients in Proprietary Nursing Homes in New York City," a pilot study made under the auspices of the Commission on Health Services of New York City, 1960, p. 27 (mimeo.).

delays in getting tests, or getting patients admitted, and inadequate records on patients coming from those institutions were also found to be serious.

The City Administrator recommended that the threefold classification of care given welfare patients, and the attendant three levels of compensation, be abandoned for one rate in 1960 on the grounds that it created administrative complexities and encouraged operators to keep patients in bed in order to claim that the maximum level of care was being given.[50] The City Administrator also recommended a rate raise.[51] Both of these recommendations were implemented. His further recommendation to transfer regulation of proprietary nursing homes to the City Department of Health was not implemented. The Commissioner of Investigation reported that nursing home operators had defrauded the city of some $3.7 million.[52] Arrangements for the reimbursement of the Department of Welfare were negotiated between the city and the nursing homes. The institutions involved reimbursed the Department, at a discounted rate, rather than forego the referral to them of welfare patients at new, higher, rates.[53]

Soon after it had become established, Mayor Wagner's administration began to add posts to the Division of Inspection. In early 1962 a new office was created to direct, among other things, the Department's regulation of nursing homes. By mid-1962 some thirty-nine positions in the Department were directly concerned with inspection. The annual average number of visits per home to the proprietaries in the city by the inspection force grew from 9.0 in 1960 to 10.3 in 1961 and to 13.8 in 1962. At times the inspectors were accompanied by investigators of the City Department of Investigations—and on occasion even by detectives on night visits.[54]

By 1966 the average number of visits had grown to 22.4. The

[50] Office of the Mayor, Division of Administration, *Proprietary Nursing Homes in New York City; Rates and Regulations,* 1960, p. 16.
[51] *Ibid.,* p. 21.   [52] *Ibid.,* p. 2.
[53] Interview with Henry J. Rosner, Assistant to the Commissioner, New York City Department of Welfare, May 14, 1963.
[54] Department of Hospitals, *Annual Report, 1962,* p. 51.

general improvement of nursing home conditions that had resulted from the reform measures had substantially reduced the number of homes unlicensed or on restricted licenses.

A NEW CODE

There was also support from the administration for the revision of the code governing proprietary nursing homes. And there was considerable support throughout the community. A study of the code was begun in 1961, aided by a $10,000 grant from the New York Heart Association and an advisory committee of some eighty persons from various governmental agencies, voluntary welfare organizations, other community groups, and representatives of the proprietary nursing homes. The new code, after public hearings and official notice, went into effect in early 1963. Exceptionally comprehensive and detailed, it was generally acknowledged to set the highest standards of any code in the country.

Prominent among the new code's features were structural standards, ratios of required nursing personnel, and the requirement that the services of a social worker, dietitian or nutritionist, and recreation leader be engaged by each home. Structural and equipment standards for new homes were comparable to Hill-Burton requirements, except that they were more comprehensive and specific. The established ratios of required nursing personnel had been the most controversial part of the old code. The new code raised the requirements, making mandatory the provision of two registered nurses for the first sixty beds, or fraction of sixty beds, and the scheduling of one of them for the night tour of duty; where a third nurse was employed, the afternoon tour had to be covered. However, a new flexibility allowed the operator to staff according to his approved bed complement—the number of operating beds, approved by the Commissioner of Hospitals—rather than by the licensed capacity of the home. The social workers, dietitians or nutritionists, and recreation leaders could each be engaged by two or more homes, but the distribution of their services was subjected to the approval of the Commissioner.

A further feature of the code deserving special notice was the requirement of some academic preparation for nursing home administrators. Along with other qualifications, the administrator of a home was required to have completed high school, or have its educational equivalent. Requirements for completed course work in hospital or nursing home administration or some other health service administration were also imposed. Such course work was made another matter subject to the approval of the Commissioner of Hospitals. Administrators of licensed homes not meeting these qualifications were allowed two years to complete them. These special educational or training requirements have counteracted, in some measure at least, the growing tendency of nursing home administrators to have non-health-oriented backgrounds that was described in the last chapter.

STRENGTHENING THE PROPRIETARY FIELD

After the crisis, the city government undertook a number of activities that definitely supported proprietary nursing homes and sought the improvement of patient care within these institutions; among them was an in-service training program for nurses' aides in homes and the raising of rates for welfare patients. In October of 1962 a series of educational television broadcasts was begun by the city's radio-television station to train aides. The undertaking was directed by the Hospitals Department's Office of Proprietary Hospitals, Nursing Homes and Home Care Services; it was the result of the combined efforts of the Department, a number of community agencies, and proprietary nursing homes. The welfare rate for nursing home patients was raised by 1965 to $355.

Other steps taken by public agencies in the city that had the effect of strengthening proprietary nursing homes included the provision for their welfare patients of systematic, physician care by bringing together the home and some outside medical care organization.

One of the major conclusions of the Mayor's Commission on Health Services, which reported in mid-1960, was that despite the repeated historical recognition of the need for greater coordination among the various participating elements, "the City's health services suffer from fragmentation."[55] Proprietary homes present a particular challenge in this respect because they so typically have little well-developed association with hospitals or other medical-related organizations. The provision of social services in homes may be expected to ameliorate this problem somewhat. Another move of significance was the arrangement, in 1962, for physician care to be provided by the Health Insurance Plan of Greater New York to a number of Old Age Assistance and Medical Assistance for Aged recipients, about 3,000 of whom were in nursing homes. HIP, a group medical practice organization, provides specialties, diagnostic services, and equipment not otherwise available to nursing home patients. There was also, at the same time, established an agreement for Lutheran Medical Center to provide continuous medical care for some ninety-eight welfare patients in one proprietary nursing home. A contract was concluded between the City Welfare Department and the Voluntary organization through which the latter was to provide total physician care, drugs, and laboratory services for the clients of the Department in the home. The arrangement provided the advantage of expediting transfer of patients between the institutions as the need dictates. A third venture begun in 1962 involved the furnishing of medical care for welfare families, including a small number of nursing home patients, by New York Hospital; a demonstration project, it has now run its course. However, the general scheme of having hospitals provide the care for nearby proprietary nursing homes proved worth while and such contracts were, in 1966, in operation covering fifteen such homes. Preparations moved forward to provide care to patients of still other proprietary homes through similar contracts with other hospitals. In one instance where no

[55] "Report of the Commission on Health Services of the City of New York, adopted July 20, 1960" (mimeo.), p. 12.

hospital was available that could be related to the nursing home concerned, a number of private practitioners were induced to sign a contract as a group to provide the needed care and to bring in specialist services as they are called for. Such progress was largely the product of the development of new coordinative steps taken by the City Health, Hospital, and Welfare Departments and involving appointments held concurrently in all these departments of physicians skilled in the organization of health care.

A further, related, development grew out of a 1963 study of patients in general hospitals in the city for thirty days or longer. The study concluded that 41 per cent of its subjects did not need acute hospital care—that other care would have been more appropriate for their needs and less expensive as well. And, while on the one hand it reported that hospital personnel were "discouraged and cynical about some of the nursing homes to which they had to refer patients," on the other hand it concluded that "undoubtedly many . . . patients are now sent to nursing homes although they do not need nursing home care."[56] As a consequence of this research a pilot project was begun in the Department of Hospitals in 1964 to establish procedures for determining the needs of long-stay patients in city or voluntary hospitals at city expense and to expedite their referral to the kinds of facilities most desirable for their particular condition.

COST ACCOUNTING

In 1962 the City Department of Welfare began to require annual cost statements, prepared by certified public accountants, from all proprietary nursing homes caring for public welfare patients. Among the cost elements included in these financial reports were depreciation, insofar as it was allowed

[56] Frank Van Dyke, Virginia Brown and Anne-Marie Thom, "Long Stay" Hospital Care, School of Public Health and Administrative Medicine, Columbia University (New York, 1963), p. 7.

by the United States Internal Revenue Service, and therefore there was consideration of capital construction costs. However, the cost statements were not used to determine the rates but only to provide for a more informed kind of negotiation process. Bargaining remained the means by which rates of payment were determined. Moreover, all homes were paid at the same rate, regardless of the services rendered or the costs incurred. Since 1966, however, under the provisions of the legislation ensuing from the work of the Folsom Committee, about which more will be said later, payments have had to be "reasonably related to the costs" of providing such service.

LOCAL ORGANIZATION OF THE INDUSTRY

As it became clear during the early 1960's that the demand by the city government for higher quality of services from proprietary nursing homes was going to endure indefinitely, several nursing home owners belatedly attempted to establish self-regulation, as Hospital Commissioner Kogel had counseled them to do in 1952. A number banded together sufficiently to engage an attorney to coordinate their efforts and serve as their spokesman before city agencies. Little progress toward self-regulation was made, however, and the organization functioned principally to voice the objections of the owners to proposed provisions of the new code, as it was being formulated.

After a period of floundering, this group consolidated in September 1963, with a variety of other groupings of proprietary nursing home owners and administrators, into one major organization, the Metropolitan Nursing Home Association.

As of early 1966, 70 of the city's 89 homes, with about eighty thousand beds, were members. The Association had a substantial budget—running over $80,000 annually—and had a full-time executive director. The Association became the primary spokesman for the homes in relations with the City Welfare Department. The Executive Director, an attorney, became counsel for the homes on many legal matters, although special counsel is sometimes engaged for particular purposes. The Association conducts all of the negotiations with organized employees of the homes, a considerable task. It also serves as the instrument through which common causes are pursued. For example, when the televised training program for nursing home personnel was conducted, a special assessment of $1.00 per bed was levied upon all of the members in order to help the City Hospitals Department and other parties involved finance the activity. Similarly, the organization conducted studies for such purposes as demonstrating to the welfare administrators and others that there have been significant increases in labor costs to the homes.

The city nursing home organization stands in sharp contrast to the upstate contingent of the State Association. It is much better organized and financed and has a fuller membership. But this consolidation and cohesion did not predate the rigorous kind of regulation and demands that the city has made upon the homes. This organized condition of the industry in the city should be seen as attributable, to a very great extent, to changes in its relationship to the government that have occurred since 1958.

PROPRIETARIES: THE IMPACT OF FEDERAL FINANCING

Federal financial assistance for proprietary nursing homes was even slower in influencing the New York City picture than it was upstate. As late as 1963 no application for FHA mortgage insurance had yet received any measure of official approval, although eleven applications were under consideration. By early 1966, however, two large institutions financed through FHA provisions—one with 154 and the other with 116 beds and representing combined mortgages amounting to $2.9 million—were in operation. The FHA at the time was committed to extend mortgage guarantees to three more homes, two of approximately the same size as those already in operation, and one giant involving a $4 million mortgage to provide 407 beds.

There are signs that, in the tough real estate market that is New York City, the nursing home industry is not as attractive as it is elsewhere—and this is especially so because of the kind of system of accountability to the public that has been established in the city. Nonetheless, it obviously has some attraction for large-scale investment—most clearly revealed by FHA information—and special attention is drawn to the scale. The development of scale in nursing homes presents, simultaneously, opportunities for great advantages and great dangers.[57]

THE GROWTH PATTERN REVIEWED

Table 8 and Figure 3 show the growth of proprietary nursing home development in the city. After a long history of slow development, a period of extremely dramatic growth began upon the city government's policy change of 1951–1952. The number of beds multiplied over threefold in six years. Then, with the attention given to these facilities by the press and the reform measures undertaken by the city administration, there began, abruptly, a decrease that was to continue through 1963. The number of homes dropped from 124 to only 87. (The number of proprietary homes in the city had not decreased since 1955, as had been the case upstate, but had continued to increase through 1958.) Beds decreased by almost a thousand.

At the lowest level in their decline, however, as Figure 3 shows, the proprietaries stood far above the voluntary and public facilities. And both 1964 and 1965 saw some increase in proprietary beds, and in 1965 an additional two homes appeared. The industry had consolidated, many of the weaker homes expiring in the process, and was now showing signs of new growth, despite having to meet the highest standards in the country. Stern regulation had been required, however, to raise it to this level.

[57] Small Business Administration loans in the city were so insignificant that they are relegated to a footnote. Only one loan to a nursing home was granted, and it was subsequently canceled in full.

Origin and Evolution of
Public Home Infirmary Care Programs

New York City's public home establishment of the 1930's was a direct descendant of the original almshouse. There were two parts, the City Home for Dependents, on Welfare Island and housed for the most part in buildings constructed around 1846, and its adjunct, Farm Colony on Staten Island. Both had come under the jurisdiction of the Department of Hospitals with its creation in 1929. There is conflicting source material about the state of the development of infirmaries in these institutions prior to 1952. Material in the files of the City Department of Hospitals speaks of the establishment of an infirmary in the City Home during the post–Civil War period. A report by the Superintendent of City Home indicates there was substantial segregation of ill and infirm persons and that there was a house medical staff as well as a visiting staff at the home in 1947.[58] But statistical data from the State Department of Social Welfare list no public infirmary facilities in New York City in 1934 or 1943, the two years prior to 1952 for which that Department has figures. From 1952 on there is general agreement between state and city information.

The 1945 construction plans of the Hospitals Department called for the replacement of City Home and Farm Colony with buildings to accommodate some three thousand ambulatory and two thousand bedfast persons. The following year, however, long-range planning was substantially revised to look toward the institutional care of the chronically and aged ill in connection with general hospitals in the various boroughs of the city. The advantages of such an arrangement were seen as having aged persons with long-term illness "on the periphery of

[58] Memorandum from Maxwell Lewis, Superintendent, City Home for Dependents, to Dr. Marcus Kogel, General Medical Superintendent, Department of Hospitals, Jan. 28, 1947. Similarly, a report in 1947 from L. T. Dermody, Superintendent of Farm Colony, indicated that some buildings at the Colony were regarded as infirmaries.

the acute general hospital where medical and nursing staffs and all the specialties are available," and the proximity of the patient to his home community. It was still thought necessary, however, to proceed with the replacement of the antiquated City Home.[59] As a matter of fact, the replacement of Farm Colony was also being considered at least as late as 1947, but the idea of having long-term care facilities in conjunction with general hospitals was consonant with the new, developing, satellite concept for city hospitals—the clustering of specialties around general care cores as distinguished from emphasizing specialized hospitals.[60]

Construction on the replacement for City Home, the Bird S. Coler Memorial Hospital and Home, was begun in 1947. Between that time and July 1, 1952, when it received its first patient, however, changes were to take effect that were to make the new institution an important link-pin in the evolution of a new kind of system of public infirmaries. First, changing perceptions of the city's needs were to alter it from a home and hospital to a chronic disease hospital and an infirmary. Second, state and federal social security amendments of 1950–1951 were to make patients of public home infirmaries eligible for welfare reimbursable by federal aid.

Simultaneously with the pilot-study[61] transfers of patients from city hospitals to private nursing homes, applications of 2,008 infirmary patients in City Home and Farm Colony were submitted to the Department of Welfare for relief under one of the federal categorical programs. About 1,800 had been accepted under one program or another by the end of 1951.[62] As Bird S. Coler opened the following year, City Home was

[59] Dr. Edward M. Bernecker, Commissioner of Hospitals, "New York City's Present Plans for its Aged in the Future," paper read at the New York State Conference of Social Work, Nov. 12, 1946.

[60] Interview with Dr. Marcus Kogel, Jan. 22, 1963. Dr. Kogel was Chairman of the Hospitals Department Planning Committee during most of 1946.

[61] See p. 187, above.

[62] Memorandum from Dr. Marcus Kogel, Chairman, to Board of Hospitals, March 1, 1952.

closed down, its bedfast patients—those accepted for categorical welfare included—being transferred to Coler and its ambulant patients to Farm Colony. Records of the State Department of Social Welfare indicate that Coler, with a total bed capacity of 1,920, had 968 infirmary beds in 1953 and 1,018 in 1954. The point is that, without a hitch, welfare clients were transferred to the new institution even though it was not a public home in the sense of having domiciliary beds. "Home" had been left in its title to make clear its relationship as an adjunct to the city's public home—now Farm Colony alone, consisting of domiciliary and infirmary beds—and its status as a successor to the old City Home.

By June 1953 the state legislature had already decided that the state would participate in reimbursing care given in infirmaries of public homes, although the decision was not to become effective until January 1 of the following year. Under the new formula, the city could make its costs for a month of infirmary care $42.50 instead of $120 for each patient it could have accepted on one of the federal categorical rolls. On June 29, 1953, the Commissioner of Hospitals wrote to the Commissioner of Welfare requesting the latter's cooperation in securing reimbursable aid for infirmary-type patients in Goldwater Memorial Hospital.[63] The City Welfare Department accordingly took the matter up with the State Department of Social Welfare, which responded as follows:

You will recall that in order to classify Bird S. Coler Memorial Hospital and Home as a public home infirmary, our Board found it necessary to distinguish clearly between the hospital and infirmary section of the facility. Hospital cases *without* public assistance status, whether in Bird S. Coler or in Goldwater Memorial Hospital, cannot qualify for public assistance.[64]

[63] Letter of Dr. Marcus D. Kogel, Commissioner of Hospitals, to Henry L. McCarthy, Commissioner of Welfare.

[64] Letter from Peter Kasius, Deputy Commissioner, State Department of Social Welfare, to Henry L. McCarthy, Commissioner of Welfare, July 27, 1953. Italics in original.

A proposal was made for a conference between city and state officials but then the matter appears to have been dropped.

In late 1954 another thread of the development of the concept of public infirmaries in hospitals became clear. Dr. Basil C. MacLean, the new Commissioner of Hospitals, declared in a press conference that the findings of a ninety-five-patient study by Dr. Howard A. Rusk had drawn the Hospitals Department's attention to the fact that many of its patients no longer required definitive hospital care. He announced the undertaking of another project by Dr. Rusk, financed by the New York Foundation, to determine what proportion of the Department's patients might be transferred to more appropriate facilities. He spoke of developing "homesteads"—accommodations with homelike furnishings and atmosphere—for custodial patients within the city hospital system. Newspaper accounts reported the potential savings involved, comparing the $20.00 a day general hospital rate with the $4.00 a day rate for domiciliary and infirmary care.[65] The following year there were continuing releases to the public concerning developing plans for infirmary-type facilities, and particular notice was taken of the potential for reimbursement of city costs.

In April of 1956 the Hospitals Department again sought, through the same channel as in 1953, to have part of Goldwater Hospital recognized as a public infirmary. In June there was a response from the State Department of Social Welfare, stressing this time not so much the requirement of separation of infirmary from other facilities as a need for infirmaries to be parts of homes to qualify under existing rules. The correspondence quoted from Bulletin 139, of 1951, stating that it

clearly defined a public home infirmary to mean 'a public medical care unit of a public home and providing continuing medical treatment and nursing care in addition to board and lodging to patients admitted upon the written recommendation of a physician.' The underlining is ours to indicate the difference between the proposed

<hr>

[65] See the *New York Times* and the *Herald-Tribune*, Nov. 17, 1954; press release, Department of Hospitals, Nov. 16, 1954.

plan for Goldwater Memorial and the plan which was approved for Bird S. Coler Memorial Hospital and Home. . . . In other words, our approval of the plan at Bird S. Coler was given not because its Infirmary was part of a hospital, but because the Infirmary was an outgrowth of the old public home.[66]

A flurry of correspondence followed between the Hospitals and Welfare departments and the City Bureau of the Budget. Then the city countered the state argument with three points. First, the Goldwater public infirmary would "likewise serve as an infirmary for the Farm Colony Public Home and [would] care for persons who, but for their need for such care, would otherwise be eligible for care in the public home." Second, the city had about 40 per cent more persons on OAA, AB, and aid to disabled rolls than upstate New York; it should therefore have more infirmary cases on categorical assistance but in fact had less. Third,

New York City could, of course, follow the Upstate lead and build separate municipal homes and infirmaries. No useful purpose to the taxpayer or the patient would be served by this development. . . . There is a very real advantage to the infirmary case in reorganizing certain of our hospitals as hospitals and homes with infirmary wings because it has the advantage of making readily available to them the hospital's superior medical facilities and resources in alleviating the patient's distress when these are required.[67]

To this argument the State Department of Social Welfare capitulated, and the Public Home Infirmary Care Program became legalized.

Meanwhile, Dr. Rusk had completed his survey of city hospital patients and the results had been published. Among his findings had been the conclusion that one out of every five

[66] Letter from Peter Kasius, Deputy Commissioner, State Department of Social Welfare, to Henry L. McCarthy, Commissioner of Welfare, June 5, 1956.
[67] Letter from Henry L. McCarthy, Commissioner of Welfare, to Peter Kasius, Deputy Commissioner, State Department of Social Welfare, Aug. 22, 1956.

patients in the chronic and general hospitals was there not because he needed the care such facilities offered but because he had no other suitable place to go.[68] The press release that reported the findings of the survey also announced the beginning of a "pilot" homestead at Goldwater Memorial. The Hospitals Department was asked to give notice when it was ready to have the new infirmary inspected by the State Department of Social Welfare. The inspection was duly carried out and approval for reimbursement was given. In August 1957 a ninety-patient unit was opened and by the end of the year it had grown to 360 beds. By segregating patients out of the chronic unit of the hospital and giving them reimbursable infirmary care, the city was paying $108 per month for many patients instead of the $420 that nonreimbursable chronic care would have cost, according to the strict arithmetical analysis. Of course, there is always the question whether infirmary-type patients, simply because they are in chronic or acute facilities, actually receive all of the care accorded other patients in such accommodations who in fact need such care.

In 1957 the Public Home Infirmary Care program spread also to City Hospital at Elmhurst, a general hospital, and in 1958 an infirmary unit was established at Queens Hospital Center. Later expansions of the program involved Coney Island Hospital and a consolidation of Seaview Hospital and Farm Colony that resulted in an addition of infirmary beds. Categorical welfare cases could be cared for in any of these institutions and reimbursement was duly forthcoming. Most public infirmary welfare cases were transferred to the Medical Assistance to the Aged rolls when that new category became operative in 1961. Under MAA, the federal government reimbursed 50 per cent of the cost and the state reimbursed 25 per cent. At rates in effect in early 1966, it cost the city $14.58 each day to keep an eligible patient in a general hospital bed and $6.12 to care for them in a public infirmary.

[68] Howard A. Rusk *et al.*, *Hospital Patient Survey* (New York: Goldwater Memorial Hospital, 1956), p. 26 *passim*.

BARRIERS TO GROWTH

The Public Home Infirmary Care program was not without problems. Growth to 3,000 beds by 1958 was anticipated in 1957; at the end of 1964 there were still only 2,465 beds. Perhaps there should be noted first the staffing difficulties, notably at Coney Island, where there was a 285-bed capacity but only a 46-bed complement until 1962, when fifty additional beds went into operation. The 72-bed infirmary at Queens was closed in 1965 to make room for a badly needed psychiatric unit. There were other problems as well, but a major barrier to growth appears to have been the opposition of the medical boards in city hospitals, particularly in large teaching hospitals.[69] Some physicians feared that the classification of persons as infirmary patients in the hospitals with which they were associated would weaken the teaching of medical students, despite protestations of the Hospitals Department leadership that infirmaries could be disassociated from medical teaching programs. The problem is well known and is not a new one. The 1946 *Report* of the Health Preparedness Commission noted that general hospitals, particularly teaching hospitals, were loathe to admit custodial cases.[70] And Eli Ginzberg made a number of caustic comments on the matter in 1949 in his *A Pattern of Hospital Care.*[71]

Eventually, however, agreement was reached in principle to the addition of infirmary beds to existing acute care facilities, involving no reduction of the latter, and the establishment of 400 PHIC beds in a new building at Bronx Municipal, a teaching hospital, has moved well through the planning stage. There are also 1,800 other beds at various stages of planning. Money for construction is, of course, one chief consideration. It should

[69] Interviews with Dr. Herman E. Bauer, Director, Bureau of Medical and Hospital Services, Department of Hospitals, May 10, 1963; and Dr. Marcus Kogel, Dean, Albert Einstein Medical College of Yeshiva University, Jan. 22, 1963. See also Herbert E. Klarman, *Hospital Care in New York City* (New York: Columbia University Press, 1963), p. 408.
[70] Leg. Doc. 66A, 1946, p. 107.   [71] See, for example, pp. 194, 198.

be noted that the city has received no Hill-Burton money for any public facilities.

UPSTATE-DOWNSTATE SCHISM

Feelings of administrators about the PHIC program provide a good example of the kind of conflict of opinion along the upstate-downstate line, characterizing much administration in the state—at least in the health field.[72] Some pockets of upstate administrative opinion have seen the PHIC program against a background of belief that during the 1940's New York City did not turn to proprietary nursing homes because it wanted to keep its hospitals full. This is probably related to the conclusion some hold that PHIC was conceived as a scheme to get money out of the state for hospital care. Simultaneously, there is other upstate administrative opinion that the city has "sat on its hands" and not moved ahead satisfactorily in expanding the program.

What these two opinions have in common is that both are critical of New York City. Individual administrators in the city also have strong feelings on the matter. One has acknowledged that he has a "jaundiced point of view" about upstate New York and others often show pique at the exercise of upstate power. The existence of these attitudes has not precluded the bridging of the upstate-downstate gap by strong friendships in individual cases, of course. Furthermore, there is no question but what there has been a substantial amount of cooperation between the state and city administrative bodies. Still, the heat generated by colliding attitudes cannot be

[72] Divergence of administrator opinion is hardly new. During the hearings of the Commission on Old Age Security, in 1929, the Superintendent of the New York City Home described the barrier to outdoor relief in the City Charter and accounted for its origin as follows: "It was felt that New York City, being largely Democratic, could not be trusted to spend money and so you people upstate stuck [the barrier] in there. That's the only explanation I ever heard for it." New York State Commission on Old Age Security, *Hearings*, State Legislative Library, Capitol, Albany (typescript), p. 1109.

ignored as an administrative problem. The following quotation makes the point:

Every acute administrator knows that bureaucratic organizations set individual against individual in a simmering conflict that siphons off much of our creative energy . . . as well as some of our productive energy. Someone has said the organization hasn't been made yet which does not burn up half its pulling power between the motor and the rear axle.[73]

[73] William Gore, "Psychiatrists as Administrators," *Public Administration Review*, XXI (Winter 1961), p. 35.

CHAPTER 7

The Fermenting Present

Policy Consolidated

The years 1964, 1965, and 1966 have been as important as any period in previous history as to change in public policy for the development of nursing-home-type facilities. Moreover, where much social policy of the past had oblique or unintended implications for long-term care institutions, the new policy characteristically represents direct confrontation with problems of the development of nursing homes and related facilities. The mass of policy change of this most recent span of years has produced broad, integrated but decentralized administrative machinery aimed at assuring that all future nursing homes will fit into a pattern of community need. It has geared this machinery into an over-all network for the making of health care policy. It has assigned the main thrust of policy development to professionals in community health—relegating the welfare administration to a lesser role—and has transferred primary supervising responsibilities of medical institutions to health professionals. It has also given birth to new, comprehensive health care programs financed through the federal social security system and federal grants in aid. And these are not all the reforms of these years.

Controlling the Number of Beds

A major break-through at the state level occurred in 1964 with the passage of the Metcalf-McCloskey Act. Part of the story of the hammering out of that legislation has been told in previous pages.¹ A rather full account is to be found as Chapter 7 of the *Report of the Joint Legislative Committee on Health Insurance Plans, 1964.*² The presentation here will more or less be limited to the changes the law brought about.

Prior to October 1, 1964, the effective date of the Act, there were serious deficiences in the state's ability to prevent the building of unwarranted hospital and nursing home beds. The Board of Social Welfare had its power to approve or disapprove charters of incorporation of voluntary institutions and the prior approval powers over proprietary nursing homes discussed in Chapter 5. It had certain other powers over proprietary hospitals, but consideration by any state agency of whether or not there was a public need for additional beds "certainly [was] not mandated and probably not authorized prior to the building of a governmental or proprietary general hospital or prior to a major expansion of any hospital."³

As Dr. Ray E. Trussell and Frank van Dyke put the matter in the 1960 Blue Cross Study:

Lacking the authority to do so, . . . neither the New York State Joint Hospital Survey and Planning Commission nor any other agency has been able to prevent the building of unnecessary beds, except when Federal funds were necessary to construction and were withheld. . . .⁴

And the Blue Cross Plan for Southern New York supplied figures on the number of new hospital beds under construction in its area to one of the meetings of the Joint Legislative

---

¹ See pp. 134–135, above.   ² Leg. Doc. No. 39, 1964.

³ *Ad Hoc* Committee on Regional Councils of the State Hospital Review and Planning Council, *Statutory and Regulatory Provisions Governing the Organization, Construction and Operation of Hospitals in New York State* (a memorandum prepared by James A. Cashen, June, 1962); quotation is from the covering letter.

⁴ *Prepayment for Hospital Care in New York State*, School of Public Health and Administrative Medicine, Columbia University (New York, 1960), p. 270. The quoted sentence concludes ". . . or to adequately implement the development of other types of facilities such as non-profit nursing homes."

Committee in 1964. The Plan estimated that the new beds would cost its subscribers some additional $80 million for the first year they were in operation. Which, Senator Metcalf said, "serves to underscore the critical need for limiting unnecessary building of hospitals or nursing homes."[5]

The core administrative structure for the control of beds had already developed in the state Hill-Burton machinery. The functions of the Joint Hospital Survey and Planning Commission—the Joint Commission, comprised of the Commissioners of the Departments of Social Welfare, Mental Hygiene and Health, had been established in 1947 to do the Hill-Burton work—had been transferred by law to the Department of Health following the Blue Cross report in 1960. The functions of the Commission's Advisory Council had similarly been transferred to a new body, the State Hospital Review and Planning Council. The Joint Commission had established informal consulting relationships with various private organizations in different regions of the state and seven regional councils had thereby evolved—although there was substantial difference among them as to the extent they had become organized and prepared to play roles in the planning of health care facilities.

In essence, the Metcalf-McCloskey Act applied the planning forces of the Hill-Burton Program to all new hospital and nursing home construction throughout the state, and strengthened and decentralized the administrative machinery involved by giving the regional councils statutory recognition and powers. However, the Board of Social Welfare was not subordinated to the Hill-Burton mechanism and was, itself, given ultimate power to determine whether or not new beds should be added.

Under the law any party desiring to erect a new medical care institution—except the State of New York—must apply to the Board of Social Welfare. The Board passes the relevant information on to the State Hospital Review and Planning

5 Joint Legislative Committee on Health Insurance Plans, 1964 *Report*, p. 72.

Council and to the Regional Council concerned. The Regional Council makes a decision as to whether there is public need for the proposed facility and refers that decision to the State Council. That Council then makes a decision; in the event that it rejects the decision of the local council it must allow the local organ to request a public hearing. The State Council refers its decision to the Board of Social Welfare. If the Board rejects the determinations of either the State or Regional Council it must hold a public hearing if either requests one. The statute provided criteria by which the Board's judgment is to be guided: (1) the public need for the facility;[6] (2) the character, competence, and standing in the community of the leaders for the proposed project; (3) financial resources; (4) such other matters as the Board shall deem pertinent. The Commissioner of Hospitals of the City of New York was charged with the responsibilities otherwise exercised by the Board in respect to proprietary hospitals and nursing homes in the city. An important indicator of the general policy drift is to be found in the following language: "In general and in cooperation with the various regional councils, the [state] council shall seek to improve the quality, efficiency and economy of health care throughout the state."[7]

The Folsom Committee and Resulting Legislation

On May 24, 1964, Governor Rockefeller, disturbed by a rising public clamor over proposals of Blue Cross plans in the state to raise their premium rates, appointed seven citizen-notables with experience in hospital affairs to a Governor's Committee on Hospital Costs. The Chairman of the Committee was Marion B. Folsom, a prominent leader in health and welfare matters and a former Secretary of the Department of Health, Education and Welfare in the Eisenhower administration.

[6] See p. 135, above, and p. 223, below.
[7] *Laws of New York, 1964*, chap. 730.

The Governor charged his committee " (1) to study the costs of general hospital care in the state and to make recommendations as to how hospitals may best provide high-quality care at the lowest possible cost and (2) to examine the present apportionment of responsibility among State agencies concerned with hospital care and to make recommendations as to how the responsibility of State Government may be most effectively carried out."[8] The Committee's work was to produce the most sweeping legislation to be found in any state in the country for the planning and systematic arrangement of health care facilities. The immediate legislative consequences sprang from the Committee's summary report, released in April 1965, and the Governor's determination to do something about the apparent derangement of the state's function and philosophy in relation to health care facilities.

Among the Committee's principal conclusions was the following:

Responsibilities for hospital affairs are now scattered among many agencies of New York State. No one agency, however, nor even the aggregate of agencies, has a comprehensive responsibility for being informed about all aspects of hospitals and related institutions and for considering institutional health care from the standpoint of the State as a whole. There is no "State" policy on hospitals and related facilities, but only a number of fragmented activities that affect these kinds of institutions. State administration in this area has, consequently been piecemeal and inadequate.[9]

Following up this finding, it recommended that the State Health Department, as most qualified of state agencies to deal with hospitals, should become the central agency for these matters. It counseled that the Department should be given full authority to require from every hospital and nursing home in the state whatever reports relating to finances, management,

[8] Governor's Committee on Hospital Costs, *Report* (New York, 1965), p. 2.
[9] *Ibid.*, p. 11.

utilization of services and quality of medical care given it found necessary for the fulfillment of its responsibility.[10]

The Committee's recommendations echoed those of earlier studies in proposing that regulatory powers over hospitals and nursing homes should be shifted from the Board and Department of Social Welfare to the Department of Health, these functions to be executed in that setting with the advice of the State Hospital Review and Planning Council. In a step of cardinal importance, the Committee recognized the anachronistic nature of the policy of requiring voluntary institutions to help finance the care of public charges through philanthropy. It advised that rates for public charges cared for by private institutions should cover full cost.[11]

A recommendation that the state establish a program of grants and loans for the construction of voluntary nursing homes and hospitals, to be administered through the existing Hill-Burton planning mechanism, represented another step taken to promote these nonprofit institutions. Note was taken of the common conclusion that one important cause of high hospital costs is the use of acute care hospitals for what would more properly be nursing home patients because of the lack of appropriate facilities. Finally, among its recommendations most relevant for the development of nursing-home-type institutions, the Committee asked for a compulsory State health insurance plan that would provide nursing home benefits and requested that the Regional Hospital Planning and Review Councils be strengthened.

The measure of cause for gratification that the Committee

[10] *Ibid.,* p. 87.

[11] *Ibid.,* p. 71. The language proposed by the Committee for the general establishment of rates was that they should be "reasonably related to the over-all costs of the particular hospital consonant with community need for the health care and teaching facilities" (see p. 87). The word "hospital" was intended to include long-term care facilities. The words "consonant with community need for health care and teaching facilities" were employed to allow opportunity for determination that the costs incurred were needed costs.

had seeing its recommendations implemented into law comes with extreme infrequency. On the heels of its summary report —and months before the release of its final report—huge important sections of its proposals had found their way to the session laws, bringing great change. Chapter 795 of the *Laws of New York, 1965* reflected the relationship of nursing homes to other kinds of institutions by including them in its broad definition of hospitals and then charged the Department of Health with the "central, comprehensive responsibility for the development and administration of the state's policy with respect to hospital and related services." It went on to grant the Commissioner of Health full authority to require reports on financial and other information as the Committee had requested and specified that the rates for public charges paid for by government throughout the state should be certified by the Commissioner of Health as being "reasonably related to the costs of providing for such services."[12]

The new law went beyond what the Committee had recommended in establishing a system of licensing—some nineteen years after the recommendation of the Health Preparedness Commission. Hospitals and nursing homes were forbidden to operate without certificates of operation. Such certificates are revokable, after a hearing, upon a finding that the institution is not complying with the law and pertinent rules and regulations. The rule-making power relating to the gathering of information and to the regulating of health care institutions is vested in the State Hospital Review and Planning Council, such rules being subject to the approval of the Commissioner of Health. The execution of the regulatory functions of the law in relation to proprietary nursing homes and hospitals in New York City were charged to the City Hospitals Department.

Also, the law exceeded the recommendations of the Committee in extending a grant of power over construction to the Commissioner of Health, thereby creating an anomalous situa-

---

[12] Public Health Law, sec. 2800.

tion. The Commissioner must now approve or disapprove all new construction of nursing homes and hospitals, after having referred applications for such proposed construction to the State and Regional Councils for their deliberation and determination. In making his decision, the Commissioner is guided by certain criteria, the most specific of which is that of "public need." The Commissioner under this law and the Board of Social Welfare under the remaining sections of the Metcalf-McCloskey Act are each charged with deciding whether there is public need for new facilities—and are provided with precisely the same criterion for the determination of that need.[13] There is no apparent device, short of resort to the courts, for the resolution of conflicting decisions that might result.

The act passed the state legislature in the summer of 1965, creating Article 28 of the Public Health Law, and became effective February 1, 1966. In June of 1966 the State Council approved a new nursing home code.

THE STATE-WIDE CODE

The Division of Chronic Disease Services of the Health Department, which worked up the new product, took the New York City code as well as the draft from the Adult Institutions Bureau as a beginning model. Its proposals reflect their origins in these respects and also anticipate some of the requirements nursing homes will have to meet to participate in the federal health insurance for the aged program (Medicare, Title XVIII), to be described below. The upstate document bears a strong resemblance to the New York City code, even borrowing exact

---

[13] Sec. 2802 of the Public Health Law and sec. 35 of the Social Welfare Law both require, the first on the part of the Commissioner of Health and the second on the part of the Board of Social Welfare, satisfaction as to "the public need for the existence of the institution at the time and place and under the circumstances proposed, provided however that in the case of an institution proposed to be established by an organization defined in subdivision one of section four hundred eighty-two-a, the needs of the members of the religious denomination concerned for care or treatment in accordance with their religious or ethical convictions, shall be deemed to be public need."

language in some instances, but it has differences that reflect three things: (1) the heterogeneous nature of the institutions it must regulate and the impracticality of demanding the kind of standards appropriate for a city home to a small, rural facility; (2) the fact that nursing home concepts have developed even since the city code was promulgated, and (3) a heightened consciousness concerning administrative management. Of course it differs also in that its purview encompasses voluntary and public as well as proprietary homes.

The code is to have state-wide application but proprietary homes in New York City must also meet any requirements of the city code that are more restrictive. Except in the case of these same institutions, which are left under the supervision of the City Hospitals Department, enforcement is carried out by health departments of local governments and the regional offices of the State Health Department. It is broad in at least one other respect. Although it recognizes differences between kinds of institutions—particularly in that public and voluntary homes are responsible for the physician care of their patients but proprietaries may not render such care—in general it is a uniform document applicable to all of the types of nursing home facilities under consideration in this study—fulfillment of another recommendation made by the Health Preparedness Commission in 1946.

Staffing standards of the upstate document reflect the variation among homes it is designed to cover. For example, they permit part-time administrators for some homes, which the city code does not do. Staffing ratios are used, but for kinds of services assignments of personnel "appropriate" to patient needs are called for—the code does not go as far as the city instrument in determining what those needs are.

The new regulations venture into some areas not covered by those of the city, and venture farther into some others. For example, where the city requires nursing personnel to be aware of the patient's dental needs and that the patient's sponsor or physician must be informed of them, the state code requires dental examinations and the drawing up of a plan for dental treatment and the maintenance of dental records by the home. Again, the former does not mention occupational therapy but the latter requires the home to arrange for such services and to develop a plan for them when they are prescribed by a physician. There are at least three specific, unique state requirements which, if met, will move the homes along the road to participation in the federal health insurance program for the aged.

These are for the systematic review of the appropriateness of utilization of the home's facilities by its patients, for an agreement or affiliation with a hospital that will facilitate the transfer of patients from one institution to the other as the need arises—or evidence that serious attempts have been made to establish such an affiliation or transfer agreement; and for the appointment of a medical advisory board or consulting physician charged with developing medical policies for the institution and generally advising the operator on medical matters.

The state code singularly promotes an administrative management point of view. This is not to say that such precursors as the city code have been unmindful of administrative considerations—personnel policies and the like—but that the new state document focuses upon and emphasizes much conceptual material developed by students of administration in a manner that makes it unusual as a regulatory document. It is replete with references to plans, programs, and job descriptions. The city code stipulates that each home must "provide individual and group activities suited to the patients' needs and interests," but under the state rules there must be an "activities program plan" complying with a fairly explicit set of directives and involving a schedule of activities planned at least one month in advance. Plans must be developed by homes for carrying out such patient services as patient dental programs, the activities program mentioned above, physical therapy, occupational therapy, diets, emergency procedures, nursing care, utilization review, and medical and social discharge. In other words, much of the work the home does is to be seen through the administrative management perspective of planning. What influence the state code will have in educating nursing home managers for effectively planned activity will depend, of course, upon the style in which it is administered. But its tone makes it an instrument worth watching.

Because life-care contracts have not been an important aspect of the financing of proprietary nursing homes no mention has been made of the fact that the city code forbids any home to make such a contract. They have been quite an important aspect of the economics of voluntary institutions, however, particularly in upstate areas. In harmony with the changing image of the voluntary organization the state code abolishes life-care contracts for all of the types of nursing home institutions under its purview.

Nonprofit Facilities: State Funds for Construction

The deepening concern over the inadequacy of nursing home facilities engendered by the discussion of, and then the passage of, the federal Medicare legislation, by the *Report* of the Folsom Committee, and by a growing general awareness of institutional medical care problems of which these two were partly an outgrowth, constituted a climate of opinion favorable to positive, direct approaches to the provision of more or better nursing home beds. Two developments with this aim that were begun in earlier years have come to fruition in the mid-1960's. One provides state grants for the construction of public nursing homes. The other provides long-term loans for building nursing homes under voluntary auspices.

PUBLIC INSTITUTIONS

The State Health Department took a policy position in 1962 that there should be state matching grants to local governments for the construction of community nursing homes. It noted that there was legislation authorizing grants of 50 per cent of the cost of construction of public hospitals by counties,[14] to be administered by the Commissioner of Health, and recommended that the statute be amended to include nursing homes and that funds be appropriated. In a statement of October 1, 1964, the Department made similar proposals and asked for help for the construction of voluntary nursing homes as well:

It is believed that an annual appropriation of approximately $10,000,000 for each of five years would greatly assist in providing more rapidly needed facilities and services for those requiring nursing home care. It is also believed that the grants would have to amount to 50 per cent of the total costs of constructing these facilities in order for the program to be attractive to the voluntary nonprofit and religious groups.[15]

This precise language was repeated again in the conclusions of a study done by the Departments of Health and Social Welfare under the auspices of an interdepartmental coordinating committee and dated May 1, 1965.[16] In these reports the Department was estimating that with a 50 per cent matching grant there was enough construction currently planned by counties and New York City to match almost $50 million in state funds.

The 1965 session of the state legislature enacted a new provision authorizing matching grants for the construction of public nursing homes by New York City or counties of the state equal to one-third of the costs.[17] The law was based upon still another study by the Health Department which involved a three-year projection. The first year's appropriation was $1,000,000; the projected appropriations requested for the second and third

[14] Public Health Law, sec. 608.
[15] New York State Department of Health, Division of Hospital Review and Planning, "Evaluation of All Types of Nursing Home Facilities in New York State and Projection of Needs and Capital Construction Costs," Oct. 1964, p. 11.
[16] Interdepartmental Health and Hospital Council, New York State Department of Health and New York State Department of Social Welfare, "A Report on Nursing Home Facilities and Home Care Services in New York State," 1965, p. 11.
[17] Laws of New York, 1965, chap. 394.

year were $4 million and $6 million. The state Hill-Burton plan, under the guidelines of which the money was to be spent, was late for the current year and none of the million was spent. The program was thus delayed for a year. The $1 million was reappropriated in 1966. It must be noted that the $1 million is a modest amount compared to the Health Department's estimate of needs.

VOLUNTARY INSTITUTIONS

The loans for voluntary nursing homes were provided, of course, as an implementation of the constitutional amendment described in Chapter 5 for that purpose. Two bills dealing with the matter were introduced into the legislature in 1966, one drafted in the New York City Housing and Redevelopment Board and the other by the State Housing and Finance Agency in consultation with the State Health Department. The New York City bill approached the implementation largely as a matter of including nursing homes under voluntary sponsorship among the cluster of other kinds of construction—such as housing, mental hygiene facilities, and university buildings —for which the agency administers loans financed through public bond issues. It provided for mortgages of up to 95 per cent of the construction cost, as much as is available under any of the other programs coming under it. It did propose that the supervision of a nursing home project should not be the responsibility of the chief fiscal officer of the local government in which the project was to be situated, as is the case with other of its programs, but a suitable official such as a health or hospital commissioner. The state bill was quite different, however, calling for a wholesale commitment of government credit and other support for the expansion of voluntary nursing home facilities.

The state proposal became Article 28-A of the Public Health Law, following Article 28, which had grown out of the Folsom Committee study during the closing hours of the 1966 session of the legislature. It provides for the establishment of "nursing home companies" by voluntary organizations under the membership corporations law, the statutory provisions by which all charitable institutions in the state take their form. To such companies there are available loans under the customary terms of the State Housing Finance Agency—loans to be amortized over fifty years at the rates of interest required to sell the bonds furnishing the money, plus costs—to cover 100 per cent of the costs of establishing a nursing home. The mortgages may include costs of land acquisition, planning, and other ancillary costs, construction and equipment costs, the costs of outfitting the institution with needed personal property, and up to 3 per cent of the total cost for working capital.

The device of the "nursing home company" provides for the setting apart of the financing of any project from that of other kinds of activities in which the voluntary agency might be engaging and thereby to establish unclouded lines of fiscal responsibility. Similarly the law calls for the creation of a separate fund for nursing home projects by the Housing Finance Agency into which all related receipts are to be paid and from which the bonds involved are to be retired. Thus there are material safeguards to assure bondholders of the soundness of their investment.

These are not all of the safeguards, however. The Commissioner of Health is empowered to appoint one member of the board of directors of each nursing home company. Further, he may determine the amounts charged by an institution for its services to assure that its income is sufficient to meet its financial obligations. He is to be co-defendant to any action brought against the company for foreclosure or legal judgement. In the event of foreclosure he may become the receiver or make an agreement with the Housing Finance Agency to take over the home and operate it or contract with some other party for its operation. As a further safeguard, the legislature and Governor are authorized to appropriate to the special fund for the retirement of bonds sold to finance the nursing homes such money as might be necessary to keep it solvent.

Article 28-A also integrates the facilities constructed through its program into the over-all state planning and regulation of health care facilities. It requires the approval of the Commissioner of Health, in addition to that of the Board of Social Welfare, for the certificate of incorporation by which nursing home companies are to be established. Such companies are subject to the regulatory powers of the Health Department over nursing homes (Article 28) and also to rules and regulations of the Commissioner promulgated specifically for them. Nor may the Housing Finance Agency make a loan until the company concerned has secured the approval of the Commissioner, such approval to be contingent upon the company's having complied with the Commissioner's specifications as to standards for the project and with the provisions of Article 28.

The new law is to provide nursing home facilities for "persons of low income." And such a person is statutorily identified as one "whose probable annual income at the time of admission and during the period of occupancy does not exceed two times the annual charges to be paid." Specific standards for eligibility are set by the Commissioner and identify, under these terms, a population somewhat different from that composed of welfare recipients.

There is now availability of complete financing by government for the creation of nursing home facilities on the one hand, and on the other the statutory requirement of Article 28 that reimbursement for public charges must be reasonably related to cost. Problems of money for voluntary organizations desiring to provide nursing home care for persons of limited means would appear to be largely over, at least if administrative implementation follows the seeming intent of the law.

Social Security Amendments of 1965

In 1930 the central political issue in New York State was whether there would be a contributory social insurance system of support for the aged or one paid for out of taxes. These differing systems were joined again in the passage of Public

Law 89-97, the Social Security Amendments of 1965. Title XVIII of the Social Security Act made available extensive health services on a contributory insurance basis, and a second new measure, Title XIX, laid the foundation for a comprehensive system of health care to be funded from taxes. It is typical of Americans to choose a "patchwork of," or "pluralistic set of"—depending upon where one's social sympathies lie—devices to get on with the job of systematic provision of health care.

Title XVIII provides a broad program of health insurance for the aged. Title XIX, in effect, forms all public assistance for medical purposes previously given under the four federal assistance categories—Old Age Assistance, Aid to the Blind, Medical Assistance to the Aged, Aid to the Disabled, and Aid to Dependent Children—into one, federally aided, comprehensive, medical assistance program; in addition it qualifies for aid under that program all persons who would be eligible for aid under one of the four historical categories if their incomes were lower, yet whose incomes are not sufficiently high to enable them to afford needed medical care.

The enactment of the health insurance provisions of the new law created great excitement, hope for a plentitude of money, and no little fear, in the nursing home field. Some nursing home administrators see the legislation as laden with new opportunities for them. But many see it as a threat, imposing standards that they will not be able to meet, and that will thereby exclude them and gratuitously mark their homes as inferior institutions. However, any home that meets the demands of the new state code or the proprietary nursing home code of New York City should have no trouble meeting the federal requirements.

MEDICARE

Under the health insurance law all persons of age sixty-five or over became entitled, on January 1, 1967, to insurance payments for care in an "extended care facility," along with other health services. An extended care facility is defined as an institution giving skilled nursing care or rehabilitation services. This care is paid for by the program only if it is received by the patient after discharge from a hospital stay of at least three days. Admission to the extended care facility must be within fourteen days of the hospital discharge. Compensation of the institution is at "reasonable cost" of the services but the patient must pay $5.00 of the cost each day after the twentieth day of his stay. The insurance contributes to only one hundred days of care during any one "spell of illness"—that is, during any period in which the patient has not been out of extended care facility and out of the hospital for at least sixty days.

In order to qualify for a fresh hundred-day period of care paid for by insurance, then, a patient must be well enough to stay out of the nursing home—or extended care facility—and out of the hospital for sixty days. The average length of stay of most nursing home patients is much longer than one hundred days, of course. The broadest study of the matter done in the state did not even measure stays in days, or months, but in years. The average patient found in a proprietary nursing home in New York at the end of 1962 had been in the home for 1.4 years.[18] A table drawn up by the Hospital Review and Planning Council of Southern New York indicates that the average length of stay in nonprofit, public, and proprietary nursing homes in southern New York during 1963 was 267 days.[19] The provisions of the health insurance legislation relating to extended care are aimed at relatively short-term, restorative care, and may be expected to strike only a glancing blow at the major problems of long-term care that so typically characterize nursing home service. They may be expected, however, to attract a good deal of talent and capital to short-term, rehabilitative services, and even to develop a fairly identifiable

[18] Milton Matz, "Nursing Homes and Related Facilities and Their Patients in New York State," Medical Economics Reports No. 1, May 1964, State Department of Social Welfare, p. 51. However, 68 per cent of the patients discharged from such homes during 1962 were terminating lengths of stay of less than one year.

[19] "Nursing Home Statistics," Sept. 1965 (mimeo.), Table 9.

body of institutions distinguished from what nursing homes have tended to be by their giving of intensive, restorative care.

The statute specified some eight conditions that must be met by an institution before it may be recognized as an extended care facility qualified to receive patients for whose care there will be reimbursement by the health insurance. Such an institution must have a transfer agreement with a hospital; medical policies developed by at least one nurse and one physician; a physician or registered nurse charged with the execution of those policies; physician supervision of the care of each patient and availability of physician care for emergencies; clinical records on all patients; twenty-four hour nursing service, and full-time employment of at least one registered nurse; appropriate procedures for administering drugs; a utilization review plan; a license or other approval if required by state or applicable local law.

The statute elaborates somewhat on its requirements for transfer agreements and utilization review. It directs that there be transfers of patients between the facility and a hospital, and vice versa, whenever such transfer is medically indicated and that there be an exchange of useful, needed information relating to the care of the patient between the institutions involved. It then proceeds, however, to direct that the transfer agreement requirement shall be deemed to have been met if a facility has attempted "in good faith" to conclude such an agreement with a hospital even though it has failed, if the Secretary of the Department of Health, Education and Welfare finds this to be in the public interest.[20] The law specifies that there must be utilization review of the professional services rendered and the medication used both from the standpoint of medical necessity and of the efficient use of resources. The review is to be conducted by at least two physicians from the institution or by a group outside the institution—or by some

---

[20] The role of voluntary and proprietary organizations in the framing of this language has been noted. See p. 131, above.

group established in a manner that meets the Secretary's approval.

A publication titled *Conditions of Participation for Extended Care Facilities*,[21] distributed by the Department of Health, Education and Welfare, elaborates the law in outlining requirements in eighteen subject areas, eight of which overlap the provisions of the law. As for the plant and equipment, it requires the facility to meet applicable local building or other codes, or in absence of such codes to meet "recognized safety standards" such as the Recommendations of the American Society of Engineers and the National Building Code of the National Board of Fire Underwriters. The specifications to which there was the most opposition during the drafting of *Conditions of Participation* were those requiring academic qualifications of nurses. Nursing home representatives pleaded that personnel shortages made the fulfillment of the requirement impossible.[22] A registered nurse directing the nursing service—without administrative responsibilities for the facility—is requisite; supervising nurses under the director of nursing must also be registered nurses. Only at the level of the charge nurse may a practical nurse—"a graduate of a State-approved school of practical nursing"—be employed; and these are required "at all times."

Even more than in the case of the New York State code, *Conditions of Participation* reflects the heterogeneous mass of institutions it is to regulate, and its impact will depend upon the manner in which its provisions are administered. There are factors that do not auger well for that administration. The provisions tend in numerous respects to be unspecific; there are no staffing ratios, for example. Moreover, a policy directive of the Department of Health, Education and Welfare, with an

[21] U.S. Department of Health, Education, and Welfare, Social Security Administration, HIM-3, March 1966.

[22] Lecture by Alfred Ercolano, Executive Director of the American Association of Nursing Homes, at Columbia University School of Public Health and Administrative Medicine, Continuation Education Unit, May 10, 1966.

eye to elevating levels of performance over time, adopts a test of "substantial compliance." Facilities are to be considered in substantial compliance with the conditions of participation if

the facility meets the specific statutory requirements of section 1961 (j) but is found to have deficiencies with respect to one or more conditions of participation which:
1. It is making reasonable plans and efforts to correct and
2. Notwithstanding the deficiencies, it is rendering adequate care and is without hazard to the health and safety of individuals being served, taking into account special procedures or precautionary measures which have been or are being instituted.[23]

Agencies designated by each state—in New York the State Health Department—will conduct the necessary inspections and make recommendations to the Secretary for the acceptance of homes as extended care facilities. Inevitably pressures upon the agencies will develop to facilitate the flow of insurance money into the respective states. Without specific criteria there is a clear danger those pressures may have unwholesome consequences. The situation in New York is considerably less dangerous than that in most states because standards here are quite high and specific.

MEDICAID

The instrument by which Title XVIII seeks to promote a deepened kind of social justice is an insurance program. That is clear. The counterpart qualities and characteristics of Title XIX need a bit more spelling out. The chief means by which it undertakes to promote social justice is by extending benefits to others than those who are impoverished. It does this primarily by providing that persons who are able to meet their own needs as to food, clothing and shelter and who, if this were not so, would qualify to receive public assistance through one of the categorical aid programs, may receive the medical assistance benefits it affords. The department of welfare of each

23 *Conditions of Participation*, p. 2.

state is charged with determining the income levels below which persons in the respective states need the medical assistance. (After a fierce political battle, however, the Department of Health was given the responsibility of administering the program in New York State.) To be eligible for any medical assistance is to be eligible for all medical assistance given, as needed, under the federal program. The federal government pays a percentage of the cost that is determined by a ratio of the state per capita income to the national per capita income; for New York the federal contribution is 50 per cent.

Other provisions of the federal legislation deserve mention. The law declared, for the first time, that children are not responsible for the costs of their parents' medical care.[24] Laws on estates of recipients were strictly limited. In a step that may evoke recollections of the problems of settlement and removal of 1788, the statute required that by July 1, 1970, the state will either pay all of the nonfederal share of the federal medical assistance program itself, relieving local governments of all financial responsibility, or otherwise "assure that the lack of adequate funds from local sources will not result in lowering the amount, duration, scope, or quality of care and services available."

Among the strategies the federal act employed to promote comprehensiveness of care is the requirement that in-patient and out-patient hospital care, other laboratory and X-ray services, skilled nursing home care, and physician services all be available as minimal services to those eligible for medical assistance by July 1, 1967. As another stratagem, it encouraged movement to nursing home facilities, where appropriate, of persons over sixty-five in state mental hospitals. The federal government had never before contributed to the support of persons in mental institutions. Now, the aged in state institutions are eligible for the federally aided medical assistance. But for them to qualify for this financial support the state must

---

[24] Wives and husbands are responsible for each other's care, and parents for the care of their children under twenty-one.

provide for plans for the care of each patient, and agencies of the state must undertake joint planning to provide suitable alternatives to state hospitalization. The use of community mental health centers and nursing homes are the two specific alternative services the state must demonstrate, to the satisfaction of the Secretary, that it is developing, in order to continue receiving federal money for the care of the mentally ill aged.

The New York Medicaid Law

As the Governor and legislative leaders prepared to implement Title XIX, New York City groups pressed hard for liberal eligibility criteria. The State's implementation of the federal legislation went farther than was required to receive federal reimbursement. It provided that not only those who would, by virtue of their age, childhood dependency, or physical condition if not their incomes, be eligible for financial aid through one of the old categories, but that even those who would not—that is, everyone in the state—could receive medical assistance if their incomes fell below the eligibility limits established by the Board of Social Welfare. Between income exemptions specified by the law and the eligibility criteria set by the Board, liberality prevailed: recipients could own their home and necessary personal property. A family of four could have an income of $6,000, have $4,000 in insurance and $3,000 in savings, and be eligible for medical assistance.[25] Under the state law the state and the local public welfare districts share equally the fiscal responsibility for the part of the cost not subsidized by the federal government. There is no federal subsidy for medical indigents who would not qualify, except for income, under one of the four categories.

Actually, there had been a precursor of the medical indigency principle recognized in the implementation of Title XIX. Since 1934, the reader may recall, local governments had been

[25] Calculated from State Department of Social Welfare, "Medical Assistance for Needy Persons," n.d. (pamphlet released May 1966).

obliged to bear the full financial burden of any hospital care they gave to persons not already receiving public assistance except, since 1961, those eligible for Medical Assistance to the Aged. In 1965 the state legislature had passed a measure— such as had been introduced in every legislature for many years —determining that the state would share 50 per cent of the cost not federally reimbursed, of all hospital care provided by local governments. The legislation recognized a class of medical indigents, to include persons "unable to meet all the costs of their care through their own income and resources, including available support from responsible relatives, although other- wise able to maintain themselves."[26] It also directed that the determination of eligibility for hospital care must be by the welfare administration, and the investigations and collection functions of the City Department of Hospitals were accordingly transferred to the City Department of Welfare.

After the passage of the bill implementing Title XIX, on April 30, 1966, a storm of protest broke out through upstate regions. A vignette illustrating the political situation may be cited from the *New York Times*:

One state Senator, who strongly supports the program, recently voiced agreement with a newsman's observation that few legislators seemed to comprehend the bill they had just debated.

"And it's a damn good thing," the Senator added, "because they never would have voted for it if they had."[27]

New York City stood to gain some $50 million annually be- cause much more of its generous provision of health care would be supported by federal money. However, participation at the level stipulated by the state law involved upstate areas more deeply than they had ever before been involved, and even with the federal grants in aid, they were obliged to spend substan- tially more local tax money for care than in the past. The wave of opposition grew to great heights and the Governor and

[26] *Laws of New York, 1965*, chap. 287.
[27] May 21, 1966. See the *Times* for May 21, 23 and 24.

leadership of the contending factions amended the law, moving it a step back from its liberal position.[28]

Still more cutbacks were to come, however. The alarm was not confined to upstate New York, but was nation-wide. In 1967 Congress set a ceiling standard for eligibility under Medicaid.[29] The following Spring the state revised its statute to comply and to cut state and local expenses further. The eligibility income level for a family of four was reduced to $5,300. More significantly, those persons who would have hardship paying medical bills but who would not qualify to receive non-health public assistance were removed from coverage.[30] This was the group for whom no federal funds were provided.

PROBABLE IMPACT OF TITLES XVIII AND XIX

The upshot of the aims of comprehensiveness and increased availability of public assistance for medical care, for the purposes of this study, is that there will be a substantially increased demand for nursing home care. The health insurance provisions of Title XVIII will increase the use of nursing homes partly as an alternative to more expensive hospital care, which is the intent of the law. It will also encourage nursing home utilization simply by making payment for the service more available than it has been before, the requisite hospitalization preceding admission to the home operating as a secondary consideration. But its most important impact will probably be in facilitating initial entry of patients to nursing homes who, upon filling out their hundred-day stay, will then be transferred to the medical assistance program of Title XIX. The main flow of patients into homes may be expected to be through the provisions of the health insurance because most all of such patients are over sixty-five and thus entitled to the benefits, and because states will want to use up those resources first, not having to contribute to them. But Title XIX also facilitates entry to homes of any who do not have the insurance, and, having no time

[28] *Laws of New York, 1966*, chap. 802.   [29] Public Law 90-248.
[30] *Laws of New York, 1968*, chap. 32.

limit, will surely end up carrying most of the financial burden for nursing home care, which is typically of such long-term character.

The Veterans' Administration and Nursing Home Beds

The year 1964 saw the advent of still another federal nursing home program. In that year the Veterans' Administration, over its objections, was charged with carrying out a three-pronged measure to furnish nursing home care to veterans. Public Law 88-450 directed the Administration to develop, within its hospitals throughout the country, at least 4,000 nursing home beds; to transfer patients needing nursing home care from its hospitals to private or public nursing homes and pay for their care there; and to administer a program of matching grants for the construction of nursing home beds in state soldier's homes and contributing to the maintenance of veterans there.

The Administration's keenest opposition was to the development of nursing home beds in its hospitals. This was so even though the new beds were to be in addition to, rather than at the sacrifice of, acute care beds. Representative Olin Teague, Chairman of the Committee on Veterans' Affairs of the House of Representatives, observed that the Veterans' Administration was "opposed to the legislation that we have pending for nursing care." The Administrator of Veterans' Affairs, Mr. John S. Gleason, Jr., responded: "At this time, anyway."[31]

Mr. Gleason acknowledged that there were about 9,400 patients in VA hospitals who should be in nursing home or similar facilities, but then went on to say: "We don't want to encroach upon the hospital care that we are now giving. This is the reason why at this time we are opposed to this."[32] He became more specific in his objections: "I might say I believe honestly, Congressman, that there would be some type of depreciation from the viewpoint of the medical profession of

[31] U.S. Congress, House, Committee on Veterans' Affairs: *VA Legislative Policy—Administrator of Veterans' Affairs*, 88 Cong., 1st Sess., 1963, p. 168.
[32] *Ibid.*, p. 173.

the nursing home, we will say, in association with the hospital."
He was joined by Dr. H. M. Engle, Acting Chief Medical Director of the Administration, who reported that

the major objection of physicians in the Veterans' Administration
to a formal association with nursing home care is, we don't think
it would represent good medical practice. . . . Further, we would
agree very definitely with the Administrator that having large numbers of nursing home patients in physical and functional contiguity with the hospital would dilute the efforts of our staff and
would make it difficult to attract and retain high caliber professional personnel.[33]

The Administrator expressed a preference for some kind of
"community" nursing home program, where patients would be
close to their own homes, but was still studying to determine
what role in it the VA should play. He saw some appropriate
relationship of the Department of Health, Education and Welfare to such an undertaking, but explained that "we wouldn't
be in favor of HEW exercising any controls over any part of
our program. This we don't look upon, however, Congressman,
as part of our program if the individual is returned to his own
community."[34]

Urged by veteran groups,[35] however, Congress went on to
enact the provisions it had been contemplating.[36] VA hospitals
were authorized to transfer suitable patients to nursing homes
in the community. As of mid-1966 the limits of the terms were
rather severe, however, and the Administration had not had
great success in New York State. Payment for care could not
exceed one-third of the per diem cost of caring for the patient
in the VA hospital from which he was transferred. Rates in the
state ran from $9.51 per day to $13.50, and were generally not

[33] *Ibid.*, p. 179.   [34] *Ibid.*, p. 169.

[35] See the testimony of Francis W. Stover, National Legislative Director,
Veterans of Foreign Wars, and John D. Fagan, Assistant Director,
Veterans of Foreign Wars, U.S. Senate, Joint Subcommittee on Long-
Term Care of the Special Committee on Aging, *Nursing Homes and
Related Long-Term Care Services*, Part 3, 88th Cong., 2nd Sess., 1964,
pp. 282–286.

[36] 72 *U.S. Statutes* 1251.

as high as the local welfare district rates for nursing home care. The VA hospitals were often able to find beds for their patients, in proprietary nursing homes, only in institutions many miles from the hospital and the veterans' homes. By mid-1966 a total of 469 patients had been placed. Pressures were developing to lift the rate ceiling.

The law also authorized the Administration to establish and operate "not less than" 4,000 nursing home beds in VA hospitals. Although the language of the law was permissive, an excerpt from the Senate Committee Report on the bill made the legislative intent clear:

While the cited authority is discretionary, let there be no doubt or misunderstanding as to the intent, purpose, and desire of the committee. The 4,000 nursing home care beds are to be provided in the immediate future and to be fully operated at the earliest practicable date. It is fully expected by the committee that every bed of this type which is placed in operation by the VA will be fully utilized for the purpose stated.[37]

By mid-1966 there were 36 nursing home beds established in VA facilities in the state, with plans to add 332 beds during the fiscal year 1967.

Public Law 88-450 authorized the appropriation of $5 million annually to be used in matching grants of up to 50 per cent of the cost of constructing nursing home facilities in either existing state soldiers' homes or in such homes to be built. It also provided that the VA could pay up to 50 per cent of the cost of furnishing nursing home care in such an institution. New York State did not move to participate in this aspect of the Veterans' Administration nursing home program.

More Than Straws in the Wind

There has been, then, a resentful, belated burst of feeling in upstate New York upon realization of the importance of the state's implementation of the new federal medical assistance program and cut-backs have resulted. Moreover, there has

[37] *U.S. Congressional Record,* 88th Cong., 2nd Sess., 1964, p. 17392.

been established a new federal nursing home program that will probably do more to fragment community health care facilities than to integrate them—although it has not yet been sufficiently effective to have much impact whatsoever. Also, the constitutional amendment providing for loans for hospital construction has not even begun; grants for public nursing homes have gotten off to only a halting start—one could make a long list of examples frustrating progress. However, if one can assume a historical perspective on matters of the present, the items of such a list are seen as backlash reactions to a major thrust of policy development, or as eddies swirling off a main stream.

There is a discernible main stream, or thrust, and it emphasizes breadth and at the same time a sense of direction. In an inexorable kind of evolution, it becomes more clearly a determination to do positive things to organize nursing homes and a broadening spectrum of other facilities into a battery of resources purposefully arranged to achieve identified goals. Seen from this vantage point, there are a number of other recent developments that are more than straws in the wind even though if observed in isolation they would reveal no trend and might even seem insignificant.

ACCREDITATION

After a long and bitter struggle, the American Hospital Association, the American Medical Association, the American Association of the Homes for the Aged, and the American Nursing Home Association have sufficiently patched up their differences to agree to a national system of accreditation of nursing homes administered by the Joint Commission on Accreditation of Hospitals. This latter body has, since 1952, managed hospital accreditation.[38] The nursing home standards are general and,

[38] For a detailed history of the preliminaries to the establishment of this program, the reader is referred to U.S. Senate, Joint Subcommittee on Long-Term Care of the Special Committee on Aging, *Nursing Homes and Related Long-Term Care Services*, Part 2, 88th Cong., 2nd Sess., 1964. About three-quarters of the volume is devoted to the accreditation matter and points of view of the various parties concerned are presented.

by and large, not severe.[39] With the exception of the specific requirement for a written transfer agreement with a hospital, they appear less demanding than the state code and the federal *Conditions of Participation* for extended facilities. The Joint Commission had, as of March 1966, not yet accredited any long-term care institutions although it published, at that time, a list of facilities that had been approved by four organizations that were its predecessors in this field.

PROPRIETARY NURSING HOME ORGANIZATION

In 1964 there began a new organization, the American College of Nursing Home Administrators. The College has a national membership of 457 members divided into three classifications—fellow, member and associate—The highest classification, fellow, requires four years of higher education, the publication of four articles in the field, and five years of responsible administrative experience in a nursing home. There are 190 fellows. The emphasis of the College is on the development of prestige through education and it is working toward the establishment of degree programs in the field of nursing home administration. Meanwhile, the State Nursing Home Association has been busy opposing the proposals for government loans and grants to voluntary and public nursing home facilities; but with little effect. Opposition to the loans was somewhat qualified. As had been the case with the Hill-Burton amendments, the proprietary home representatives wanted proprietaries to be included as beneficiaries, but, barring that, were opposed to the passage of the measure.

WELFARE ADMINISTRATIONS BROUGHT UNDER THE MERIT SYSTEM

The 1965 legislature took heed of the many criticisms that had been leveled at the local administration of welfare in most upstate areas. New Yorkers may now look forward to having matrons of county homes other than the wives of Welfare Com-

[39] Joint Commission on Accreditation of Hospitals, *Standards for Accreditation of Extended Care Facilities* (Chicago, n.d.).

missioners or Deputy Commissioners. Since January 1, 1966, chief executive positions in county or city public welfare departments throughout the state have been under the merit system. Appointments are for five-year terms and according to qualifications established by the Board of Social Welfare. However, incumbents in office at the end of 1965 were, by the law, deemed "qualified."[40]

[40] *Laws of New York, 1965,* chap. 1071.

CHAPTER 8

Conclusion

Recapitulation and Observations

During the 1930's many leaders in the public health and welfare fields misread history, losing track of the specialization in institutions that had been developing. Special institutions had been established for children, for the mentally ill, and for others. The next logical step was the development of a special institution for sick, aged people of limited means—of whom there were increasing numbers. But in their haste to reject the philosophy of indoor relief and rid the country of the almshouse, leaders overlooked the unfolding historical pattern. The members and staff of the State Commission on Old Age Security, of 1930, did not make this mistake. They studied the problem and saw clearly that there was already a great need for long-term, institutional care for the aged sick and that such need would grow in the future. Their decision to recommend the exclusion of persons in institutions from the benefits of the Old Age Security Act of 1930 and to relegate the problem of institutional care to a lesser priority than the pension provision, admonishing the legislature to give their matter further attention, was a judgment in strategy. Perhaps their judgment was best. Historical perspective—one might say *even* historical perspective—does not enable us to decide.

"We didn't know what was going to happen," is the way Luther Gulick explained the decision. That statement epitomizes one of the central predicaments confronting those who would guide social policy. Nonetheless, as propitious an opportunity to set policy in a groove toward the systematic provision of institutional care would never again be presented. And in fact, the cast that their decision gave policy, purely unintended, operated against the development of a rational system of nursing home facilities for at least the next two decades, and in many respects, longer than that. The need was not met. But it did not go away. Instead, it grew. As it grew, inexorably, makeshift arrangements to cope with it sprang up—as primitive proprietary nursing homes. In time, they became part of the institutional forms for the rendering of health care. Contending with the deficiencies that grew out of the makeshift character of the new arrangements has been one of the central threads of public policy in relation to nursing-home-type facilities as it has formed and consolidated.

The sociologist Robert S. Lynd has remarked that "it scarcely requires saying that organized power tends to be most alert and active precisely at the hinge-points of change, where new options, or loss of customary ones, impend."[1] It seems that it was not so much considerations of power as of lack of foreknowledge that determined that the option would not be attempted. There was no organized power in opposition to the Commission's belief that modern institutional care should be provided. But there was an absence of recognition of what the future held. Ironically, it is part of the heritage of the 1930 decision that today there is organized power that operates against the system of public institutions that the Commission believed in. The proprietary nursing home associations opposed the Hill-Burton legislation for nursing home facilities. They opposed the proposals for state loans and grants for the construction of voluntary and public nursing-home-type facilities. As they gain in public acceptance—which may be problematical—they may be expected to become more effective in their opposition.

[1] Robert S. Lynd, "Power in American Society as Resource and Problems," *Problems of Power in American Democracy*, ed. Arthur Kornhauser (Detroit: Wayne State University Press, 1957), p. 20.

From the 1930's on through the early 1960's nursing-home-type institutions were more strongly affected by public policy not directed at them than by that designed to influence them. Policy affecting the facilities was much like the forces shaping a whirlpool. An abundance of tangential influences give the whirlpool form, but the vortex is a vacuum. Laws aimed at abolishing the almshouse cramped the development of the public infirmary, and to some extent the voluntary institution. Welfare administrators, faced with a legitimate need to place clients, found a way to evade the law by using proprietary nursing homes, channeling to them the ever-increasing growth potential. In a seller's market, without rates being based on cost, and with virtually no regulation to maintain standards, the proprietaries experienced an explosive growth. The unbalance was aggravated when, in an effort to shore up the fiscal condition of local governments, the state reimbursement formula was shifted to make it even more profitable for local governments to place clients in proprietary institutions rather than public homes. And the battle of upstate conservatism versus New York City liberalism in relation to the provision of free hospital care postponed the day when the public institutions would stand on an even footing with proprietaries in the matter of reimbursement. For thirty years, there really was little or no policy on nursing home facilities at the state level. Yet, policy intended to deal with other affairs affected them profoundly and broadly.

By the statement that there was little or no policy on nursing-home-type facilities is meant simply that no body of sufficient significance to have influence had considered these facilities, determined what was to be desired from them, and designed specific, or even general, steps to be taken to promote the desiderata. Voluntary and public institutions languished in neglect. Proprietaries profited by accident and absence of attention. There was virtually no public recognition of the condition that existed or understanding of how it had come about—that it was an artifact of public policy supposedly unrelated to such facilities. The complexity and interlinkage of such matters is difficult to comprehend, especially by the broad public.

In New York City, by contrast, the lapse of attention to nursing home problems was relatively brief. After a firm historical policy of refusal to use proprietary facilities for public charges the city, under bed-shortage pressures that resulted at least in part from the Depression and World War II, shifted its position in 1952. There occurred then a growth in proprietaries even more dramatic than that upstate. Again, regulation was inadequate, a seller's market prevailed and there was not a close relationship between the costs of services rendered and what the homes were paid. Obviously and beyond question, the owners or operators found the business profitable.

The city is a place where the stakes are high and things are done on a grand scale. After only six years attention was brought forcefully to bear upon flagrant abuses. Policy again took shape. Regulation was strengthened—even rigidified—in time cost accounting statements were required, and steps were taken to expand the public and especially the voluntary sectors of the field. The constitutional amendment to provide capital financing for voluntary institutions and the implementing legislation that followed were sparked by New York City's public policy concern.

There had been some attenuated threads of policy directed at nursing-home-type facilities all along, of course. The localities of Mount Vernon and New York City began licensing and regulation in 1929. The statutory legitimization of the use of proprietary homes for welfare recipients in 1944—an acquiescence to a *fait accompli*—was policy in a sense. (It was an example of man being managed by his affairs rather than his managing them, however. Much policy is, and must be, molded in this fashion—a consequence of the indispensable need for policy of some kind and the absence of foreknowledge or prevision.) The disposition of the public welfare administrators to pay voluntaries less than cost for the care of public charge patients was also policy, but it was policy at cross-purposes with the need to provide more high-quality facilities. (Perhaps the holders of this philosophy thought voluntaries would expand without being compensated for full cost. If so, they lacked knowledge.) There had long been a general kind of state regulation of voluntary institutions, local governments had been responsible for the appropriate operation of all public institutions, and in 1951, a state code of sorts had been made applicable to proprietary homes. During the latter part of the 1950's and the early 1960's upstate supervision was strengthened somewhat and the milestone New York City code went into effect. One consequence of this elevation of standards was the stimulation of a trend for nursing homes to become big business operations and attract sophisticated people with business orientations.

Over the years policy was not only strengthened, it was also broadened, and took on a clearer sense of direction. In 1950 the malnourished state of public infirmaries, and the part that the social security law had played in their malnutrition, was recognized and remedied by the federal legislature. In 1954 the state obstruction to the use of these institutions was also removed. The same year saw federal legislation, the Hill-Burton Act, make a positive effort to promote an adequate supply of high-quality nursing-home-type facilities rationally arranged in relation to other health care resources on a community wide basis. This program has been of far more importance in establishing broad organizational perspectives and imparting rational organization to health care institutions in the state than in supplying facilities, so far as nursing homes are concerned. The administrative idea was of far more significance than the money involved.

Meanwhile more and more people were using nursing-home-type facilities and hospitals—and paying higher and higher charges. There developed an alarm that the services these institutions had to offer would be priced out of the market for many who needed them. This public concern constituted a potential, if not a demand, for change to be instituted. Public policy embracing nursing-home-type institutions along with other health care facilities within a broad administrative network, and with authority and an unmistakable purpose, followed. In 1964 the Metcalf-McCloskey Act strengthened the state Hill-Burton administrative mechanism and broadened its jurisdiction to include all medical care institutions in the state. All new facilities would now be part of an over-all pattern designed for the most efficacious rendering of care. The Folsom Committee legislation followed in 1965. It charged one agency, the State Health Department, with the development of positive public policy relating to all health institutions in the state, gave untrammeled authority for their regulation, and empowered it almost without limits to gather information to promote the conduct of these functions. It also decreed that voluntary institutions, and proprietaries as well, be paid the full cost of caring for the public charges whom they accept.

To meet the other part of the financial problem for voluntary agencies the legislature has, in 1966, implemented the constitutional amendment sparked by New York City for the construction of nursing homes to be used by persons of low income. Between the loans and the full-cost provisions of the Folsom legislation, many of the difficulties voluntaries have experienced with money should be solved. This represents a conclusion that although the voluntary organization should not be relied upon for financial resources to carry public responsibilities in this era of rising costs and demands, it is well equipped to render services, and that it should be utilized for the assets it has to offer. Also, there has been since 1965 a modest program of state grants for public nursing home construction. With the growing crescendo of attention to nursing home problems reaching climax, one might say there is now public policy on nursing homes.

By and large the control of splintering effects of some unarticulated federal programs is provided for by the state administrative structure. Although the Federal Housing Administration loan guarantees may continue to produce more proprietary homes than many would like to see, each new home must fit into the state plan and the new Health Department code will promote, although not guarantee, the association of homes with hospitals and demand relatively high standards in staffing. (Historically, however, proprietary institutions have presented the greatest challenge to regulation and there is no apparent reason to assume that that will not continue to be the case.) The Veterans' Administration program for nursing home beds in state soldiers' homes and VA hospitals has not yet produced serious problems. It is to be hoped that the state will watch the matter with care. The health insurance provisions of the Social Security Amendments of 1965 may be expected to promote the association of nursing homes with hospitals and to elevate the quality of care somewhat. With its comprehensive approach, and the additional amounts of money that it will make available for nursing home care, Title XIX of the amendments fits into the state's purposes, although amendments to improve its administration will probably prove necessary.

Public Policy and Its Development

One of the major problems for public policy that this history reveals is that the community found itself putting its resources into a set of facilities that was not of its choice. It would appear that if public money is spent there is a concomitant responsibility that it be well spent, and that this requires at least some examination of alternative means by which it might be spent and the selection of that means that appears most reasonably calculated to achieve the intended consequence. However, there had been no decision by the community or its representatives in 1930 or 1935 to use proprietary nursing homes. The community and its representatives had not recognized that there was a need to be met (even though it had been called to their attention), had made no provision to meet it, and therefore had not seized their opportunity to decide what instruments they would use to perform the indispensable function of caring for the aged sick. To right this condition—that is, to make some choice and undo the decisionless condition—remained as a task for public policy. A kind of choice has now been made and there has been a decision to promote voluntary and public institutions.

This task, however, was only an aspect of the essential function that public policy had to perform. In simple societies, where whole work processes are carried out by individuals or small groups or other small social structures, organizational problems are not severe. Modern society has improved its performance both as to the amounts of its goods and services produced and as to their effectiveness through the division of labor—that is, specialization. We have not only many specialized disciplines and professions, we have also specialized institutions. In this manner we more appropriately suit the service to the need. But once labor has been divided a second step, and a challenging one, becomes immediately necessary—putting its product together. The essential problems in organizing our affairs may be seen as constituting two fundamental steps: selecting, developing, and utilizing reasonably appropriate specialized facilities and services to perform the desired function; and harmonizing the specialized activities so that each complements the other in a satisfactory fashion. These two steps are now incorporated in the intent of public policy in New York relating to nursing homes.

But how did this come about? If it is as simple as the two paragraphs above appear to indicate, why was it not the case thirty-five years ago? It has come about now only because of increasing recognition of the need for good nursing homes and an increased awareness of the extent to which, in an era of specialization, there is an organizational need to relate things to each other. But this has all come from experience and was not seen thirty-five years ago. The community "didn't know what was going to happen." Did the community decide? Did the community default?

Public policy grows out of needs, or opinions about needs, and therefore forces, that build up in the community. Examples of such forces taken from this study might be the decision to bar public assistance to persons in institutions; the practical need of a social welfare investigator to find someone who would care for a sick, destitute old lady; the recommendation of the Health Preparedness Commission that assistance be allowed to inmates of public institutions and that there be an expansion of voluntary nursing home beds; the Public Health Service's desire to promote voluntary and public beds; federal legislators' opinions that nursing homes should be seen as business enterprises; the fear of local governments of a post–World War II depression; the arguments of local Welfare Commissioners that they should not come under the merit system. Such forces may go through a certain legitimizing procedure, perhaps becoming ceremonially officialized as legislation or perhaps only becoming accepted administrative procedure. But as this happens they become the content of what official policy there is.

But such forces spring from independent considerations and from a variety of groups, each having its own special perspective. Therefore they may complement each other, or fail to complement each other even where there is a potential for fruitful concerted action. They may clash or stalemate each other. That the relevance they have for each other has not emerged from some natural ordering process, that rational order has not come about automatically, and that the consequences of the lack of order are costly to substantial segments of the public, tend strongly to be learned only by experience. The first rule of decision making is to identify the problem, but frequently it proves that man's knowledge is not sufficient to identify the problem until it becomes manifest in practice.

The problem became manifest. Most people, by far, had either been oblivious to the growing importance of nursing homes, their significance for themselves and their families, or saw the matter from a point of view that inclined them to let things go their own course. But when disclosures by the press revealed that the public was being defrauded of large sums of money by nursing home operators, nursing homes suddenly took on a new kind of importance. When muckraking press exposés talked about abuses and neglect of patients, these institutions became even more a subject of public concern. Finally, when a number of groups became indignant about rising hospital costs, more people began to see the nursing home as a relatively inexpensive alternative for many cases, and as such, an institution to be cultivated, promoted and watched with care. When this happened new forces were thrust into the calculus of public policy that gave it a breadth, force and purpose it had not had before. If the problem is defined similarly by enough people, that definition in itself may virtually be the solution to the problem. Most planning and organizing problems are matters of getting support from those involved rather than technical questions of fact. The making of policy is largely a social process—the development of opinion. And many events which, from historical perspective, appear as defaults are attributable to the state of opinion in the particular cases involved.

The public is notoriously fickle, however, and to rely solely upon aroused public opinion for effective long-run policy is an enterprise doomed to failure. Wise men use the public support at the time it is available to bring about basic institutional changes that will assure the continuance of the policy they advocate when public concern has dissipated. This has been done to some extent in the case at hand. But the regulation of proprietary nursing homes may be expected to become a problem again when the public turns its attention elsewhere.

Moreover, as broader sections of the public become concerned and exert pressures—thereby making public policy more representative of the community as a whole—they do not obliterate the specialized opinions and forces; they simply present a countervailing thrust to them. The policy resultant of these "moments of force" may still be expected to bear some marks of the more specialized opinion. A broadening of policy is the result, however, and over time there may be a lingering effect. There has been much concern of late with planning in the health care field. Planning has slowly taken on a mantle of respectability. The concept of planning—of ordering elements into an over-all system—has become one of the important forces contributing to the shaping of public policy in this area. There is a propensity on the part of experts and, to some extent, even to the public at large, to see an increasing number of elements in relation to each other. The story of public policy in relation to nursing homes has been one of broadening administrative boundaries to encompass more and more phenomena within the considerations upon which policy is based. This trend may be expected to continue.

APPENDIX I

Master Tables

In 1946 the New York State Health Preparedness Commission concluded that there were no less than 844 (presumably proprietary) nursing homes in New York State (see note f, Table 3M). This exceeds considerably the peak reached during the 1950's, according to the most reliable data, and illustrates well the problem encountered repeatedly in attempting to trace accurately the growth of nursing home facilities during the years before 1952. It is patent that homes functionally not the precursors of what are now considered nursing homes are included in this estimate, and that the absence of widely accepted definitions of facilities in the nursing home field must indefinitely plague the researcher. The problem is essentially the same whether one speaks of voluntary, proprietary, or public facilities: identifying function as part of the process of verifying home and bed figures. It is a problem that cannot be completely solved even when dealing with data for the most recent years. It is believed, however, that the data for the tables that follow are sufficiently sound to indicate clearly the general contours of the development of facilities, even though there is no way to prove them definitively accurate.

Table *1M*. Growth of nursing-home-type facilities, 1934–1964

Time and place	Public Infirmaries		Voluntary Private home for aged infirmary		Voluntary Inc. nursing & convalescent homes		Voluntary Total		Proprietary Nursing homes		Total	
	Homes	Beds	Homes	Beds	Homes	Beds	Homes	Beds	Homes	Beds	Homes	Beds
Mid-1930's												
Upstate	47	2,129	40	443	15	1,093	55	1,536	20	325	122	3,990
N.Y.C.	—a	—	32	1,213	10	709	42	1,922	8	116	50	2,038
Totals	72		72	1,656	25	1,802	97	3,458	28	441	172	6,028
Early 1940's												
Upstate	45	3,461	30	390								
N.Y.C.	—	—	26	1,186								
Totals	56		56	1,576					44	884		
Early 1950's												
Upstate	44	4,191	80	934	29	1,645	109	2,579	603	11,027	756	17,797
N.Y.C.	2	1,311	58	2,891	8	894	66	3,785	76	2,801	144	7,897
Totals	46	5,502	138	3,825	37	2,539	175	6,364	679	13,828	900	25,694
1961												
Upstate	37	6,110	84	1,672	28	1,693	112	3,365	496	13,995	645	23,470
N.Y.C.	6	1,918	54	3,397	7	1,202	61	4,599	107	9,420	174	15,937
Totals	43	8,028	138	5,069	35	2,895	173	7,964	603	23,415	819	39,407
1964												
Upstate	39	6,666	68	1,991	27	1,797	95	3,788	446	15,358	580	25,812
N.Y.C.	6	2,465	48	3,923	6	1,137	54	5,060	87	8,805	147	16,330
Totals	45	9,131	116	5,914	33	2,934	140	8,848	533	24,163	727	42,142

A note on data. All of the tables of this study are based, to a substantial extent, on data from the files of the State Department of Social Welfare.

The Division of Hospital Review and Planning of the State Health Department, in administering the Hill-Burton program, also gathered information relating to nursing-home-type facilities, but its figures have been judged not quite as suitable for the purposes of this study as those of the Welfare Department. Differences between the two sets of data are generally related to the former agency's historical concern with construction of physical plant and the latter's concern with reimbursement. Some of the more important specific differences are: The Social Welfare Department listed bed complement, that is, the number of operating beds, and the Health Department reported bed capacity, that is, the number of potential beds the physical plant affords, rather than the complement. Social Welfare listed after 1957 only approved public infirmaries, that is, those that meet standards for state and federal reimbursement; Health listed all beds reported by the locality as public infirmary beds whether approved for reimbursement or not. The Health Department included as nursing home facilities some proprietary and voluntary nursing home units in hospitals (see note c, Table 5) that were not included as nursing home facilities in Social Welfare figures. The Health Department did not list infirmaries of private homes for the aged that have less than four beds; the Department of Social Welfare included all such infirmaries. Also, the criteria of definition used by the two agencies differed enough that, in marginal cases, a given institution might be classified as a nursing-home-type facility by one of them and not by the other.

One substantial advantage offered by Social Welfare figures is that they are available back to the mid-1930's, although they are not historically complete since that period. The Health Department's responsibilities for gathering the relevant data began only in 1954 with the Hill-Burton nursing home program.

For comparison, the year 1963 from Table 1 is presented below with State Health Department data (New York State Department of Health, Division of Hospital Review and Planning, *New York State Program for Construction of Hospital and Related Facilities, Sixteenth Annual Revision, 1964-1965*, pp. 154-157) substituted in all places where Department of Social Welfare figures are used in the original Table 1M (all figures except those for proprietary beds in New York City). In this Health Department material facilities under construction are included as to numbers (of facilities) but not as to numbers of beds. The "Total" column includes nursing home units of hospitals not represented in other columns—491 beds in 13 hospitals upstate and 427 beds in 3 hospitals in New York City.

	Public		Voluntary								Proprietary		Total	
	Infirmaries		Private home for aged infirmary		Inc. nursing & convalescent homes		Total				Nursing homes			
	Homes	Beds	Homes	Beds	Homes	Beds	Homes	Beds			Homes	Beds	Homes	Beds
1963														
Upstate	45	6,392	51	1,763	33	2,000	84	3,763			502	14,044	644	24,690
N.Y.C.	8	2,438	51	3,984	8	1,300	59	5,284			87	8,551	157	16,700
Totals	53	8,830	102	5,747	41	3,300	143	9,047			589	22,595	801	41,390

Table 2M. Growth of nursing-home-type facilities in public infirmaries, 1934–1964

Years	Upstate		New York City		New York State	
	Homes	Beds	Homes	Beds	Homes	Beds
1934	47	2,129	—ᵃ	—	47	2,129
1943	45	3,461	—	—	45	3,461
1952	44	4,191	2	1,311	46	5,502
1953	46	4,450	2	1,549	48	5,999
1954	44	4,545	2	1,610	46	6,155
1955	43	4,708	2	1,290	45	5,998
1956	43	5,110	2	1,290	45	6,400
1957	42	5,242	4	1,784	46	7,026
1958	35	5,023	4	1,784	39	6,807
1959	35	5,268	6	1,902	41	7,170
1960	36	5,513	6	1,918	42	7,431
1961	37	6,110	6	1,918	43	8,028
1962	37	6,030	6	2,124	43	8,154
1963	37	6,200	6	2,381	43	8,581
1964	39	6,666	6	2,465	45	9,131

Source. Files, New York State Department of Social Welfare.
ᵃ Dashes indicate no facilities.

Note. The decrease in upstate beds from 1957 to 1958 results from the Social Welfare Department's decision to include only approved beds in its enumeration of public infirmary facilities. The records indicate that on January 11, 1957, there were 372 unapproved infirmary beds. How many of these were sufficiently upgraded by the time the 1958 census was taken to be included in the 1958 figures and how many were dropped from the classification of infirmary beds is unknown.

Table 3M. Proprietary nursing home growth, 1929–1965[a]

Years	Upstate		New York City		New York State	
	Homes	Beds	Homes	Beds	Homes	Beds
1929			12[b]	148[b]		
1935	20[c]	325[c]	8[c]	116[c]	28	441
1939					133[d]	2,186[d]
1940			44[b]	884[b]		
1944			51[•]	1,449[•]		
1945			52[•]	1,431[•]	400[f]	5,110[f]
1946			58[•]	1,770[•]	447[f]	6,139[f]
1947			62[b]	1,933[b]		
1949	591[g]	8,554[g]	70[b]	2,317[b]	661	10,871
1951			73[b]	2,503[b]		
1952	603[h]	11,027[h]	76[b]	2,801[b]	679	13,828
1954	636[h]	11,822[h]	95[b]	4,699[b]	731	16,521
1955	632[h]	12,810[h]	106[b]	5,737[b]	738	18,547
1956	635[h]	13,654[h]	113[b]	7,195[b]	748	20,849
1957	604[h]	13,380[h]	121[b]	8,218[b]	725	21,598
1958	597[h]	14,441[h]	124[b]	9,489[b]	721	23,930
1959	564[h]	14,326[h]	119[b]	9,392[b]	683	23,718
1960	525[h]	13,718[h]	113[b]	9,354[b]	638	23,073
1961	496[h]	13,995[h]	107[b]	9,420[b]	603	23,415
1962	478[h]	13,279[h]	91[b]	8,704[b]	569	22,001
1963	455[h]	14,170[h]	87[b]	8,551[b]	542	22,721
1964	446[h]	15,358[h]	87[b]	8,805[b]	533	24,163
1965	433[h]	16,082[h]	89[b]	8,900[b]	422	24,982

[a] Blank spaces indicate that no data have been found.

[b] Files, New York City Department of Hospitals. Years 1947–1965 are from annually compiled "List of Proprietary Nursing Homes," where available.

[c] *Directory of Hospitals and Dispensaries,* (4th ed.; New York State Department of Social Welfare, 1935). The upstate figures represent institutions classified as "Medical Convalescent Homes for Adults," but whose descriptions appear to identify them as nursing homes. The data for New York City are taken from pp. 221–222, VIII, "Proprietary Nursing Homes in New York City under Jurisdiction of City Department of Hospitals." A 1946 report (see note e) that discusses the growth of proprietary nursing homes during the 1920's invites the conclusion that the 1929 figure overstates and the 1935 total understates the number of facilities.

ᵈ "Hospital and Other Institutional Facilities and Services, 1939," *Vital Statistics—Special Reports,* Vol. 13, No. 33, Bureau of the Census (Washington, 1942), p. 306.

ᵉ *Survey of Proprietary Nursing Homes in New York City,* Research Bureau, Welfare Council of New York City (November 1946). For 1944, see p. 10. For 1945 and 1946, see p. 8. The study discusses proprietary growth for earlier years on pp. 2–3.

ᶠ *Planning for the Care of the Chronically Ill in New York State— Some Medical-Social and Institutional Aspects,* New York State Health Preparedness Commission, Leg. Doc. (1946) No. 66A (Albany, 1947) pp. 25, 122.

The home and bed totals given are only for nursing homes certified for use by local departments of public welfare in July 1945 and May 1946. The Commission reported that there were many more homes in the state and cited an additional 419 homes listed by the Division of Vital Statistics, New York State Department of Health, to arrive at a minimum total of 844 nursing homes for October, 1946.

It is not certain whether the data include homes of both voluntary and proprietary ownership or only the latter. Subsequent discussion on pp. 25–26, covering rates for public assistance patients, implies that locally certified homes were overwhelmingly, if not exclusively, proprietary in ownership. As the introductory note to these tables indicates, the figure 844 is unreasonably high given the present-day conception of what constitutes a nursing home. Quite obviously the criteria used by the Commission differed considerably from those used today. The number of certified facilities seems much more reasonable and therefore is used here.

ᵍ This estimate is derived basically from figures for upstate New York found in: *A Survey of 754 Proprietary Nursing and Boarding Homes for Adults in New York State,* (Albany: Department of Social Welfare, 1950). However, although in Table 1 of the survey the "Number and Bed Capacity of Private Nursing Homes in Upstate New York, By County, 1949," is given, in fact, this census included not just proprietary nursing homes but convalescent and adult homes as well, or all "proprietary establishments offering bed care" (see p. 1). Thus, the 754 homes with 9,590 beds represented a total in excess of the number of proprietary nursing homes and beds at that time. To arrive at figures for these facilities, the homes and beds in 1949 were presumed to be distributed among nursing and other facilities in the same proportion as they were in November 1952.

ʰ "List of Provisionally Approved Private Proprietary Nursing Homes, and Private Proprietary Convalescent Homes in Upstate New York," Bulletin No. 135a, May 1, 1952; 135b, Nov. 13, 1952; 135d, July 15, 1955; 135g, Nov. 24, 1958, Department of Social Welfare, State of New York (Albany). "Directory, Proprietary Nursing Homes and Proprietary Convalescent Homes in Upstate New York," Jan. 1, 1962, Jan. 1, 1963, Jan.

1, 1964, Jan. 1, 1965, Jan. 1, 1966, New York State Department of Social Welfare (Albany).

Data for 1952 for Erie and Suffolk counties were obtained through the counties' Departments of Health; for Westchester, through Area No. 5 Office of the Department of Welfare.

Table 4M. Growth of nursing-home-type facilities in private homes for the aged infirmaries, 1934–1964

Years	Upstate		New York City		New York State	
	Homes	Beds	Homes	Beds	Homes	Beds
1934	40	443	32	1,213	72	1,656
1943	30	390	26	1,186	56	1,576
1952	80	934	58	2,891	138	3,825
1953	92	1,038	58	2,374	150	3,412
1954	95	1,239	56	2,638	151	3,877
1955	95	1,235	59	2,880	154	4,115
1956	93	1,284	57	3,046	150	4,330
1957	88	1,348	57	3,061	145	4,409
1958	89	1,376	57	3,168	146	4,544
1959	89	1,469	56	3,328	145	4,797
1960	84	1,490	55	3,353	139	4,843
1961	84	1,672	54	3,397	138	5,069
1962	57	1,601	50	3,582	107	5,183
1963	63	1,891	50	3,575	113	5,466
1964	68	1,911	48	3,923	116	5,834

Source. Files, New York State Department of Social Welfare.

Table 5M. Growth of nursing-home-type facilities in incorporated nursing and convalescent homes, 1935–1964

Years	Upstate		New York City		New York State	
	Homes	Beds	Homes	Beds	Homes	Beds
1935[a]	15	1,093	10	709	25	1,802
1950[b]	29[c]	1,645	8[d]	894	37	2,539
1954[b]	28	1,594	8	984	36	2,578
1956[b]	31	1,645	8	951	39	2,596
1957[b]	34[e]	2,064	8	966	42	3,028
1958[b]	33	1,941	8	1,046	41	2,987
1959[b]	31	1,868	8	1,194	39	3,062
1960[b]	30	1,896	7	1,161	37	3,057
1961[b]	28	1,693	7	1,202	35	2,895
1962[b]	30	1,843	7	1,221	37	3,064
1963[b]	31	1,968	8	1,271	39	3,239
1964[b]	27	1,797	6	1,137	37	2,934

[a] *Directory of Hospitals and Dispensaries,* (4th ed.; Department of Social Welfare, State of New York, 1935). Included are "medical convalescent homes for adults" and facilities for incurables, chronic invalids, etc., that might have been regarded as chronic disease hospitals but were subsequently reclassified as nursing homes. Jarrett in 1933 made this comment about those in New York City: "These institutions, although they have been in the past regarded as institutions for medical care and for convenience are grouped in this study with 'chronic hospitals,' are usually not equipped as hospitals and are rarely able to give their patients more than custodial care." Mary C. Jarrett, *Chronic Illness in New York City,* Vol. II: *The Care of the Chronic Sick by Different Types of Voluntary Agencies* (New York: Columbia University Press, 1933), p. 40.

[b] Totals for 1950 to 1964 are taken from the files of the New York State Department of Social Welfare. For these years homes used exclusively for children are omitted. One 75-bed home open only in the summer but appearing in the Department's list of incorporated nursing and convalescent homes until 1963 is included through 1962.

[c] Excludes four homes with 344 beds, believed to be proprietary, and four homes with 129 beds whose location and ownership could not be determined. An absence of data from 1954 onward indicates that these latter ceased to operate.

[d] Excludes seven homes, 444 beds, believed to be proprietary.

[e] Includes the Hopsick Falls Health Center, 11 beds, which was formerly

considered a hospital. The Valeria Home, 233 beds, makes its first appearance on the list in 1957. Jarrett in her 1928 census of convalescent homes includes this facility for adults with 125 beds. *The Care of the Chronic Sick*, Appendix Vb. However, it was not included in the Welfare Department data from 1935 to 1956.

Table 6M. Growth in population, aged and nursing-home-type beds[a]

Period	Population	Aged	Per cent aged	Total beds[c]	Total beds per 1,000 aged	Ownership					
						Public		Proprietary		Voluntary	
						Beds	BPTA	Beds	BPTA	Beds	BPTA
Mid-1930's											
Upstate	5,840,883[b]	455,384[b]	7.80	3,990	8.76	2,129	4.68	325	0.71	1,536	3.37
N.Y.C.	7,192,721[b]	339,461[b]	4.72	2,038	6.00	—	—	116	0.34	1,922	5.66
Totals	13,033,604	794,845	6.10	6,028	7.58	2,129	2.68	441	0.55	3,458	4.35
Early 1940's											
Upstate	6,024,147[b]	507,945[b]	8.43			3,461	6.81				
N.Y.C.	7,454,995[b]	414,419[b]	5.56			—	—	884	2.13		
Totals	13,479,142	922,364	6.84			3,461	3.75		—		—
Early 1950's											
Upstate	6,938,235[b]	653,222[b]	9.41	17,797	27.24	4,191	6.42	11,027	16.88	2,579	3.95
N.Y.C.	7,891,957[b]	605,235[b]	7.67	7,897	13.05	1,311	2.17	2,801	4.63	3,785	6.25
Totals	14,830,192	1,258,457	8.49	25,694	20.42	5,502	4.37	13,828	10.99	6,364	5.06
Early 1960's											
Upstate	9,000,320[b]	873,763[b]	9.71	23,470	26.87	6,110	7.00	13,995	16.02	3,365	3.85
N.Y.C.	7,781,984[b]	813,827[b]	10.46	15,937	19.58	1,918	2.36	9,420	11.57	4,599	5.65
Totals	16,782,304	1,687,590	10.06	39,407	23.35	8,028	4.76	23,415	13.87	7,964	4.72
1964											
Upstate	9,740,409[d]	954,263[d]	9.79	25,812	27.04	6,666	6.97	15,358	16.09	3,788	3.96
N.Y.C.	7,780,000[d]	922,353[d]	11.85	16,330	17.70	2,465	2.67	8,805	9.54	5,060	5.48
Totals	17,520,409	1,876,616	10.71	42,142	22.45	9,131	4.86	24,163	12.87	8,848	4.71

[a] Dashes indicate no facilities. Blank spaces indicate that no data have been found.

[b] Decennial data from the United States Bureau of the Census, except that of the mid-1930 figures include half the increase between 1930 and 1940. The aged represent persons 65 years of age or older.

[c] Bed data are from Tables 2 through 4B. The columns headed BPTA show beds per thousand aged. New York State Health Department data, not used in this table, include as nursing-home-type facilities five units in hospitals that are not included in Department of Social Welfare figures (see note, Table 1). The distribution of these units, the beds involved and the resultant beds-per-thousand-aged figures, follows:

Period	Total			Ownership								
				Public			Proprietary			Voluntary		
	Hosp.	Beds	BPTA	Hosp.	Beds	BPTA	Hosp.	Beds	BPTA	Hosp.	Beds	BPTA
1963												
Upstate	4	170	.17	—	—	—	1	102	.10	3	68	.07
N.Y.C.	1	354	.39	—	—	—	—	—	—	1	354	.39
Totals	5	524	.56	—	—	—	1	102	.10	4	422	.46

[a] Files, New York State Department of Health, computed in the manner described in New York State Department of Health, *Provisional Annual Tables for 1963*, Supplement to *Monthly Vital Statistics Review*, Vol. XLIV, No. 13 (April 1964), note c, p. 241.

APPENDIX II

Analysis of Questionnaire Circulated by New York State Nursing Home Association

In July 1962, the New York State Nursing Home Association distributed a questionnaire among its members for the purpose of learning about their educational background. Eighty-one persons, approximately one-half of the membership, responded. The completed questionnaires indicated the following:

Fifty-nine of the administrators had some health care training:

M.D. degree	1
Registered Nurses	33
Practical Nurses	18
Nursing training only	7

Among these fifty-nine were found persons with the following higher educational qualifications:

Master's degree	2
Bachelor's degree	3
Some college only	5
Total	10

Twenty-two persons had no health care background. Among them were persons with the following higher educational qualifications:

Master's degree	2
Law degree	2
Some graduate work only	3
Bachelor's degree only	4
Some college only	5
	—
Total	16

Figures about high-school graduation reveal something relating to the age of the administrators as well as to the level of their education. The number of persons who had not graduated from high school was seven. For two others the date of graduation could not be determined. Among the 72 remaining, 6 had graduated before 1920, indicating that—if they graduated at age seventeen—they were at least fifty-nine years old in 1962. The same arithmetic reasoning indicates that only 4 were under thirty, 11 were thirty to thirty-nine, 21 were forty to forty-nine, and 30 were fifty to fifty-nine.

Sixty questionnaires identified the home with which the administrator was associated. Through the State Department of Social Welfare's directory, it was possible to establish the sizes of the homes for these respondents, who were then classified according to whether or not they had any medical background.

Forty-six had health care training:

M.D. degree	1
Registered nurses	27
Practical nurses	12
Nursing training only	6

Among these were 9 with higher academic qualifications:

Master's degree	1
Bachelor's degree only	3
Some college only	5

Fourteen had no formal health care training; but among them were eleven with higher educational qualifications:

Master's degree	2
Bachelor's degree	4
Law degree only	2
Some college only	3

The average size of the homes with which the first group of administrators—those with medical background but less academic background—were associated was 28.2. The corresponding figure for the second group—those without medical training but with more academic preparation—was 41. Considering the sizes of the groups, one must conclude that, on the average, those managing the larger homes had substantially more nonmedical academic preparation.

It must be noted that the conclusions drawn on page 159 of this study rest on extremely limited data. The information was not gathered with rigorous methodology; and at the time the questionnaires were answered by these small numbers of people, there were some 478 proprietary nursing homes in operation upstate.

APPENDIX III

Chronology of Major Policy Junctures

1788   State legislation fixes towns and cities as financial and administrative bases for poor relief.

1824   State County Poorhouse Act adopts indoor relief policy. Requires county almshouses, county-wide financing; but excepts 38 of 54 counties.

1849   General statutory reauthorization to use towns as base for financing relief. Significant compromise with principle of outdoor relief.

1867   Board of State Commissioners of Public Charities created. (Changed to State Board of Charities in 1873 and to State Board of Social Welfare in 1929.)

1875   State law forbids care of children in almshouses.

1876   Local law imposes severe limitations upon outdoor relief in downstate New York.

1890   State relieves local government of cost of care of patients in state mental hospitals.

1898   Charter of Greater New York City prohibits outdoor relief.

1929   New York City Department of Hospitals established and charged with inspecting and licensing proprietary nursing homes.

1929   State Public Welfare Act adopts principle of outdoor relief "whenever practicable" (New York City excepted), yet provides for institutional care. Permits towns to continue as financial bases and provides for county Welfare Officers—to be elected or appointed at county option.

1930   State Commission on Old Age Security recommends county homes be upgraded to infirmaries or hospitals.

1930   State Old Age Security Act provides a pension for aged. Pensions not to be received in any institution except when recipient temporarily hospitalized. Pensions financed half by state and half by county governments, administration under state supervision.

1935   Federal Social Security Act makes grants-in-aid to aged and blind relief programs available to states. Persons in private institutions, but not public, made eligible for such programs.

1936   State law implements federal aid for the aged. Local governments left dependent upon own resources for care in public institutions and in private institutions of "custodial, correctional, or curative character," and in cases where patient in need of "continued institutional care."

1936   State assumes 40 per cent of costs of home relief—leaving local governments 60 per cent—but includes no institutional care in the program.

1937   State law discontinues federal and state aid for relief of aged in hospitals who were not receiving old age assistance prior to hospitalization.

Late 1930's,

early 1940's   Local welfare officials use separate applications for maintenance and for medical care of welfare cases in nursing homes. Institutions defined by State Department of Social Welfare as places for more than eight people.

1940   State Department of Social Welfare establishes "standards of suitability" for private homes for the aged to meet before admitting public assistance beneficiaries.

1941   Nonprofit convalescent homes included among those charitable institutions whose charter must be approved by State Board of Social Welfare.

1943   State Department of Social Welfare study of 109 upstate nursing homes finds them inappropriate facilities for sick people.

1944   State law and Bulletin 105 of State Department of Social Welfare specifically designates private nursing homes as places where recipients of reimbursable welfare might live. Local government certification of nursing homes required.

1946   State Health Preparedness Commission recommends state regulation of nursing homes, and state reimbursement of welfare expenditures for patients in public homes.

1946 State share of costs to local government of providing welfare increased to 80 per cent, leaving public infirmary and hospital care to be paid for solely by localities.

1947 "Fur coat" scandal in New York City aggravates upstate-downstate division and doubts about wisdom of reimbursement formula.

1948 New York City Hospitals Department average occupancy rate reaches 100.8 per cent.

1949 Proposals for state and local governments to assume equal proportions of all welfare costs stumble on New York City's liberal hospitalization policy.

1950 Federal Social Security Act amendments establish new welfare category, aid to permanently and totally disabled, and provide that persons may receive federally aided welfare while in public medical institutions (except those institutionalized because of mental illness or tuberculosis).

1950 Staff Report to Special Committee of the Joint Committee on Interstate Cooperation finds operation of public homes an independent and neglected function. Recommends state aid to be extended to hospital and public home care.

1950 State Department of Social Welfare reports on study of upstate proprietary nursing homes. Recommends education and regulation by state.

1951 State law includes proprietary nursing homes among institutions regulated by State Board of Social Welfare. Rules and regulations for private nursing homes promulgated, require homes to *register*.

1951 State implements flow of federal money to welfare cases in public infirmaries and hospitals but does not begin contributions itself for infirmary care or hospital cases initiated in hospitals. Bulletin 139 promulgates state standards upon which federal reimbursement for welfare cases in public infirmaries is contingent.

1951–
1952 New York City shifts policy on use of nursing homes for welfare patients from limited, convalescent care use to long-term, custodial care. Encourages nursing homes to expand, transfers long-term patients in voluntary homes to reimbursable welfare categories.

1952 New York City begins operating an infirmary in a city hospital. Federally aided welfare cases admitted.

1954 Local share of welfare costs changed by state law from 20 per cent to 50 per cent after federal contribution. State participation broadened to include public home care and indefinite hospitalization of OAA, AB, AD, and home relief cases on lists before hospitalized.

1956 State Bulletin 119a stipulates standards for infirmaries of private homes for the aged to meet to receive operating cost-level payments (up to a ceiling) for welfare cases.

1956 State law changes requirements for proprietary nursing homes, requires prior approval before they may begin to operate, and establishes special enforcement procedures relating to them.

1957 Spread of New York City infirmaries in city hospitals approved by State Department of Social Welfare. Program expanded.

1959 State rules require prior approval for new construction of proprietary nursing homes.

1958 New York City begins investigation of proprietary nursing homes.

1959 New York City Mayor's reform program for proprietary nursing homes begins.

1959 Law makes Federal Housing Administration guarantees of 75 per cent of mortgages on proprietary nursing homes available.

1960 State code for private homes for the aged promulgated.

1961 Insurable proportion of FHA loans for proprietary nursing homes raised to 90 per cent.

1963 New York City code for proprietary nursing homes becomes effective.

1964 Metcalf-McCloskey Act requires prior approval of all new construction and reconstruction of nursing homes by strengthened State Hill-Burton Agency and Board of Social Welfare.

1965 Law growing out of Folsom Committee Study designates State Health Department as agency responsible for supervision, data gathering and for over-all policy related to health care institutions. Stipulates that care of public charges shall be at rates reasonably related to cost.

1965   State Constitution amended to allow long-term loans by government to voluntary institutions for the construction of nursing home facilities for people of low income.

1965   State assumes half of financial responsibility for costs of hospital care given by local governments and not reimbursed by federal aid.

1965   Social Security amendments provide health insurance for the aged, including care in qualified nursing homes, and provide federal reimbursement as a spur to comprehensive, well-integrated health care programs for persons falling into welfare categories except for income.

1966   State legislature implements 1965 Social Security amendments with liberal eligibility criteria, requiring even care for medical indigents for whom federal reimbursement is not available.

1966   State legislature implements constitutional amendment to provide long-term, low-interest loans for the construction and outfitting of voluntary nursing homes.

1966–
1967   Cutbacks at state and national level on social security measures of 1965–1966.

Index